NOTICE TO PURCHASER
The viewer attached
to the inside back cover is essential
for the proper use
of this text

GROUP THEORY
AND SYMMETRY
IN CHEMISTRY

Lowell H. Hall

CHAIRMAN
DEPARTMENT OF CHEMISTRY
EASTERN NAZARENE COLLEGE

GROUP THEORY
AND SYMMETRY
IN CHEMISTRY

6 4 2 2 6

McGRAW-HILL BOOK COMPANY
New York, St. Louis, San Francisco, London
Sydney, Toronto, Mexico, Panama

to
DORLA,
SHERRIE AND MARK

preface

In recent years the use of techniques adapted from principles of group theory and the use of point-group symmetry symbols have increased rapidly in several areas of chemistry. Understanding most journal articles on such topics as infrared spectra, quantum chemistry, and molecular structure depends upon a knowledge of methods and terminology derived from group theory, which is generally not included in the usual undergraduate–graduate course sequence. New editions of some of the leading textbooks in physical and inorganic chemistry are now attempting to make up this deficiency.

This present volume is intended for upper-division undergraduate and first-year graduate work in the chemistry curriculum. In addition, all or part of this material may be helpful to those whose graduate training lies behind them and who are now venturing into new areas where symmetry and group theory take on importance.

The material included in this book ranges over several topics at more than one level of difficulty. Hence the individual reader may find a chapter or two either a review or somewhat advanced. For instance, the typical chemist who is familiar with symmetry may wish to skip Chap. 2 on symmetry elements, or the graduate student may only skim Chap. 8 on hybrid orbitals. Thus, some chapters are somewhat elementary by way of introduction and for the sake of completeness; other chapters are advanced so as to prepare the reader for topics of current research.

The manuscript upon which this book is based grew out of a one-semester first-year graduate chemistry course given for 3 years at the Florida Atlantic University, Boca Raton, Florida. I have supposed that the reader has had training in chemistry which includes an introduction to quantum theory as in a typical physical-chemistry course and a general knowledge of algebra and calculus. When mathematical techniques, such as group theory and matrices, are important, these techniques are either reviewed or developed in detail in the text.

Since the book deals with the description of molecular structure in some detail, I have introduced computer-drawn stereoscopic illustrations. I believe that viewing these stereoscopic diagrams will aid the reader in gaining a feel for the symmetry of molecular structure. However, I also feel strongly that there is no substitute for working directly with molecular models both in understanding the textual material and in solving specific problems.

Many problems have been included since I believe that often little learning takes place unless the reader becomes actively involved in the relationship between concept and application. Actual problem solving is one means of bringing about the involvement.   Some of the problems are designed to give the reader practice in using definitions, some are real practical problems which the chemist meets, and some (the most difficult) lead to a deeper insight of the textual material when the solution is properly obtained.

I wish to express appreciation to Prof. Walter S. Koski, who inspired my interests in problems related to molecular structure, and to Prof. Dean W. Robinson, who first introduced me to the elegance and usefulness of group-theoretical techniques.   Further, I wish to thank Prof. Samuel F. Clark, who encouraged me to pursue the writing of the manuscript, and to C. K. Johnson, for the use of his program ORTEP in producing the stereoscopic illustrations.   For their excellent secretarial assistance and patience I wish to thank my wife, Dorla, who produced the first and last typewritten drafts, and Mrs. Joan Bleau for the intervening draft.

Lowell H. Hall

thumbnail sketch of the chapters

Chapter 2 deals with the symmetry of molecules in a formal manner. Although the average reader has some familiarity with the symmetry description of molecular structure, Chap. 2 is designed to formalize his knowledge of symmetry through a discussion of the relationship between symmetry operations and symmetry elements.

Chapter 3 is entitled Elements of Group Theory. The chapter does not give a *full* presentation of group theory, for it deals with those selected portions of group theory considered necessary for laying a firm foundation for the structure built in later chapters. The inquisitive reader is urged to accept the challenge of using group-theory texts for more intensive study.

Chapter 4 combines the principles introduced in Chaps. 2 and 3 to achieve a systematic identification and classification of symmetry point groups. Emphasis is placed upon working directly with the symmetry operations of the specific groups so that the reader's newly developed knowledge of group-theoretic principles is exercised. The aim of the chapter, however, is not exclusively that of sharpening the tools of group theory. A flow-chart scheme is developed for determining the point-group symmetry of a molecular structure quickly and accurately. Many examples are provided for practice.

In Chap. 5 matrices and vectors are introduced and shown to be the link between the abstract algebra of group theory and the problems of molecular geometry to which applications are made in later chapters. Matrix algebra is reviewed and applied to symmetry operations in some detail. Representation theory is introduced and shown to be the key in making applications to problems of physics and chemistry. Matrix theory is carefully related to the group-theory formalism developed earlier.

Representation theory is developed further in Chap. 6 as the reader is led into the heart of the theoretical part of the book. Several theorems are presented, but not without proofs which require considerable reflection on the part of the reader. Although complex algebraic manipulation might tend to interfere, the emphasis is always upon the conceptual development of the proof. Where algebraic equations are necessary, they are liberally interspersed with statements designed to act as direction signs among the maze of symbols. In addition, a glossary of symbols is appended to Chap. 6. The equations developed in Chap. 6 are shown to be not only quite simple in algebraic form but also easy to apply to specific cases. Again, several examples and exercises are provided for experience.

Beginning with Chap. 7, applications are made to specific chemical subjects, the first being molecular vibrations with specific attention to infrared and Raman spectra. The concept of normal modes of vibrations is introduced through a classical-mechanical analysis of the vibrations of a molecular system. The force laws which describe the bonding forces in a molecular system are left in a generalized form. The relation of internal coordinates of interest to chemists—bond-stretching vectors and bond-angle deformations—to the normal modes of vibration is described in detail so that functional-group analysis may be understood properly.

The determination of spectral-transition selection rules is shown to be a quantum-mechanical problem. The solution of the problem is outlined under the simple-harmonic-oscillator approximation, and selection rules are related to the symmetry of the normal modes. Attention is drawn to the fact that selection rules based on the harmonic-oscillator approximation may be violated, and examples are given. Overtone and combination bands and the polarization of Raman spectra are discussed. Several examples of normal-mode analysis are given.

Chapters 8 to 11 discuss molecular electronic structure. Construction of hybridized atomic orbitals is taken up first in Chap. 8 because of its general simplicity and its usefulness in later chapters. First, methods are given for the determination of the proper orbitals to be combined to give hybrid orbitals of the desired symmetry. A list of all of the important hybrid orbitals is given in table form. Both sigma and pi bonding systems are treated. The techniques used for the construction of the hybrid orbitals are then developed in detail with several examples.

Molecular-orbital theory is then treated in its LCAO MO form in Chap. 9. The variational method is used to derive the secular equations and to show that the formal structure of MO theory can be reduced to an eigenvalue problem. To avoid obscuring the details of the symmetry orbital method, the simple Hückel treatment of organic pi systems is discussed first. Many detailed examples are worked out, and several results are presented in table form. Then the sigma bonding systems of BH_3 and C_2H_6 are treated to lay a basis for the development of more sophisticated methods which make use of high-speed digital computers.

To introduce the reader to the use of symmetry in more sophisticated methods of quantum chemistry, the results of extended Hückel calculations are presented and analyzed for BH_3 and C_2H_6.

Chapter 10 deals with selection rules for electronic spectra. The basis for selection rules has already been given in Chap. 7. Thus, many examples are given in the several areas of interest to chemists. Such topics as vibronic coupling and polarization are included.

The final chapter deals with the specific area of the coordination compounds of transition metals. Although MO theory may be used as a basic formalism for the understanding of coordination compounds, the ideas of crystal-field theory (or ligand-field theory) prove most useful in describing the splitting of the free-atom states of metal atoms caused by the lowering of the symmetry of its surroundings in the coordination compound. The use of symmetry in determining splitting is described, and correlation diagrams are introduced. Starting with the one-electron case in the octahedral field, the discussion proceeds through the cases of the 10 d electrons and the tetrahedral case. Magnetic properties and spectral transitions are then considered.

contents

1

introduction: the relation of group theory and symmetry to chemistry

"A thing of beauty is a joy forever." So wrote Keats in "Endymion." In "Ode on a Grecian Urn" the poet also wrote ". . . beauty is truth, truth beauty." The symmetrical appearance of the urn no doubt helped inspire the poet; the esthetic appeal of the urn was enhanced by the symmetry of its design. In applying properties of symmetry to the understanding and solution of certain problems in chemistry, we find that the basic esthetic appeal of symmetrical objects is paralleled by a certain elegance in the mathematical description of nature because symmetry plays a fundamental role in physical theory.

1.1 SYMMETRY, A FAMILIAR THEME

Symmetry is a familiar theme in our world. The human body, for instance, possesses a certain symmetry, albeit an imperfect one. The right half of the body is related to the left half as if the right were obtained by reflection of the left across a mirror plane, which can be imagined to

1

divide right from left. Notice that there are two each of every human body part not located on the mirror plane—two arms, two hands, two eyes, two ears, and two nostrils in the nose—but only one each of those located on the mirror plane—one nose and one mouth.

The human hands serve as another example of human body symmetry. Hold your hands out thumbs up and palms parallel. You will notice again that the right hand is the mirror image of the left hand. Now hold your left hand out with the thumb pointing directly away from you with the palm up, fingers pointing to the right. Place your right hand above the left with the palm down; your right thumb points directly at you and the right-hand fingers point to the left. The relation of your hands is now that of inversion, and the center of inversion is a point located midway between the palms of your hands. If you connect a line between any point in your right hand, e.g., the crease behind a knuckle, and the center of inversion, the extension of that line an equal distance will terminate at a point on your left hand which is equivalent to the initial point on your right hand.

Symmetry is exhibited in many other objects found in nature such as in crystal habits, which may take the shape of a cube, an octahedron, a square plate, or a needle. A regular geometric solid is regular because of its symmetry: a tetrahedron, a cubooctahedron, an icosahedron, a pentagonal dodecahedron. The arrangement of the equilibrium positions of atomic nuclei may often be similar to certain geometric solids, and molecular (and ionic) structure may likewise possess symmetry.

In molecular structure symmetry is a simplifying theme. The usefulness of the symmetry simplification lies in reducing the complexity of the physical theory used to understand and describe molecular structure. Molecular structure may be thought of in some situations as a giant geometry problem. The relationships of the various symmetry-related parts of a molecular structure may be used to simplify the mathematics of the theory. Symmetry may also be defined as that property of a substance which is common to all physical properties of the substance.

There is also a symmetry which may be associated with collections of numbers. When a law of combination of the numbers is specified, e.g., addition or multiplication, the collection of numbers takes on certain properties, and an algebra can be constructed on those properties.

1.2 GROUP THEORY, ORGANIZER OF OUR NOTIONS

The algebra based upon the law of combination of a collection of numbers (or unspecified symbols) is called *group theory*. The fact that the elements of the group need not be numbers is important here, for we are interested in the relation of symmetry to physical theory. Let us put our notions of symmetry relations on a more definite basis by defining a symmetry transformation: a transformation which preserves the distances between all pairs of points in a body and brings the body into coincidence with itself is called a *symmetry operation*. It will become evident in later discussions that there is a correspondence between symmetry operations and the group properties expressed in group theory. Hence, group theory has become known as the algebra of geometry.

Because of the systematic nature of group theory we shall use this abstract theory as the basis for organizing our notions concerning symmetry, as a means not only of developing useful equations but also of classifying shapes, functions, and molecular structure. We shall be able to determine the appropriate collections of symmetry operations necessary for the required physical descriptions. We have found that certain restrictions are placed upon the collections of operations. One restriction deals with the relative orientation of the symmetry elements (mirror planes and inversion centers). For a finite body all the symmetry operations must leave at least one point unmoved. Clearly rotations about nonintersecting axes or reflections across nonintersecting planes will introduce a translation: the body will be moved in space and not brought into coincidence with itself. Hence, all symmetry elements in a molecular symmetry group must intersect in a point. Such groups are therefore called *point groups*.

1.3 MATRICES, THE VEHICLE OF OUR NOTIONS

Symmetry transformations may take on the form of algebraic equations in which the initial set of coordinates (x, y, z) is related to the transformed set (x', y', z').

$$x' = t_{11}x + t_{12}y + t_{13}z$$
$$y' = t_{21}x + t_{22}y + t_{23}z$$
$$z' = t_{31}x + t_{32}y + t_{33}z$$

For example, inversion of a point through a center of inversion yields the following equations:

$$x' = -1 \cdot x + 0 \cdot y + 0 \cdot z$$
$$y' = \quad 0 \cdot x - 1 \cdot y + 0 \cdot z$$
$$z' = \quad 0 \cdot x + 0 \cdot y - 1 \cdot z$$

Rotation in the xy plane through an angle θ about the z axis may be written

$$x' = \quad (\cos \theta)(x) \quad + (\sin \theta)(y) + 0 \cdot z$$
$$y' = (-\sin \theta)(x) + (\cos \theta)(y) + 0 \cdot z$$
$$z' = \quad\quad 0 \cdot x \quad\quad + \quad 0 \cdot y \quad + 1 \cdot z$$

Such transformation equations can be written in matrix form.

$$\begin{bmatrix} x' \\ y' \\ z' \end{bmatrix} = \begin{bmatrix} t_{11} & t_{12} & t_{13} \\ t_{21} & t_{22} & t_{23} \\ t_{31} & t_{32} & t_{33} \end{bmatrix} \begin{bmatrix} x \\ y \\ z \end{bmatrix}$$

The rotation matrix, for example, is written

$$\begin{bmatrix} x' \\ y' \\ z' \end{bmatrix} = \begin{bmatrix} \cos\theta & \sin\theta & 0 \\ -\sin\theta & \cos\theta & 0 \\ 0 & 0 & 1 \end{bmatrix} \begin{bmatrix} x \\ y \\ z \end{bmatrix}$$

A matrix is simply an array of numbers which represents a mathematical quantity such as an operator or a symmetry transformation. The elements of the array are the coefficients of the initial coordinates in the transformation equations. In this manner matrices can be constructed to represent symmetry operations, and a simple equation can represent the action of a symmetry operation.

$$\mathbf{X'} = R\mathbf{X}$$

Then for rotation

$$R = \begin{bmatrix} \cos\theta & \sin\theta & 0 \\ -\sin\theta & \cos\theta & 0 \\ 0 & 0 & 1 \end{bmatrix}$$

The vital link between the geometric description of molecular structure necessary for physical theory and the mathematical formalism of abstract group theory, then, is matrix theory. On the one hand matrices can be used to describe symmetry operations, and on the other hand they can be used to represent groups in the sense of the abstract algebra of group theory. The formal system of mathematics which embodies the connection between matrix theory and group theory is known as *representation theory*.

What is the importance of symmetry in physical theory? How is symmetry useful? We may be able to classify mathematical functions and molecular structures according to some point-group symmetry-classification scheme, but what purpose does such classification serve?

1.4 QUANTUM MECHANICS, THE FUNDAMENTAL NOTION

Symmetry enters the picture at a level more fundamental than the symmetry of external forms. The postulates of quantum mechanics, along with the Schrödinger equation, must be used in dealing with chemical problems of molecular and electronic structure. In quantum mechanics the symmetry of a molecular system appears in the mathematical form of the potential-energy function which describes the system. Thus, the symmetry of the potential function has a profound influence upon the solutions to the Schrödinger equation.

The Schrödinger equation may be written as an operator equation

$$\mathcal{3C}\psi_i = E_i\psi_i \tag{1.1}$$

$\mathcal{3C}$ is the hamiltonian operator for the system. In the language of quantum mechanics $\mathcal{3C}$ is an operator which stands for the sum of the kinetic and potential energies of all the particles in the system. Calculations in quantum mechanics require one to solve the Schrödinger equation (1.1) to determine the allowed energies of the system E_i and the wave functions ψ_i. Since the wave functions for molecular systems are complex functions of many variables, any means whereby the descriptions of the functions can be simplified by using symmetry is welcomed. Because of the particular form of the Schrödinger equation an examination of the symmetry of the hamiltonian operator reveals useful information concerning the symmetry of the wave functions, as shown by the following simplified development. (See the appendix to this chapter for an expanded treatment.)

For simplicity in our present purpose we can write the hamiltonian operator in its classical form as the sum of the kinetic and potential energies for the system.

$$H = T + V = \frac{1}{2} \sum_{i=1}^{N} m_i v_i{}^2 + V(r_1, r_2, r_3, \ldots, r_N) \tag{1.2}$$

where m_i is the mass of the ith particle and v_i is its velocity. $V(r_1, r_2, r_3, \ldots, r_N)$ represents the potential-energy function which describes the system.

Both the kinetic- and potential-energy parts of the hamiltonian are mathematical functions and, as such, can be described in symmetry terms. Consider the two simple functions graphed; Fig. 1.1a shows the potential-energy curve for a simple harmonic oscillator (which might describe the bond force in a diatomic molecule). The function $V(x) = \frac{1}{2}kx^2$ is symmetric with respect to reflection across the abscissa, whereas the function shown in Fig. 1.1b is *not* symmetric with respect to reflection across the abscissa.

The more complicated functions which describe molecular potential functions can be classified with respect to the point-group symmetry of the molecule, and the symmetry of the hamiltonian operator has a direct relationship to the symmetry classification of the wave functions. The results may be generalized as follows: in an operator equation of the

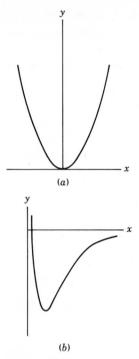

Fig. 1.1   (a) The function $y = \frac{1}{2}kx^2$ is symmetric with respect to reflection across the y axis. (b) This function is not symmetric with respect to the y axis.

eigenvalue type such as the Schrödinger equation the wave functions will possess the same symmetry properties as the operator ℋ.

The usefulness of this classification scheme becomes apparent when we consider the kinds of integrals involved in the quantum-mechanical solution of a problem.   The value of a physically observable quantity p (such as the intensity of a spectral transition) is expressed as the expectation value of its corresponding operator P.

$$p \rightarrow \langle P \rangle = \int \psi_m^* P \psi_n \, d\tau \tag{1.3}$$

From the theory of calculus we can state that an integral will not vanish (will not have the value zero) when the integrand is invariant under all the symmetry operations of the space involved.   The integrand must be totally symmetric with respect to all the appropriate symmetry operations if the integral is to have a nonzero value.   The key statement, then, is that we can determine the possible zero values of an integral such as Eq. (1.3) simply by classifying the symmetry of its constituent functions.

The eigenvalue form of Eq. (1.1) can be put into a more useful form for our present purposes, as shown in Eq. (1.4).

$$\{H - E_i \mathbb{1}\}\psi_i = 0 \tag{1.4}$$

The quantity in braces represents a matrix whose elements are integrals of the following type

$$H_{ij} = \int \psi_i^* \mathcal{K} \psi_j \, d\tau \tag{1.5}$$

The ordering of the functions ψ_i in a sequence such that zero values occur in blocks in the matrix $\{H - E_i \mathbb{1}\}$ allows for a great reduction in the problem. Herein lies one source of the great usefulness of symmetry in applications to problems in chemistry; the procedure is called *block diagonalization* of the secular determinant.

1.5 APPLICATIONS TO PROBLEMS IN CHEMISTRY

There are three broad areas in chemistry to which the basic concepts of point-group symmetry and group theory together may be applied: molecular structure, molecular vibrations, and electronic structure.

In describing the geometry of molecules and complex ions one may simply list the symmetry elements present in the structure. However, the symmetry operations can be organized into a collection of groups with the aid of group theory. Each group can be identified with a simple but systematic symbol. One can then describe a structure simply by giving the proper point-group symbol. Such a classification scheme is very useful.

The problem of molecular vibrations is intimately related to infrared and Raman spectroscopy, one of the fundamental experimental areas of chemistry. The vibrations of molecular species can be described in terms of the cooperative ways in which the atoms vibrate (normal modes of vibration). The normal-mode description can be related readily to the forces between the various atoms through the notions of bond stretching and bond-angle deformations. Normal-mode analysis is performed with the aid of the point-group classification scheme and other group-theory principles. Further, the intensity of the various spectral bands is a basic quantum-mechanical problem which can be treated in part by group-theory techniques. The result is a set of selection rules which can be used to help interpret infrared and Raman spectra in terms of molecular structure.

Group-theoretical principles can be used as an aid in constructing both equivalent and nonequivalent hybrid atomic orbitals. First, the appropriate orbitals can be determined in order to give a set of orbitals leading to the desired symmetry. Then, the correct mathematical form can be determined.

The methods derived from group theory and symmetry may be applied to solving problems in molecular-orbital (MO) theory because in its basic formalism MO theory is written as an eigenvalue problem. Whether one is dealing with simple Hückel theory or with an advanced self-consistent-field theory, the group-theoretical techniques are useful both in performing calculations and in understanding results. Methods based upon group theory may be used to simplify the eigenvalue problem and to classify the MO wave functions. Once the wave functions are classified on a symmetry basis, a set of selection rules can be produced for use in the interpretation of ultraviolet and visible (electronic) spectra.

When one is dealing specifically with coordination compounds of the transition metals, the ideas of crystal-field theory are needed in addition to other theories of electronic structure (such as MO theory). Energy-level splitting of the d electron levels due to the interactions with the coordination ligands and the dependence of the splittings upon the strength of the interactions can be treated with the same group-theoretical techniques.

We shall not discuss here certain topics (principally of atomic physics) on which symmetry also has great influence, e.g., angular momentum, electron-spin interactions, and parity. Further problems related to groups, such as space groups in crystal physics and crystallography, are also omitted.

The notion of classification schemes based upon a symmetry description of matter and its interactions taken together with the principles of abstract group theory yields techniques which aid in the solution and understanding of problems of great importance to chemistry.

APPENDIX TO CHAPTER ONE

For simplicity in the following development we can use the classical-mechanical form of the hamiltonian function for N particles, which can be written

$$H = T + V = \sum_{i=1}^{N} T_i + V = \sum_{i=1}^{N} m_i \dot{r}_i^2 + V(r_1, r_2, \ldots, r_N) \quad (1.6)$$

where T = kinetic energy
V = potential energy
$\dot{r}_i$ = velocity of particle i

The wave functions ψ_i are the solutions to the Schrödinger equation, and each one possesses (belongs to) an energy E_i. In the nondegenerate case there is one and only one wave function for each energy.

The Schrödinger equation has the form of an eigenvalue equation in which the wave functions ψ_i are the eigenfunctions and the energies E_i are the eigenvalues. Symmetry plays an important role in solving problems in physical theory because of the nature of the eigenvalue equation.

Let us consider the Schrödinger equation in the nondegenerate case. First we examine the symmetry properties of the hamiltonian operator. Equation (1.7) shows that the kinetic-energy term T is symmetric with respect to all symmetry operations because the spatial coordinates appear raised to the second power. Let R stand for a symmetry operation.

$$RT = R \left(\sum_{i=1}^{N} m_i r_i^2 \right) = \sum_{i=1}^{N} m_i \dot{r}_i^2 = T \qquad (1.7)$$

because

$$R\dot{r}_i^2 = \dot{r}_i^2 \qquad (1.8)$$

Thus, the hamiltonian $\mathfrak{R}$ (or H) directly possesses the symmetry of the potential function.

Let us say, for example, that $V(\mathbf{r})$ [$= V(r_1, r_2, r_3, \ldots, r_N)$] is symmetric with respect to symmetry operation R.

$$RV(\mathbf{r}) = V(\mathbf{r}) \qquad (1.9)$$

For example, in the simple harmonic oscillator $V(x) = \frac{1}{2}kx^2$, and $V(x)$ is symmetric with respect to reflection across the y axis, i.e., the change of x into $-x$ and $V(-x) = V(x)$. Equation (1.10) represents the action of R on the Schrödinger equation. Since E_i is a numerical constant,

$$R\mathfrak{R}\psi_i = RE_i\psi_i \qquad (1.10)$$

R may be interchanged with E_i (R commutes with E_i). Since $\mathfrak{R}$ is totally symmetric ($\mathfrak{R}$ possesses the full symmetry of the system as indicated by the potential function), R may also be interchanged with $\mathfrak{R}$ since it has no effect on $\mathfrak{R}$. Hence, Eq. (1.10) may now be rewritten

$$\mathfrak{R}(R\psi_i) = E(R\psi_i) \qquad (1.11)$$

Equation (1.11) says that the function $R\psi_i$ is also an eigenfunction of $\mathfrak{R}$ belonging to energy eigenvalue E_i. However, since in this case the solutions are nondegenerate, $R\psi_i$ must simply be a constant times ψ_i.

$$R\psi_i = c\psi_i \qquad (1.12)$$

Suppose now that R is an operation such that when performed twice, the system is returned to its original configuration; that is R performed twice is an identity or unit operation.

$$R \cdot R = R^2 = 1 \tag{1.13}$$

Then, a repeat of the operation on Eq. (1.12) leads to Eqs. (1.14) and (1.15).

$$R \cdot R \cdot \psi_i = R(c\psi_i) = c(R\psi_i) = c^2\psi_i \tag{1.14}$$

and

$$R^2\psi_i = 1 \cdot \psi_i = \psi_i \tag{1.15}$$

Thus

$$c^2 = 1 \quad \text{and} \quad c = \pm 1$$

Therefore, the wave functions ψ_i must be even or odd functions. A similar result is obtained when the approach is generalized to include both the degenerate cases and operations which yield the identity operation when performed n times successively. The result may be generalized as follows: in an operator equation of the eigenvalue type in which the operator is a linear operator the eigenfunctions may be classified with respect to the symmetry properties of the operator.

2
molecular
symmetry
elements

In considering the overall features of the structures of various molecules one finds certain general principles very useful for describing molecular geometry. Certain aspects of molecular geometry are similar to certain features of regular geometric solids: the tetrahedral orientation of carbon-hydrogen bonds in methane, the octahedral arrangement of the fluoride ions in the $FeF_6{}^{3-}$ complex ion, the icosahedral structure of the dodecaborohydride ion, $B_{12}H_{12}{}^{--}$, and the triangular arrangement of the nitrate ion. The geometrical equivalence of related parts of a regular solid suggests a chemical equivalence of atoms which occupy the analogous sites in molecules.

In this chapter we shall discuss the notion of equivalent atoms and the operations which relate such atoms. We first define certain purely geometrical entities known as *symmetry elements* and show how to recognize their presence in a molecular structure. Then we consider the various symmetry elements individually and investigate symmetry operations, which we shall consider as being generated by each symmetry element.

Finally we consider small (or limited) collections of symmetry elements. We shall find that an assemblage of certain elements implies the presence of certain others. This discussion leads naturally into the presentation of the material of Chap. 3, where we shall find a formal organization of the ideas concerning molecular symmetry. The basis for this formal organization is abstract group theory.

2.1 SYMMETRY ELEMENTS

We have already implied the basic nature of a symmetry operation. When performed on a molecular structure, a symmetry operation is a movement or manipulation of that structure from an initial position to a final position (or orientation) such that the initial and final positions (orientations) are indistinguishable both geometrically and physically. Thus, the effect of the symmetry operation is to interchange equivalent atoms in the structure, and thereby it cannot affect either the physical or the chemical properties of the molecular system. The symmetry operation carries the molecular system into a configuration which is equivalent to its original configuration but not necessarily identical to it.

In order to develop a firm foundation on which to build, let us develop the notion of symmetry operations from a geometrically more fundamental concept, that of the symmetry element. A symmetry element, by definition, is a geometrical entity which generates symmetry operations, i.e., a plane, line, or point with respect to which symmetry operations can be performed. The types of symmetry elements and operations encountered in molecular symmetry are summarized in Table 2.1.

Before entering into the detailed discussion of each symmetry ele-

Table 2.1   Symmetry elements and the operations generated

Element	Operation
Symmetry point or center (inversion center)	Inversion through the center
Symmetry line or proper axis (rotation axis)	Rotation about the axis
Symmetry plane (mirror plane)	Reflection through the plane
Improper symmetry axes (compound axes):‡	
Rotatory reflection axis	Successive application of rotation about the axis and reflection through the plane perpendicular to the axis
Rotatory inversion axis	Successive application of rotation about the axis and inversion through a center lying on the axis

‡ The two improper (compound) axes produce an equivalent set of operations (see Prob. 2.3).

ment and its set of operations, we need to introduce and define the identity operation. The identity operation is a "do-nothing" operation, an operation in which all parts of the molecular structure (or geometrical solid) remain in their original position, an operation in which the initial and final positions are in fact identical. It is usually given the symbol E (German *Einheit*). It must be included in this chapter for the sake of completeness and in Chap. 3 because of mathematical necessity.

2.2 THE SYMMETRY CENTER AND THE INVERSION OPERATION

The operation of inversion through a center transforms all the points of a structure into an inverted configuration. This operation may be more easily understood in terms of the operation on a general cartesian point (x, y, z). Consider a cartesian coordinate system in which the center of symmetry is located at the origin $(0, 0, 0)$, as shown in Fig. 2.1.

The action of the operation transforms the coordinates (x, y, z) into their respective negatives $(-x, -y, -z)$, and the two points are said to be related by the operation of inversion. Under the inversion operation the two points (x, y, z) and $(-x, -y, -z)$ are geometrically equivalent, and atoms which might occupy such points in a molecule are thus chemically equivalent. It should further be observed that inversion produces an enantiomer of the original.

We can symbolize the inversion operation by the equation

$$i \cdot \begin{bmatrix} x \\ y \\ z \end{bmatrix} = \begin{bmatrix} -x \\ -y \\ -z \end{bmatrix}$$

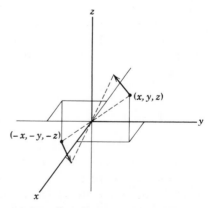

Fig. 2.1 Coordinate system illustrating the inversion operation.

Let us now observe the result of applying the inversion operation successively, as symbolized for two successive inversions by the equation

$$i \cdot i \cdot \begin{bmatrix} x \\ y \\ z \end{bmatrix} = i \cdot \begin{bmatrix} -x \\ -y \\ -z \end{bmatrix} = \begin{bmatrix} -(-x) \\ -(-y) \\ -(-z) \end{bmatrix} = \begin{bmatrix} x \\ y \\ z \end{bmatrix} \tag{2.1}$$

In the language of geometry we have returned to the original (or identical) configuration. The successive application of the inversion operation is equivalent to the identity operation. In fact repetition of the inversion operation an even number of times produces the same effect as the application of the identity operation. These repetitions of inversion may be summarized

$$i \cdot i \cdot \cdot \cdot i \cdot \cdot \cdot i = i^n = \begin{cases} i & n \text{ odd} \\ E & n \text{ even} \end{cases}$$

Thus, the symmetry (or inversion) center generates two operations, the inversion operation and the identity operation.

Let us now consider the possibility that there exists an operation which will precisely undo the inversion-through-a-center operation. Even if such an operation exists, the reader may object to considering an apparently unnecessary extra feature. However, consideration of the *undoing* operation is necessary for conceptual completeness, and it is just this type of completeness which is demanded by the rigor of the abstract group theory which we consider in Chap. 3.

We can see from previous discussion, as shown in Eq. (2.1), that application of the inversion operation twice returns the system to its original configuration. Thus, the inversion operation will undo itself. An operation which produces the effect of reversing a given symmetry operation is called the *reciprocal* of that operation and is symbolized by the superscript -1. The inversion operation is its own reciprocal. This statement, along with other properties of the reciprocal operation is summarized by

$$i \cdot i^{-1} = i^{-1} \cdot i = E$$
$$i^{-1} = i$$

Many molecular structures possess a center of symmetry; Table 2.2 lists molecules whose structures are centrosymmetric.

Notable among the structures which do not possess a center of symmetry (noncentrosymmetric) are the tetrahedral structure of CH_4, the trigonal bipyramidal structure of PF_5, and the eclipsed conformation of C_2H_6.

**Table 2.2   Molecular structures possessing
a center of symmetry‡**

Molecule	Location of center
N≡N	Center of N≡N bond
O=C=O	On the carbon atom
H—C≡C—H	Center of C≡C bond
$\begin{array}{c} \text{H} \qquad\quad \text{H} \\ \diagdown \qquad \diagup \\ \text{C=C} \\ \diagup \qquad \diagdown \\ \text{H} \qquad\quad \text{H} \end{array}$	Center of C=C bond
$\left[\begin{array}{c} \text{Cl} \qquad \text{Cl} \\ \diagdown \quad \diagup \\ \text{Pt} \\ \diagup \quad \diagdown \\ \text{Cl} \qquad \text{Cl} \end{array}\right]^{-1}$	On the platinum atom

‡ See Figs. 1 to 4 for Table 2.2 for more
examples.

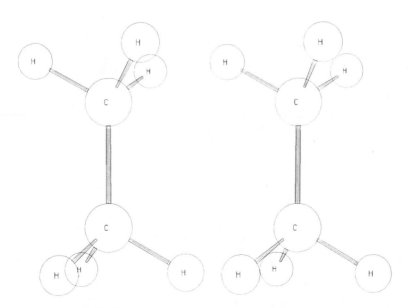

Fig. 1 for Table 2.2   Ethane (staggered), C_2H_6, has a center of symmetry
at the center of the C—C bond.

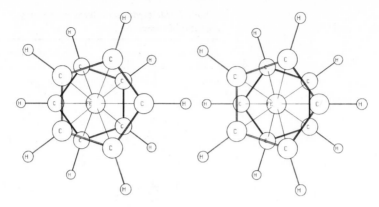

Fig. 2 for Table 2.2   Ferrocene (staggered), $(C_5H_5)_2Fe$; inversion center on the iron atom.

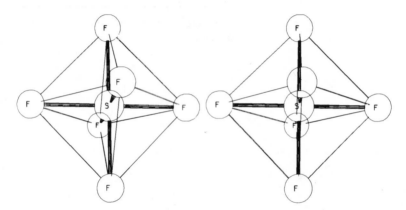

Fig. 3 for Table 2.2   Sulfur hexafluoride, SF_6; inversion center on the sulfur atom.

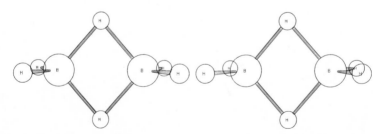

Fig. 4 for Table 2.2   Diborane, B_2H_6; center of inversion located midway between the boron atoms.

2.3 THE SYMMETRY AXIS AND THE ROTATION OPERATION

The symmetry axis is a line about which rotation through a given angle brings the structure into coincidence with itself. If the rotation operation is repeated several times, the structure must eventually be brought to a position which is identical with its original position; i.e., the structure will have gone full circle to its starting point. If the number of repetitions is the integer n, then

$$n\theta = 2\pi$$

and

$$n = \frac{2\pi}{\theta}$$

The integer n is termed the *order* of the axis, and the axis is given the symbol C_n. In addition the values of θ are restricted to values given as 2π divided by an integer.

Depending upon the order of the axis, a symmetry axis may generate several operations. In the case of the twofold axis two operations are generated: (1) a rotation of $2\pi/2 = 180°$ and (2) a rotation of $360°$. The symbol $C_n{}^m$ is used for the operation of rotation in which the angle of rotation is given as m $(360°/n)$. Thus, the symbols for the two operations generated by a twofold axis are

$$C_2 \begin{cases} C_2{}^1 \\ C_2{}^2 \end{cases}$$

Since the $C_2{}^2$ operation (rotation through $360°$) produces the same effect as the identity operation, the $C_2{}^2$ operation is equivalent to the identity operation, and we may write the twofold operations as

$$C_2 \begin{cases} C_2{}^1 \\ C_2{}^2 = E \end{cases}$$

When we consider the four operations generated by the fourfold axis, we discover that one of the operations, $C_4{}^2$, or rotation through an angle of $180°$, is equivalent to the $C_2{}^1$ operation. Thus, the operations generated by the fourfold axis may be listed as

$$C_4 \begin{cases} C_4{}^1 \\ C_4{}^2 = C_2{}^1 \\ C_4{}^3 \\ C_4{}^4 = E \end{cases}$$

A similar situation arises in the consideration of the sixfold operations. The $C_6{}^2$ operation is equivalent to the $C_3{}^1$ operation generated by a three-

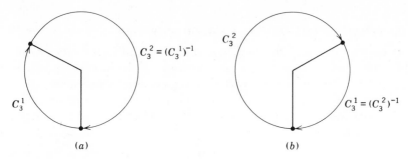

Fig. 2.2   The threefold rotations and their reciprocals.

fold axis.   (See Prob. 2.5 for the construction of a table of the operations generated by the axes of orders 1 to 6.)

The reciprocals of rotation operations are also rotation operations. The operation which will reverse the effect of rotation through 180° is also the rotation through 180°.   The reciprocal of the $C_3{}^1$ operation is, however, the $C_3{}^2$ operation, as can be seen in Fig. 2.2.   That this is true may easily be seen in the general equation

$$C_n{}^m(C_n{}^m)^{-1} = C_n{}^m C_n{}^p = E = C_n{}^n$$

Therefore

$$m + p = n$$

or

$$p = n - m$$

Thus, $C_5{}^1$ is the reciprocal of $C_5{}^4$ and so forth.   (Further exercise may be obtained in Prob. 2.5.)

Table 2.3 contains a list of molecular structures which possess symmetry axes.

For a detailed discussion of the action of the rotation operation on a general cartesian point see Chap. 5.

2.4   THE SYMMETRY PLANE AND THE REFLECTION OPERATION

When an object is placed a given distance in front of a mirror, an observer located at the same position as the object perceives that the image of the object is located an equal distance behind the mirror.   Thus, the reflection operation transforms the object into its *mirror* (enantiomorphous) *image*.

Table 2.3 Molecular structures which possess rotation axes ‡

Molecule	Location of axis
$O=C=O$	A C_∞ axis collinear with the O—C—O direction
$H \quad\quad H$ $C=C$ $H \quad\quad H$	A C_2 axis along the C=C bond
F $\mid$ B $F \quad F$	A C_3 axis perpendicular to the molecular plane through the boron atom
$\left[\begin{array}{cc} Cl & Cl \\ & Pt \\ Cl & Cl \end{array}\right]^{-1}$	A C_4 axis perpendicular to the molecular plane through the platinum atom
benzene structure	A C_6 axis perpendicular to the molecular plane through the center of the ring and C_2 axes along C—H bonds and bisecting each C—C bond.

‡ See Figs. 1 to 8 for Table 2.3 for more examples.

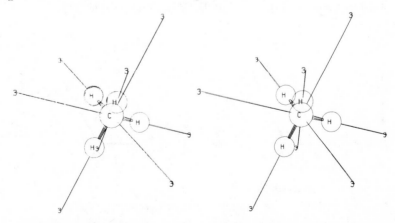

Fig. 1 for Table 2.3 Methane, CH_4; threefold axes along each C—H bond and twofold axes bisecting each H—C—H bond angle.

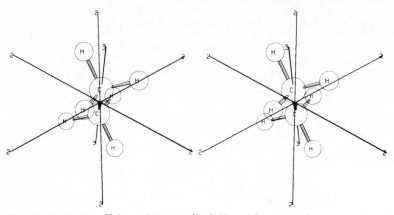

Fig. 2 for Table 2.3   Ethane (staggered), C_2H_6, with axes as shown.

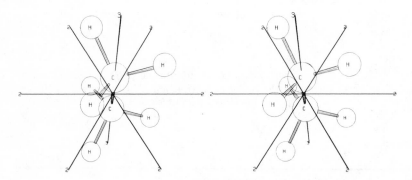

Fig. 3 for Table 2.3   Ethane (eclipsed), C_2H_6, with axes as shown.

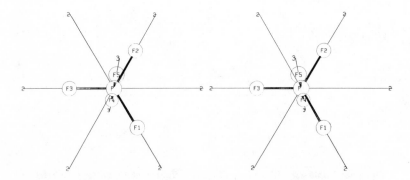

Fig. 4 for Table 2.3   Phosphorous pentafluoride, PF_5, with axes as shown.

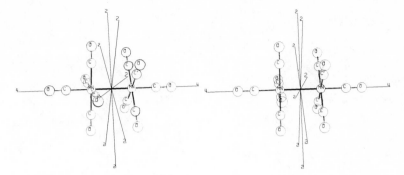

Fig. 5a for Table 2.3 Manganese decacarbonyl, $Mn_2(CO)_{10}$, with axes as shown.

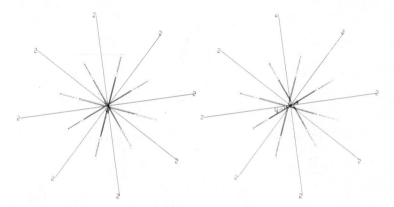

Fig. 5b for Table 2.3 Manganese decacarbonyl, $Mn_2(CO)_{10}$, with axes as shown.

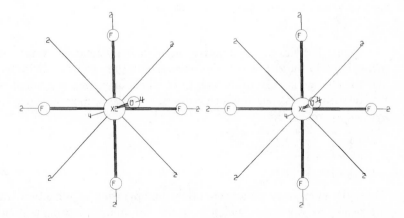

Fig. 6 for Table 2.3 Tetrafluoro xenonoxide, XeF_4O, with axes as shown.

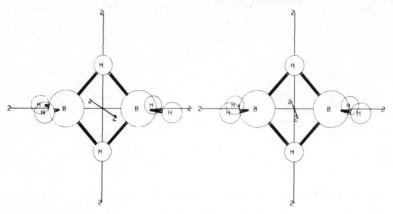

Fig. 7 for Table 2.3   Diborane, B_2H_6, with axes as shown.

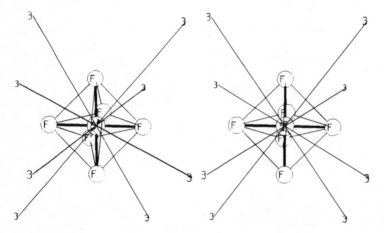

Fig. 8 for Table 2.3   Sulfur hexafluoride, SF_6, with axes as shown.

Figure 2.3 shows a symmetry plane, usually referred to as a mirror plane, lying in the xz plane.   In this case only the y coordinate is changed, and the change is only to its negative.   This operation is symbolized by the following equation, in which σ (German *Spiegel*, mirror) is used as the symbol for reflection:

$$\sigma \begin{bmatrix} x \\ y \\ z \end{bmatrix} = \begin{bmatrix} x \\ -y \\ z \end{bmatrix}$$

Thus, the symmetry plane generates the operation of reflection through the plane, an operation which produces an enantiomorphous image (as does the inversion operation also).

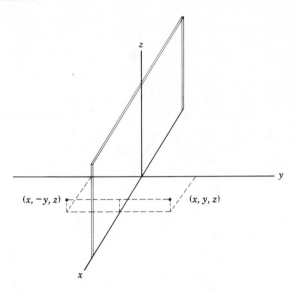

Fig. 2.3 Coordinate system illustrating reflection in a mirror in the *xz* plane.

Since successive application of reflection returns the system to its original configuration, it is seen that reflection is its own reciprocal.

$$\sigma \cdot \sigma^{-1} = \sigma^{-1} \cdot \sigma = E$$
$$\sigma^{-1} = \sigma$$

Table 2.4 lists molecular structures which possess symmetry planes.

Table 2.4   Molecular structures which possess mirror planes‡

Molecule	Location of mirror planes
N≡N	An infinite number of planes containing the N≡N bond; a plane perpendicular to the N≡N bond at the bond center
H\C=C/H (H/ \H)	Two planes perpendicular to the molecular plane, one containing the C=C bond and one perpendicular to the C=C bond through its center
F–B (F/ \F)	The molecular plane and three planes perpendicular to the molecular plane each containing a B—F bond
S=C=S	An infinite number of planes containing the molecular axis in addition to a plane perpendicular to the molecular axis containing the carbon atom.

‡ See Figs. 1 to 5 for Table 2.4 for more examples.

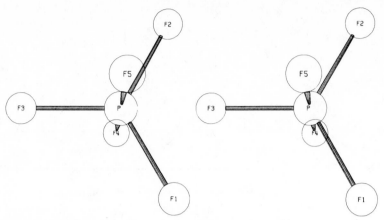

Fig. 1 for Table 2.4   Phosphorous pentafluoride, PF_5.

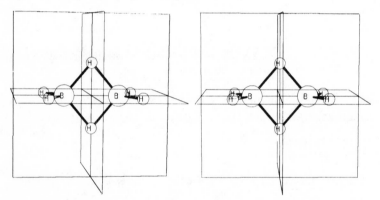

Fig. 2 for Table 2.4   Diborane, B_2H_6, showing the three mutually perpendicular mirror planes.

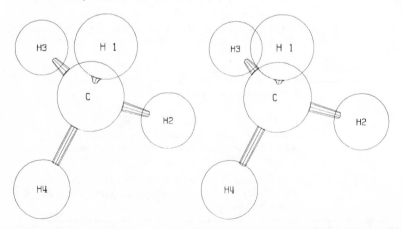

Fig. 3 for Table 2.4   Methane, CH_4, with six mirror planes such as the one defined by H_1—C—H_2.

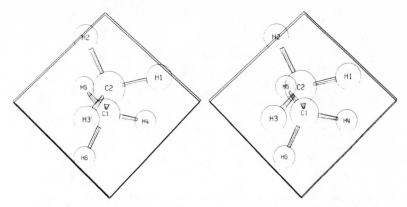

Fig. 4 for Table 2.4   Ethane (eclipsed), C_2H_6, showing the horizontal mirror plane.

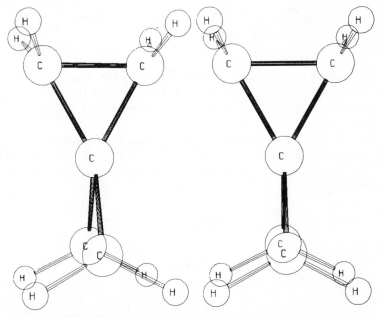

Fig. 5 for Table 2.4   Spiropentane, C_5H_8, with two mirror planes, each defined by one of the three-membered rings.

2.5   THE IMPROPER AXIS AND THE OPERATION OF IMPROPER ROTATION

The *improper axis*, so called, is actually a compound element composed of a symmetry axis perpendicular to a symmetry plane neither element of which necessarily generates its own symmetry operations independently. Each operation consists of a rotation immediately followed by a reflection. The symbol for the nth-order improper axis is S_n, and the compound

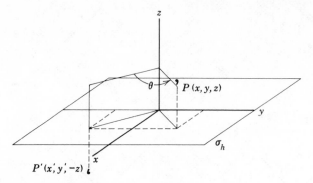

Fig. 2.4 Coordinate system illustrating the improper rotation. The rotation axis is in the conventional vertical direction perpendicular to the horizontal mirror plane.

nature of the improper axis is shown by

$$S_n = \sigma_h C_n$$

The geometrical relation of the elements which constitute the improper axis is shown in Fig. 2.4 along with two points related by an improper rotation. The symmetry plane is given the subscript h because of its conventional horizontal orientation.

The improper axis generates a series of operations denoted as $S_n{}^m$, and each operation comprises a series of operations each of which is a rotation through an angle θ $(= 2\pi/n)$ followed by reflection in the horizontal plane.

$$\overset{m \text{ times}}{S_n{}^m = \sigma_h C_n{}^1 \cdot \cdot \cdot \sigma_h C_n{}^1}$$

or

$$S_n{}^m = \sigma_h{}^m C_n{}^m$$

because

$$\sigma_h C_n{}^1 = C_n{}^1 \sigma_h$$

There are two observations to be made at this point:

1. For m odd, $\sigma_h{}^m = \sigma$ and $S_n{}^m = \sigma C_n{}^m$.
2. For m even, $\sigma_h{}^m = E$ and $S_n{}^m = C_n{}^m$.

Further, we note a difference in the operations generated by S_n depending on whether n is even or odd. When n is odd,

$$S_n{}^n = \sigma_h{}^n C_n{}^n = \sigma_h$$

and the symmetry plane must exist independently of the improper axis. Further, consideration of the next to last operation, $n - 1$, and the $n + 1$ operation

$$S_n^{n-1} = \sigma_h^{n-1} C_n^{n-1} = E C_n^{n-1} = C_n^{n-1}$$
$$S_n^{n+1} = \sigma_h^{n+1} C_n^{n+1} = E C_n^1 = C_n^1$$

shows that the proper symmetry axis must also exist independently. That both the symmetry plane and proper axis exist independently of the improper axis is not necessarily true of the improper axis of even order. Let us consider this question in more detail by examining several of the improper axes and the operations they generate, starting with those of even order.

The improper axis of order 2 generates two operations. These operations can be more readily pictured by using Fig. 2.4 and considering the effect of operation on the general cartesian point (x, y, z).

1. The first operation consists of rotation through 180° followed by reflection in the xy plane:

$$S_2^1 = \sigma_h C_2^1$$

and

$$S_2^1 \begin{bmatrix} x \\ y \\ z \end{bmatrix} = \sigma_h C_2^1 \begin{bmatrix} x \\ y \\ z \end{bmatrix} = \sigma_h \begin{bmatrix} -x \\ -y \\ +z \end{bmatrix} = \begin{bmatrix} -x \\ -y \\ -z \end{bmatrix}$$

2. The second operation is obtained by following the first operation with another 180° rotation and reflection in the xy plane:

$$S_2^2 \begin{bmatrix} x \\ y \\ z \end{bmatrix} = S_2^1 \begin{bmatrix} -x \\ -y \\ -z \end{bmatrix} = \begin{bmatrix} -(-x) \\ -(-y) \\ -(-z) \end{bmatrix} = \begin{bmatrix} x \\ y \\ z \end{bmatrix}$$

It is easily seen that these two operations are equivalent to the two operations generated by a symmetry center. Thus, the improper axis of order 2 is usually referred to by its equivalent name, *center of inversion*.

$$S_2 \equiv i$$

How many operations are generated by an even-order improper axis? To answer this question let us consider the meaning of the equation

$$S_n^n = \sigma_h^n C_n^n$$

Since n is even,

$$\sigma_h^n = E \qquad \text{and} \qquad C_n^n = E$$

Thus,

$$S_n{}^n = E$$

and the number of operations generated (E included) is n because the sequence of rotation-reflection need be performed only n times to return the system to its initial point.

As a final case of even-order improper axes let us consider order 4 and the operations generated: $S_4{}^1, S_4{}^2, S_4{}^3, S_4{}^4$. We can write these operations in somewhat more detail as follows:

$$S_4{}^1 = \sigma_h C_4{}^1 = S_4{}^1$$
$$S_4{}^2 = \sigma_h{}^2 C_4{}^2 = C_4{}^2 = C_2{}^1$$
$$S_4{}^3 = \sigma_h C_4{}^3 = S_4{}^3$$
$$S_4{}^4 = \sigma_h{}^4 C_4{}^4 = E$$

On this basis we observe that a twofold proper axis exists, along with the fourfold improper axis. In general we find that the existence of an S_n axis requires the presence of a $C_{n/2}$ axis. The improper axis of order n generates $n/2$ improper rotations, $n/2 - 1$ proper rotations, and the identity, for a total of n operations.

Let us now turn our consideration to the odd-order improper axes. We shall find that odd-order improper axes imply (or require) the independent existence of both the proper axis of the same order and the symmetry plane perpendicular to the axis. To demonstrate this feature let us examine in some detail the operations generated by an S_5 improper axis. The operations and their equivalents are

$$S_5{}^1 = \sigma_h C_5{}^1 = S_5{}^1$$
$$S_5{}^2 = \sigma_h{}^2 C_5{}^2 = C_5{}^2$$
$$S_5{}^3 = \sigma_h{}^3 C_5{}^3 = \sigma_h C_5{}^3 = S_5{}^3$$
$$S_5{}^4 = \sigma_h{}^4 C_5{}^4 = C_5{}^4$$
$$S_5{}^5 = \sigma_h{}^5 C_5{}^5 = \sigma_h$$
$$S_5{}^6 = \sigma_h{}^6 C_5{}^6 = C_5{}^1$$
$$S_5{}^7 = \sigma_h{}^7 C_5{}^7 = \sigma_h C_5{}^2 = S_5{}^2$$
$$S_5{}^8 = \sigma_h{}^8 C_5{}^8 = C_5{}^3$$
$$S_5{}^9 = \sigma_h{}^9 C_5{}^9 = \sigma_h C_5{}^4 = S_5{}^4$$
$$S_5{}^{10} = \sigma_h{}^{10} C_5{}^{10} = E C_5{}^5 = E$$

Note that

$$C_n{}^{n+p} = C_n{}^p$$

Thus, the S_5 improper axis generates 10 ($= 2 \times n$) operations which may be considered as follows:

$$S_5 \begin{cases} C_5{}^1,\ C_5{}^2,\ C_5{}^3,\ C_5{}^4 \\ S_5{}^1,\ S_5{}^2,\ S_5{}^3,\ S_5{}^4 \\ \sigma_h \\ E \end{cases}$$

In general, an improper axis of odd order n implies the independent existence of a proper axis of order n as well as the symmetry plane perpendicular to the proper axis. Thus, the total of $2n$ operations may all be expressed as some combination of rotation with reflection but not necessarily independently of each other.

Table 2.5 lists some molecular structures which possess improper axes.

Table 2.5   Molecular structures which contain improper rotation axes‡

Molecule	Location of improper axis
F B F F	An S_3 axis perpendicular to the molecular plane through the boron atom
⌈Cl Cl⌉⁻ Pt ⌊Cl Cl⌋	An S_4 axis perpendicular to the molecular plane through the platinum atom

‡ See Figs. 1 to 5 for Table 2.5 for more examples.

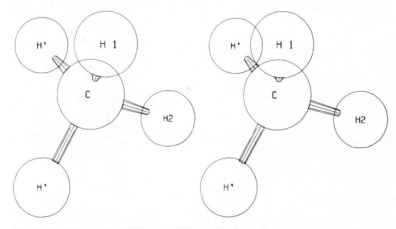

Fig. 1 for Table 2.5   Methane, CH_4, with four S_4 axes, each bisecting a H—C—H bond angle.

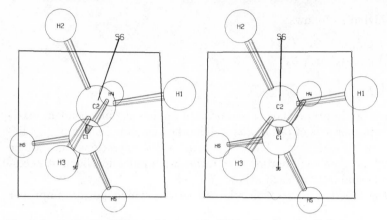

Fig. 2 for Table 2.5   Ethane (staggered), C_2H_6, showing the S_6 improper axis.

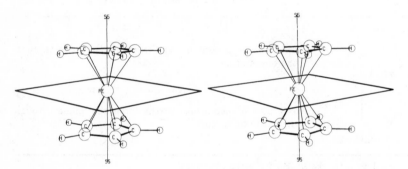

Fig. 3 for Table 2.5   Ferrocene (eclipsed), $(C_5H_5)_2Fe$, showing the S_5 improper axis.

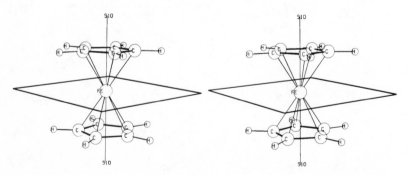

Fig. 4 for Table 2.5   Ferrocene (staggered), $(C_5H_5)_2Fe$, showing the S_{10} improper axis.

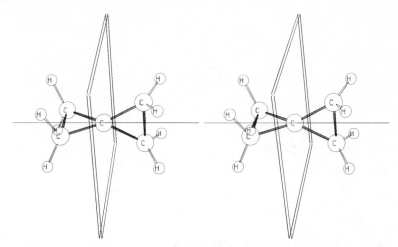

Fig. 5 for Table 2.5 Spiropentane, C_5H_8, showing the S_4 improper axis (unlabeled).

2.6 SYMMETRY ELEMENTS OF INFINITE ORDER

We have considered only symmetry elements which generate a finite number of operations. However, the molecular axis of a linear molecule generates an infinite number of rotation operations, and the molecular axis contains an infinite number of symmetry planes. A rotation about the molecular axis through any angle will, of course, leave the linear molecule undisturbed. Thus, the symmetry axis along the molecular axis of a linear molecule is given the symbol C_∞.

A molecule such as N_2 or $CH{\equiv}CH$ also possesses an improper axis of infinite order, since rotation around the molecular axis through any angle followed by reflection through the symmetry plane which bisects the central bond ($N{\equiv}N$ or $C{\equiv}C$) brings the system into self-coincidence. We shall return to these operations briefly in Chap. 4.

2.7 COLLECTIONS OF SYMMETRY ELEMENTS

In Chap. 3 we shall develop the elements of group theory which will allow us to deal with "complete" collections of symmetry operations in a formal manner. Let us first consider two examples of small groups of symmetry elements and indicate how the collection of certain symmetry elements implies the existence of another element.

Consider the symmetry elements shown in Fig. 2.5. We shall discuss the equivalent points generated by two of the mutually perpendicular twofold axes shown in the figure, those along the x and y directions. The $C_2(x)$ operation changes the general cartesian point I (x, y, z) into point II

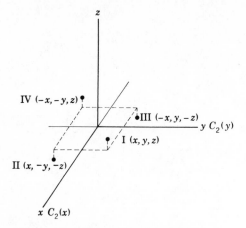

Fig. 2.5 Coordinate system and four labeled points showing that two mutually perpendicular twofold axes generate a third mutually perpendicular twofold axis.

$(x,\ -y,\ -z)$. The $C_2(y)$ axis changes the general cartesian point into point III $(-x, y, -z)$ and point II $(x, -y, -z)$ into point IV $(-x, -y, z)$. The two axes produce four equivalent general points. However, we should observe that point I is also related to point III by a twofold operation along the z axis.   A similar relation exists between points II and IV. Thus, the two twofold axes in the x and y directions imply a third twofold axis mutually perpendicular to the first two along the z axis.

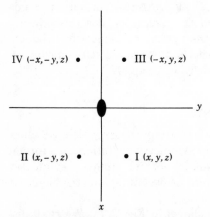

Fig. 2.6 Coordinate system and four labeled points showing that a vertical n-fold axis containing a mirror plane generates a total of n vertical mirror planes.

A similar situation arises in the system in Fig. 2.6, a vertical twofold axis and a single vertical symmetry plane containing the twofold axis. The four general points shown in the figure are generated in the following way:

$$\sigma I \rightarrow II$$
$$C_2{}^1 I \rightarrow IV$$
$$\sigma IV \rightarrow III$$

However, we can see that points I and III are related as if there were a symmetry plane in the yz plane. Thus, a twofold axis with a single symmetry plane containing the symmetry axis implies the existence of a second symmetry plane perpendicular to the first. This specific case may be considered in a more general fashion, as in Prob. 2.6: a proper axis of order n containing at least one vertical mirror plane must have a total of n vertical mirror planes. In Chap. 4 we shall consider this problem further in somewhat more detail.

PROBLEMS

2.1. Show in a *general* manner that the presence of an odd-order improper axis implies the existence of a proper axis of the same order and a symmetry plane perpendicular to the axis.

2.2. Write the symbols for the operations generated by the improper axis of order 6 and determine whether any of the operations are equivalent to the simpler operations of rotation or reflection. Is a proper axis implied in this case? An independent horizontal symmetry plane?

2.3. Consider the compound axis of rotation-inversion. Show that the improper-rotation axis produces the same set of equivalent points as the rotation-inversion axis: try axes of order 3, 4, and 6. What about the axis of order 2?

2.4. Consider the possibility that there exists a rotation axis which generates an operation $C_n{}^1$ in which the rotation angle θ is defined as $2\pi/n$, where n is not an integer. Show that such an assumption is inconsistent with the definition of a symmetry operation.

2.5. List the symmetry operations generated by each of the symmetry axes of order 1 to 6 along with any equivalent operations and the reciprocals for each operation. Construct a table with the following headings:

Order   Symbol   Equivalent   Reciprocal
                   Operations

2.6. Show that in the general case the existence of an n-fold axis of rotation together with at least one symmetry plane which contains the axis requires the existence of a total of n such symmetry planes. (Pursue the technique of Sec. 2.7 in a general manner.)

2.7. List all the symmetry elements in each of the following molecules:
- (*a*) C_5H_6, cyclopentadiene (nonplanar carbon skeleton)
- (*b*) C_5H_6, cyclopentadiene (planar carbon skeleton)
- (*c*) $C_5H_5^-$
- (*d*) CH_4; CH_3Cl; CH_2Cl_2
- (*e*) H_2CCO, ketene
- (*f*) *cis*-N_2F_2; *trans*-N_2F_2
- (*g*) B_2H_6, diborane
- (*h*) C_3H_6, cyclopropane
- (*i*) C_6H_{12}, cyclohexane, chair form and boat form
- (*j*) Cl_3PO, trichlorophosphine oxide
- (*k*) $H_2C_2C_2O_3$, maleic anhydride
- (*l*) $C_{10}H_8$, naphthalene
- (*m*) $(C_6H_6)_2Cr$, dibenzenechromium
- (*n*) PF_5
- (*o*) imidazole; pyrazole
- (*p*) C_2H_6, ethane, staggered and eclipsed
- (*q*) SO_2
- (*r*) IF_7

2.8. In the ion FeF_6^{3-}, which is octahedral, what symmetry elements are destroyed if two trans F^- ions are moved further away from the Fe^{3+} than the other four F^- ions? What symmetry elements remain?

2.9. Consider an octahedron in which two opposite triangular faces are pulled apart a short distance. Make a drawing looking down on these two triangular faces. What symmetry elements remain? (This figure is called a *trigonal antiprism*.) Compare your list of symmetry elements with those obtained in Prob. 2.8 for the undistorted FeF_6^{3-} ion.

REFERENCES

Cotton, F. A.: "Chemical Applications of Group Theory," chap. 4, Interscience Publishers, Inc., New York, 1964.

Daniels, F., and R. A. Alberty: "Physical Chemistry," 3d ed., chap. 13, John Wiley & Sons, Inc., New York, 1966.

Hochstrasser, Robin M.: "Molecular Aspects of Symmetry," chaps. 1 and 3, W. A. Benjamin, Inc., New York, 1966.

Jaffé, H. H., and Milton Orchin: "Symmetry in Chemistry," chaps. 2 and 3, John Wiley & Sons, Inc., New York, 1965.

Schonland, D. S.: "Molecular Symmetry," chap. 2, D. Van Nostrand Company, Inc., Princeton. N.J., 1965.

3

elements
of
group
theory

In this chapter we deal with abstract group theory. We shall find that group theory is not concerned with the nature of the elements which comprise the group but with the consequences of the law of combination of the elements of the group, dealing with the formal structure which evolves from the combination law. Thus, group theory may be studied completely in the abstract using only the group multiplication table to describe the group. Because of the rather intimate relation of group theory to principles of geometry, group theory may be thought of as an algebra of geometry.

For the purpose of illustration, however, we shall introduce concrete groups in this chapter. Certain of the examples will involve molecular symmetry operations to prepare for the formal connection established between abstract group theory and molecular symmetry in Chap. 4.

3.1 DEFINITION OF A GROUP

A group is a collection of elements which is closed under a single-valued associative binary operation, which contains a single element satisfying the identity law, and which possesses a reciprocal element for each element of the collection.

Let us consider the various parts of this definition in some detail.

1. *Collection.*   A specified number.

2. *Elements.*   The constituents of the group (which may be abstract and only given symbolic names such as alphabetic letters).

3. *Binary operation.*   The basic law which defines the combination of elements; the operation may be the familiar addition, subtraction, or multiplication in the algebraic sense, or it may be the successive application of symmetry operations to a geometrical figure; the combination is defined *only* for two elements at a time.

4. *Single-valued.*   The combination of two elements yields a unique result.

5. *Closed.*   The combination of any two group elements must yield another element in the group.

6. *Associative.*   The associative law of combination must hold. Consider three elements of a group: A, B, C.   When these are combined, the following equation must hold:

$$(AB)C = A(BC)$$

The parentheses indicate that the quantities contained within them must be combined before being combined with the elements outside the parentheses.   The associative law states that the order with respect to the parentheses is immaterial.

7. *The identity law.*   There must be an element in the group which in combination with all elements leaves them unchanged.   This element is called the *identity* or *unit element,* and it commutes with all elements of the group.   The identity is given the symbol E.   For the group elements A, B, and C the following sets of equations define the identity:

$$EA = A \qquad EB = B \qquad EC = C$$
$$EA = AE \qquad EB = BE \qquad EC = CE$$

8. *A reciprocal element.*   For each element A in the group there must be an element called the *reciprocal,* A^{-1}, such that the following equation holds:

$$AA^{-1} = A^{-1}A = E$$

(see Prob. 3.1).

The definition of a group requires the presence of an element which commutes with all other elements in the group.   However, group multiplication is not commutative in general: $AB \neq BA$.   A group in which the multiplication (combination) is completely commutative is called an *abelian group.*

Let us now consider the following two equations involving elements of a group containing a, b, c, x, y, and E:

$$xa = b$$
$$ay = c$$

Let us show that such equations have a unique solution by performing the following manipulations:

$$
\begin{aligned}
b &= bE &&\text{definition of identity}\\
&= ba^{-1}a &&\text{definition of reciprocal}\\
&= (ba^{-1})a &&\text{law of association}
\end{aligned}
$$

also

$$b = xa$$

Therefore

$$b = (ba^{-1})a = xa$$

and finally,

$$ba^{-1} = x \qquad \text{Q.E.D.}$$

Thus, it is possible to construct a table whose entries are products (combinations) of all group elements. Such an array is called the *group multiplication table*. Since there is an identity operation, there must be one row and one column which simply repeat the row and column headings. Because multiplication is unique, each row and column will contain each group element once and only once.

3.2 MULTIPLICATION TABLES AND ISOMORPHISM

Let us consider three groups and construct their multiplication tables: (1) the group of the threefold rotations of an equilateral triangle, (2) the group of integers modulo 3 under addition, and (3) a purely abstract group of three letters. By definition, two groups whose multiplication tables are identical are said to be *isomorphous;* there is a one-to-one correspondence between the elements of the two groups. We shall see that the three groups described above are isomorphous.

Let us consider the purely abstract group first. It consists of the letters A, B, and E, and its multiplication table is

	E	A	B
E	E	A	B
A	A	B	E
B	B	E	A

The order of the elements as they are taken in combination is, of course, very important. We shall adopt the usual convention that an entry is produced by column heading left-multiplied by row heading as shown by the following illustration.

	$\cdots\cdots\quad\cdots\cdots\quad\cdots\cdots\quad C\quad\cdots$
$\cdots$	$\cdots\cdots\quad\cdots\cdots\quad\cdots\cdots\quad\cdots\cdots\quad\cdots\cdots$
$\cdots$	$\cdots\cdots\quad\cdots\cdots\quad\cdots\cdots\quad\cdots\cdots\quad\cdots\cdots$
B	$\cdots\cdots\quad\cdots\cdots\quad\cdots\cdots\quad D\quad\cdots$
$\cdots$	$\cdots\cdots\quad\cdots\cdots\quad\cdots\cdots\quad\cdots\cdots\quad\cdots\cdots$
$\cdots$	$\cdots\cdots\quad\cdots\cdots\quad\cdots\cdots\quad\cdots\cdots\quad\cdots\cdots$

In this case the element D is produced as follows:

$$BC = D$$

(Note that this convention is identical to that for the combination of matrices.) All the information we have concerning the abstract group is contained in the multiplication table. Indeed, this is all the information necessary for the study of this group! The power of methods built upon group-theoretical considerations is that physical systems—no matter how apparently different or unrelated—whose symmetries are based on the same group multiplication table can be treated by the same mathematical formalism.

Let us now consider the group of the threefold rotations of an equilateral triangle by referring to Fig. 3.1. We have labeled the vertices of the triangle to make the effect of the various rotations easier to see. Figure 3.1a to c demonstrates the application of a single operation. Figure 3.1d shows the successive application of the $C_3{}^2$ operation, an example of the combination or multiplication of these two operations (group ele-

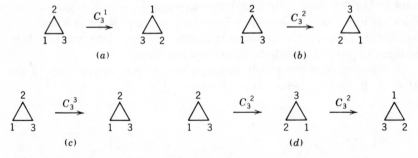

Fig. 3.1   The properties of the threefold rotations of a triangle.   (a) Action of $C_3{}^1$; (b) action of $C_3{}^2$; (c) action of $C_3{}^3$; (d) action of $C_3{}^2$ followed by $C_3{}^2$.

ments).   On the basis of these figures we can construct the multiplication table

	$C_3{}^3 = E$	$C_3{}^1$	$C_3{}^2$
$C_3{}^3 = E$	E	$C_3{}^1$	$C_3{}^2$
$C_3{}^1$	$C_3{}^1$	$C_3{}^2$	E
$C_3{}^2$	$C_3{}^2$	E	$C_3{}^1$

Finally, let us consider the integers modulo 3 under addition.   The law of combination is addition.   The following equations illustrate the results of group multiplication:

$$0 + 0 = 0 \qquad 0 + 1 = 1 \qquad 0 + 2 = 2$$
$$2 + 0 = 2 \qquad 2 + 1 = 0 \qquad 2 + 2 = 1$$

The multiplication table then is

	0	1	2
0	0	1	2
1	1	2	0
2	2	0	1

Because of the manner in which these three multiplication tables have been prepared, the fact that they are identical (apart from the symbols used) is readily apparent.   Examination of the three tables establishes the one-to-one correspondence of these groups as follows:

$$A \rightarrow C_3{}^1 \rightarrow 1$$
$$B \rightarrow C_3{}^2 \rightarrow 2$$
$$E \rightarrow C_3{}^3 \rightarrow 0$$

We also observe that these groups are abelian.   The abelian nature of a group is readily detected in the appearance of the multiplication table: the entries in the table are symmetrically disposed across the diagonal (the principal diagonal runs from upper left to lower right).

3.3 SUBGROUPS AND COSETS

For the purpose of discussing the definitions, meanings, and uses of subgroups and cosets let us consider the operations generated by certain of the symmetry elements of a square as shown in Fig. 3.2.   The operations we shall use here are E, $C_4{}^1$, $C_4{}^2 = C_2{}^1$, $C_4{}^3$, σ_v, σ_v', σ_d, and σ_d'.   The subscripts on the symmetry-plane symbols (σ_v, etc.), which serve here as

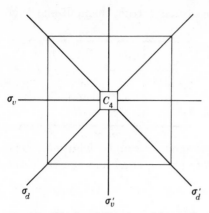

Fig. 3.2   The fourfold axis and four mirror planes of the symmetry of a square.

merely identifying or distinguishing labels, will take on added significance in Chap. 4.

A *subgroup* is a subset of the elements of a group, the subset also being a group.   The number of elements in a subgroup is usually smaller than g, the order of the group.   The set of all the elements of a group is, of course, also a subgroup.   Such a subgroup of the whole group is called an *improper subgroup*, as is the subgroup composed only of the identity element.

There is a problem in determining all the subgroups of a given group. We shall consider two methods for determining subgroups.   The second method is a pictorial technique, which is useful in considering molecules of related symmetries.

A group element may be combined with itself to produce another element in the group.

$$a \cdot a = a^2 = c$$

Let us denote the collection of elements generated by an element and all its powers as the *generation of the element* and give such a collection the symbol $\{a\}$.   Thus, $\{b\}$ denotes the element b and all its powers, and $\{ab\}$ denotes all the powers of a plus all the powers of b plus all the powers of the product ab.   Any group which can be generated entirely from one element is called a *cyclic group*.   The lowest positive integer n which satisfies the following equations is called the *order* of the element:

$$a^n = E$$

and

$$a^{n+1} = a$$

Thus, the generation of each group element is a subgroup. However, each element does not necessarily generate a subgroup distinct from all others generated by the remaining group elements.

Let us consider the symmetry operations of the square, given earlier. Table 3.1 lists all the subgroups which are generated by elements and their powers. All those above the crossrule are generated by a single element, and, hence, these subgroups are all cyclic.

Table 3.1 Generators and subgroups of some of the operations of the square

Subgroup elements	Generator	Order
σ_v, E	σ_v	2
σ_v', E	σ_v'	2
σ_d, E	σ_d	2
σ_d', E	σ_d'	2
$C_4{}^2$, E	$C_4{}^2 = C_2{}^1$	2
$C_4{}^1$, $C_4{}^2$, $C_4{}^3$, E	$C_4{}^1$ or $C_4{}^3$	4
E (improper)	E	1
σ_v, σ_v', $C_4{}^2$, E	σ_v, σ_v'	2
σ_d, σ_d', $C_4{}^2$, E	σ_d, σ_d'	2
$C_4{}^1$, $C_4{}^2$, $C_4{}^3$, σ_v, σ_v', σ_d, σ_d', E (improper)	σ_v, σ_d	2

Let us now consider generations of the product of two operations. Any generator consisting of the identity and another group element yields no new subgroups. We find that $\sigma_v\sigma_v'$ does produce a new subgroup involving the $C_4{}^2$ operation.

$$\{\sigma_v\sigma_v'\} \equiv \sigma_v, \sigma_v', C_4{}^2, E$$

Likewise $\{\sigma_d\sigma_d'\} = \sigma_d, \sigma_d', C_4{}^2, E$. Finally, the generation of $\{\sigma_v\sigma_d\}$ yields the whole group and is thus termed an improper group. In this manner one can determine all the subgroups systematically.

The second method is a pictorial method based on a systematic technique of destroying symmetry elements. Let us first consider Fig. 3.3a, which shows the location of all the equivalent points of the geometrical group under consideration. The darkened circles represent the equivalent points, i.e., symmetry-related points, of the group. By selectively making certain points nonequivalent the elements of the various subgroups are revealed. Figure 3.3b shows the result of attaching three extra symbols to the equivalent points. The following collections of elements are still groups although certain of the symmetry elements may no longer exist; consider Fig. 3.3b *three times, once* for each symbol *alone*.

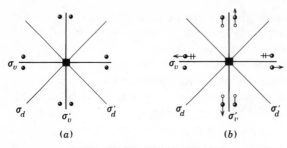

(a) $\qquad\qquad\qquad\qquad$ (b)

Fig. 3.3 (a) All the equivalent points of a particular group of the square; (b) symbols used in reducing the symmetry of the set of equivalent points.

1. When the symbol $\rightarrow$ is added to Fig. 3.3a, only the fourfold axis remains. Hence $C_4{}^1$, $C_4{}^2$, $C_4{}^3$, E must be a subgroup.
2. When the symbol $\updownarrow$ is introduced, only σ_v' remains valid. Hence σ_v', E must be a subgroup.
3. The symbol φ destroys all operations but the following, which must be a subgroup: σ_v, σ_v', $C_4{}^2$, E.

If one proceeds in this manner systematically, all the subgroups can be located. In the same manner the skilled observer may be able to see structural similarities in pairs of molecules by consideration of the various operations by subgroups.

Let us now consider a group G and a subgroup of G denoted H. Consider the collection of products of all elements in H with an element in G. This collection is called a *coset*. If multiplication (combination) is from the right, the coset is termed a *right coset* and written

$\qquad Ha \qquad$ where $a \in G$

The symbol $\in$ is read "is a member of." Let us suppose that the group G contains the following elements: a, b, c, d, q, r, s, and e. Subgroup H is composed of the last four elements: q, r, s, and e. Then, the following are right cosets:

$$
\begin{array}{lll}
qa & qb & qc \\
ra & rb & rc \\
sa & sb & sc \\
ea & eb & ec
\end{array}
$$

Notice that if the element q is a member of H, $q \in H$, then

$\qquad Hq = H$

It is possible to form left cosets when the multiplication is from the left.

Let us consider two useful theorems which are stated as lemmas.

Lemma one: All right cosets of a subgroup H of group G contain the same number of elements.

Since the elements of the cosets are simply products of elements in group g, the elements Ha, etc., must all be distinct.   Thus, the number of elements in any coset of H is simply equal to the order of subgroup H.

Lemma two: If two cosets contain one element in common, they contain all elements in common.

Suppose that two cosets Ha and Hb have one element, u, in common:

$$u = h'a = h''b \qquad h', h'' \in H$$

Then Hb contains every element of the type

$$ha = hh'^{-1}h'a = hh'^{-1}h''b = ha \qquad hh'^{-1}h'' \in H$$

found in Ha, and similarly Ha contains every element in Hb.   Thus

$$Ha = Hb \qquad \text{Q.E.D.}$$

Since any coset Ha must contain the identity, a group G is exhausted by its right cosets.   In this manner we can see that all the right cosets of a subgroup H form a collection of nonoverlapping subsets, each subset possessing the same number of elements as H does.   This conclusion for finite groups brings us to the statement of the *theorem of Lagrange:* The order of a subgroup must be a divisor of the group order.   This theorem may be stated in terms of an equation:

$$nh = g \qquad n = 1, 2, 3, \ldots$$

3.4 CLASSES OF GROUP ELEMENTS

Element A is said to be *conjugate* to element B when the two elements are related as follows:

$$A = X^{-1}BX$$

This relation is also known as a similarity transformation, and A is said to be similar to B under X.   Because of the reciprocal relation of X^{-1} and X, the similarity transformation has a certain symmetry: B is also similar to A.

$$B = XAX^{-1} = Y^{-1}AY \qquad \text{where } Y = X^{-1}$$

Further, if C and D are conjugate to another element in the group, F, then C and D must be conjugate to each other.

$$C = U^{-1}FU \qquad \text{and} \qquad D = V^{-1}FV$$

From the second of these relations it follows that

$$F = VDV^{-1}$$

and

$$\begin{aligned} C &= U^{-1}(VDV^{-1})U \\ &= (U^{-1}V)D(V^{-1}U) \end{aligned}$$

It may easily be shown that

$$U^{-1}V = (V^{-1}U)^{-1}$$

(see Prob. 3.3). Thus

$$C = (V^{-1}U)^{-1}D(V^{-1}U)$$

Since $V^{-1}U$ is also an element in the group, say W, we can write the following equation which shows that C and D are conjugate:

$$C = W^{-1}DW$$

By definition a class of elements is a collection of group elements which are conjugate to one another. The procedure for determining the classes in a group involves working out all the similarity transformations for each element. Those sets of elements which transform into themselves are then the classes. Let us consider a specific example, the symmetry operations generated by the symmetry elements of the ammonia molecule as shown in Fig. 3.4.

The operations of this group are $C_3{}^1$, $C_3{}^2$, σ_v, σ_v', σ_v'', E, and the multiplication table is

C_{3v}	E	σ_v	σ_v'	σ_v''	$C_3{}^1$	$C_3{}^2$
E	E	σ_v	σ_v'	σ_v''	$C_3{}^1$	$C_3{}^2$
σ_v	σ_v	E	$C_3{}^1$	$C_3{}^2$	σ_v'	σ_v''
σ_v'	σ_v'	$C_3{}^2$	E	$C_3{}^1$	σ_v''	σ_v
σ_v''	σ_v''	$C_3{}^1$	$C_3{}^2$	E	σ_v	σ_v'
$C_3{}^1$	$C_3{}^1$	σ_v''	σ_v	σ_v'	$C_3{}^2$	E
$C_3{}^2$	$C_3{}^2$	σ_v'	σ_v''	σ_v	E	$C_3{}^1$

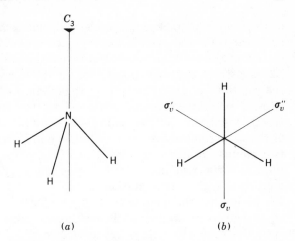

Fig. 3.4 The structure of ammonia showing (*a*) the threefold axis and (*b*) the three vertical minor planes as viewed down the threefold axis.

With the aid of the multiplication table it is possible to work out the classes of this group. Let us start with σ_v.

$$E\sigma_v E = \sigma_v$$
$$\sigma_v\sigma_v\sigma_v^{-1} = \sigma_v\sigma_v\sigma_v = \sigma_v E = \sigma_v$$
$$\sigma_v'\sigma_v\sigma_v'^{-1} = \sigma_v'\sigma_v\sigma_v' = \sigma_v'C_3^{1} = \sigma_v''$$
$$\sigma_v''\sigma_v\sigma_v''^{-1} = \sigma_v''\sigma_v\sigma_v'' = \sigma_v''C_3^{2} = \sigma_v'$$
$$C_3^{1}\sigma_v C_3^{1-1} = C_3^{1}\sigma_v C_3^{2} = C_3^{1}\sigma_v'' = \sigma_v$$
$$C_3^{2}\sigma_v C_3^{2-1} = C_3^{2}\sigma_v C_3^{1} = C_3^{2}\sigma_v' = \sigma_v''$$

If we continue this procedure, we find that σ_v, σ_v', and σ_v'' are all in the same class. The reader may finish this procedure in Prob. 3.5.

We shall return to the question of determining classes in Chap. 4 after we have formally developed the systematic classification of molecular point groups; the classes will assume a useful geometrical meaning.

PROBLEMS

3.1. Show that the requirement that each group possess an identity operation E such that

$$EA = AE = A$$

plus the requirement that the product of any two elements be another element in the group (the closed requirement) implies the existence within the group of a reciprocal element for each group element. Consider the group composed of A, B, C, D, E, and F. Let element E assume the role of the identity.   Pick out one element and combine it with all others, being careful to observe the single-valued-product restriction.   An examination of the list of products will reveal the desired result.

3.2. Construct multiplication tables for the following two groups: (a) all the rotations of an equilateral triangle (six, including the identity and twofold and threefold rotations), and (b) the group of permutations of three symbols; i.e., let (bc) stand for the permutation of b and c; then, two of the six permutations are $A = (a)(bc)$ and $F = (abc)$.   Show that these two groups are isomorphous.   (This isomorphism may be expressed in terms of a theorem due to Jordan: every finite group is isomorphous with a group of regular permutations.)

3.3. Show that the reciprocal of the product of two or more elements is equivalent to the product of the reciprocals, taken in reverse order.   Consider the product of three group elements; for simplicity consider the equation $W = XYZ$ and right-multiply by $Z^{-1}Y^{-1}X^{-1}$.

3.4. Show that every element is conjugate to itself.

3.5. Find all the classes in the group of elements generated by the symmetry elements of the ammonia molecule: $C_3{}^1$, $C_3{}^2$, σ_v, σ_v', σ_v'', and E.

3.6. What kind of group is it in which all right cosets are also left cosets, that is, $aH = Ha$, where H is a subgroup of group G and $a \in G$?

3.7. Show that the only group of order 3 is a cyclic group.   *Hint:* Use the theorem of Lagrange.

3.8. Show that all groups of prime order must by cyclic.

3.9. A concrete example of a group is called a *realization* of a group, e.g., a set of permutations, a set of numbers under a specified law of combination, a collection of symmetry operations.   Give as many realizations as you can determine for the group of order 3 and of order 4.

3.10. (a) Consider the n roots of unity.   Show that these roots form groups under the law of algebraic multiplication.   Consider their relation to the groups composed of rotations.

(b) Cyclic groups are abelian groups in which the elements may be written $R_1 = R, R_2 = R^2, \ldots, R_g = R^g = E$.   Show that the elements of the irreducible representations may be written in terms of the n roots of unity as follows for element R of the jth irreducible representation:

$$\Gamma_j(R) = e^{2\pi i j/g}$$

3.11. (a) Find all the elements of each class in the group of the square: E, $C_4{}^1$, $C_4{}^2 = C_2{}^1$, $C_4{}^3$, σ_v, σ_v', σ_d, σ_d'.

(b) Repeat for the group of the fourfold rotations: E, $C_4{}^1$, $C_4{}^2 = C_2{}^1$, $C_4{}^3$.

(c) Repeat for the following group: E, $C_4{}^1$, $C_4{}^2 = C_2{}^1$, $C_4{}^3$, $C_2{}^1$, $C_2'{}^1$, $C_2''{}^1$, and $C_2'''{}^1$.   The additional C_2 axes lie in the plane of the square at right angles to the fourfold axis.

(d)   Can you develop any general rules for placing symmetry operations into classes without resorting to the performance of all the similarity transformations?

REFERENCES

Birkhoff, G., and S. MacLane: "A Survey of Modern Algebra," 3d ed., The Macmillan Company, New York, 1960.

Hammermesh, M.: "Group Theory and Its Applications to Physical Problems," Addison-Wesley Publishing Company, Inc., Reading, Mass., 1962.

Heine, V.: "Group Theory in Quantum Mechanics," Pergamon Press, New York, 1960.

Higman, B.: "Applied Group-theoretic and Matrix Methods," Dover Publications, Inc., New York, 1964.

Margenau, H., and G. M. Murphy: "The Mathematics of Physics and Chemistry," chap. 15, D. Van Nostrand Company, Inc., Princeton, N.J., 1956.

Tinkham, M.: "Group Theory and Quantum Mechanics," McGraw-Hill Book Company, New York, 1964.

Wigner, E. P.: "Group Theory," Academic Press Inc., New York, 1960.

4
point groups: identification and classification

In this chapter we establish the formal connection between molecular symmetry and abstract group theory. We demonstrate that a complete set of symmetry *operations* constitutes a group in the abstract mathematical sense when the law of combination is defined as "the successive application of operations." The key word is "complete"; examination of the definition of a mathematical group will reveal the requirements for completeness.

Once the group nature of molecular symmetry operations is established, we can pass on to the problem of the identification and classification of symmetry point groups. We shall find that the systematic classification scheme developed here will enhance and reinforce the chemical intuition of the reader. The correct recognition of the point group of a molecular structure provides useful information concerning the chemical equivalence of atoms in a molecule and the relationships which may exist between various conformations of a system. Since symmetry relations are exact in a mathematical sense, the information mentioned above is also exact.

Since molecular symmetry operations can be classified into mathematical groups, all the power of the formal structure of group theory—in the form of theorems and equations—can be brought to bear upon the study of various physical systems whose properties can be described by, or related to, symmetry point groups.

4.1 COMPLETENESS OF COLLECTIONS OF OPERATIONS

The requirement that a set of group elements be closed under the binary operation defined for the group provides the basis for the definition of the completeness of a collection of symmetry operations. The effect of the successive application of two symmetry operations must be equivalent to the effect of an operation which is also a member of the group. We have already seen in Chaps. 2 and 3 that products of symmetry operations are also symmetry operations. The present question is the determination of closed collections of operations.

In order to demonstrate the closed nature of collections of symmetry operations we shall examine each collection separately and in detail. We shall show that the collection is closed by showing that it is possible to construct a multiplication table for the collection of operations.

We now introduce a device (or construction) which will prove useful not only in the development of multiplication tables but also in such practical problems as determining the multiplicity of equivalent positions in the point groups. This device is known as the *stereographic projection*. We shall omit discussion of the historical development of the stereographic projection and consider it only as a means of representing point groups. Figure 4.1 shows the stereographic projections of 32 point groups. For each point group there are two diagrams, one showing the equivalent positions of the group and one displaying the symmetry elements. Small polygons represent proper axes, and boldface lines represent mirror planes. The equivalent general positions of the group are represented by circles; closed circles for those above the plane of the paper and open for those below. Table 4.1 defines all the symbols used in the point-group diagrams.

Let us consider as a specific example the full symmetry of an equilateral triangle, as shown in Fig. 4.2. The symmetry elements of this triangle are as follows: a threefold (proper) symmetry axis C_3, an improper threefold axis S_3 collinear with the proper axis, three (vertical) symmetry planes σ_v, three twofold axes C_2 perpendicular to the C_3 axis and contained in the symmetry planes, and finally a (horizontal) mirror plane σ_h perpendicular to C_3 and containing the three C_2 axes. These elements generate a total of 12 symmetry operations: E, $C_3{}^1$, $C_3{}^2$, $S_3{}^1$, $S_3{}^5$ $(= S_3{}^2)$, σ_v, σ_v', σ_v'', C_2, C_2', C_2'', σ_h. Let us now demonstrate how the stereographic

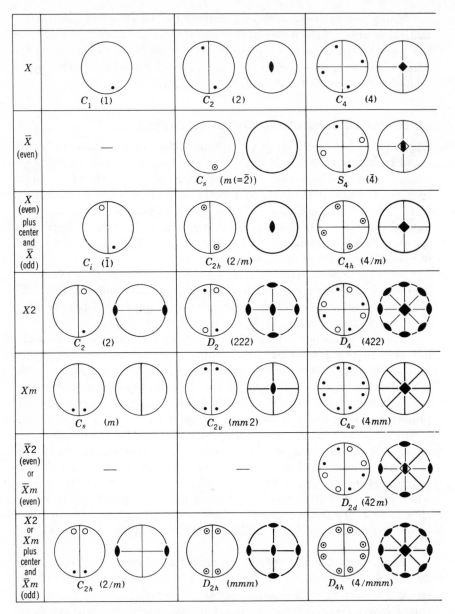

Fig. 4.1 Stereographic projection and sets of equivalent points for the 32 crystallographic point groups.   See Table 4.1 for an explanation of the symmetry symbols and Sec. 4.3 for a discussion of point-group symbols.   (*Taken by permission from Norman F. M. Henry and Kathleen Lonsdale (eds.), "The International Tables for X-ray Crystallography," vol. I, pp. 26–27, Kynoch Press, Birmingham, England, 1965.*)

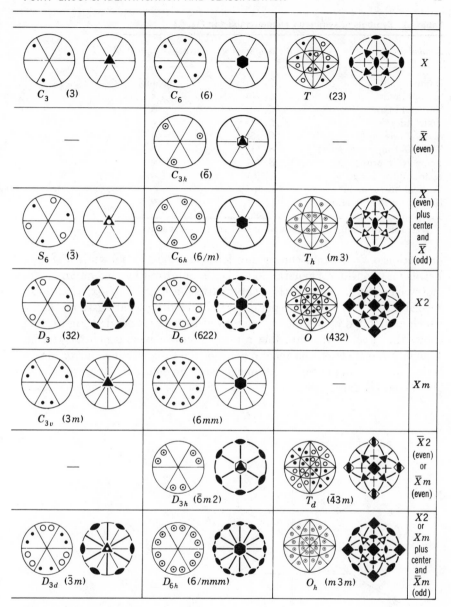

Fig. 4.1   *(Continued)*

Table 4.1 Symbols of symmetry elements used in Fig. 4.1

Symbol name	Written symbol	Graphical symbol
Onefold axis	C_1 (1)	None
Twofold axis	C_2 (2)	❙
Threefold axis	C_3 (3)	▲
Fourfold axis	C_4 (4)	◆
Sixfold axis	C_6 (6)	●
Threefold improper axis‡	S_3 $(\bar{3})$	△
Fourfold improper axis	S_4 $(\bar{4})$	◈
Sixfold improper axis	S_6 $(\bar{6})$	◍
Vertical mirror plane	σ_v or σ_d	−
Horizontal mirror plane	σ_h	○

‡ Here used to mean the compound axis of rotation-inversion.

projection of this group can be developed in steps, as shown in Fig. 4.3. Let us first consider a general point, i.e., a point not located on any symmetry element (a point with general cartesian coordinates x, y, z, not a special point). Then other points are obtained by locating those points which are related by symmetry operations to the first point. Figure 4.3a shows the effect of the threefold rotations on the general point. In Fig. 4.3b only the effect on the general point of the three vertical mirror planes is shown. The figure would become more symmetrical if the mirror planes also acted on these resultant points. Figure 4.3c shows the analogous

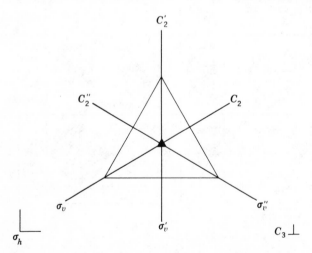

Fig. 4.2 The full symmetry of an equilateral triangle showing the relative orientations of the symmetry elements. The threefold axis is perpendicular to the plane of the paper through the center of the triangle.

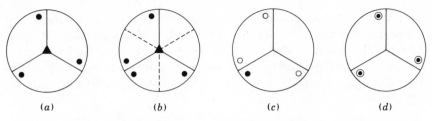

Fig. 4.3 Development of the stereographic projection of the group of the triangle. (a) Equivalent points generated by the threefold axis; (b) equivalent points generated by the three vertical mirror planes acting only on the initial general point; (c) equivalent points generated by the twofold rotations acting only on the initial general point; (d) equivalent points generated by the improper rotations.

effect of rotations about the three twofold axes, and Fig. 4.3d shows the effect of the threefold improper rotations. When all the operations are allowed to act on the general point in all possible combinations, the diagram of Fig. 4.4a is obtained. The relative positions of the symmetry elements are shown in Fig. 4.4b.

It is now quite easy to obtain the products of various symmetry operations by reference to Fig. 4.4a. One may readily determine that a proper rotation C_3^1 followed by a rotation about C_2 is equivalent to S_3^5 and that C_3^1 followed by σ_h is equivalent to S_3^1. The following can also be verified:

$$C_2\sigma_v = \sigma_h$$
$$\sigma_v C_3^1 = \sigma_v''$$

In this manner one may show that the "complete" set of operations generated by all the symmetry elements of an equilateral triangle does form a closed set.

The demonstration that the set of operations meets all the requirements of a group may now be rapidly concluded. The group possesses an identity element, the leave-it-alone or do-nothing operation E. We

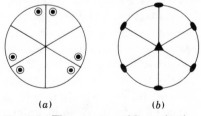

Fig. 4.4 The stereographic projection of the group of the triangle. (a) The set of equivalent points and (b) the set of symmetry elements.

have already discussed the nature of the reciprocal of an operation, and
the reader may verify readily that there exists within the group a reciprocal for each operation; that is, $C_3{}^2$ is the reciprocal of $C_3{}^1$ and vice versa
(as are $S_3{}^1$ and $S_3{}^5$), and all other operations are their own reciprocals.
Therefore, the set of 12 operations of the triangle constitutes a group.

4.2 THE MOLECULAR POINT GROUPS

Let us now proceed to the systematic classification of molecular point
groups. We shall adopt a scheme which might be called the *axis-of-
highest-order scheme*. On this basis, point groups can be divided conveniently into three types:

Type I.   Low symmetry: groups possessing only one symmetry ele-
          ment.
Type II. Intermediate symmetry: groups which may be *discussed* in
          terms of a single rotation axis (but which may *possess* more
          than one rotation axis): this type is subdivided into S, C, and
          D groups.
Type III. High symmetry: related to regular geometric solids (which
          possess more than two rotation axes of order greater than 2) or
          to linear structures.

In principle, rotation axes of any order are possible in molecular systems; symmetry arguments can place no restrictions upon the order of
rotation axes which might exist in an isolated molecule (when only one
axis is present). In practice, however, few molecules and ions exist with
structures which possess an axis of order higher than 6. The practical
upper limit to our consideration of rotation axes will be set at the order
8. The reader may easily extend these considerations to higher-order
axes.

In crystal lattices, on the other hand, rotation axes of only five different orders are permissible because of the space-filling requirements of the
crystal lattice. The permissible orders are 1, 2, 3, 4, and 6. (Consider
paving your bathroom floor with pentagons!) When the number of rotation axes is restricted in this way, only 32 point groups are possible.
These are often called the 32 *crystallographic point groups*, and they are
usually the ones for which drawings are given (as in Fig. 4.1). We shall
not restrict our attention here to the crystallographic point groups but
include a total of 57 point groups in our considerations.

A brief mention of point-group symbols and notation should be made
here. There are currently two widely used systems of point-group notation, the Schoenflies and Hermann-Mauguin (or International) systems.

The Schoenflies symbols were introduced by spectroscopists, and the Hermann-Mauguin symbols are used primarily by crystallographers. We shall use both systems here (often putting the International symbol in parenthesis following the Schoenflies symbol) so that the reader will become familiar with both methods. We shall not attempt to set forth any set of rules for obtaining the symbol from a list of symmetry elements. The method of symbol naming will be developed as each group is discussed.

TYPE I POINT GROUPS: LOW SYMMETRY

There are four groups which are generated by a single symmetry element and possess only one or two symmetry operations:

1. C_1 (1)   Structures which possess no symmetry other than the identity belong to group C_1.

2. C_i ($\overline{1}$) C_i is the Schoenflies symbol for the group generated by an inversion center alone. The symmetry operations are inversion and the identity.

3. C_s ($\overline{2}$ or m)   These are the symbols for the group which contains the reflection operation as well as the identity.

4. C_2 (2)   The group generated by the axis of order 2 contains the 180° rotation operation and the identity. This group is discussed in the next section.

Examples of structures possessing type I point groups are shown in Fig. 4.5.

Let us now proceed to a discussion of the type II groups. All these groups possess at least one rotation axis. When the list of symmetry elements contains more than one symmetry axis, it will be found helpful to center the discussion around the axis of highest order. When there are several axes of the same order, a choice must be made: one must determine the axis which is unique in the sense of symmetry or one must pick an axis arbitrarily. We shall see that a molecular axis or the normal to the molecular plane can serve as a guide in the choice.

TYPE II POINT GROUPS: THE S, C, AND D GROUPS

1. In Sec. 2.5 it was shown that an improper axis of even order n generates $n/2$ improper rotations, $n/2 - 1$ proper rotations, and the identity, for a total of n operations. The improper axis of odd order generates $2n$ operations: $n - 1$ proper rotations, $n - 1$ improper rotations, the reflection operation (across a mirror perpendicular to the improper axis), and the identity. The collections of operations generated by improper axes of both even and odd order are groups, as can be determined from an examination of the multiplication tables for orders 3 and 4 shown in Tables 4.2

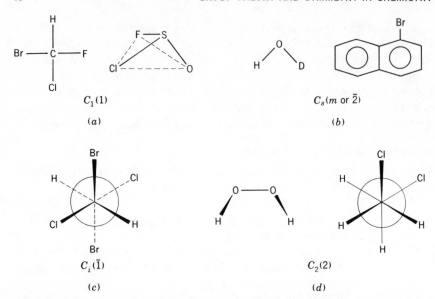

Fig. 4.5 Examples of molecules belonging to type I point groups. (*a*) C_1 (1): HFClBrC and ClFSO; (*b*) C_s (*m* or $\bar{2}$): HDO and 2-bromonaphthalene; (*c*) C_i ($\bar{1}$): 1,2-dibromo-1,2-dichloroethane; (*d*) C_2 (2): hydrogen peroxide and 1,2-dichloroethane.

and 4.3.   The groups derived from even-order axes are termed S_n ($\bar{n}$) groups, whereas groups of odd-order improper axes are called C_{nh} (n/m) because of the independent existence of the horizontal mirror plane.

The S_n groups (*n* even) possess *n* elements each of which commutes with every other element; thus, each element is in a class by itself.   If a group contains the operations generated by an improper axis in addition to operations generated by other elements (such as twofold axes perpendicular to the improper axis and mirror planes, both vertical and horizontal but not including an inversion center and other high-order axes), the group is either a *C* or *D* group.

Table 4.2 Multiplication table for a group generated by an improper axis of order three

$S_3 = C_{3h}$	E	S_3^1	S_3^2	C_3^1	C_3^2	σ_h
E	E	S_3^1	S_3^2	C_3^1	C_3^2	σ_h
S_3^1	S_3^1	C_3^2	E	S_3^2	σ_h	C_3^1
S_3^2	S_3^2	E	C_3^1	σ_h	S_3^1	C_3^2
C_3^1	C_3^1	S_3^2	σ_h	C_3^2	E	S_3^1
C_3^c	C_3^2	σ_h	S_3^1	E	C_3^1	S_3^2
σ_h	σ_h	C_3^1	C_3^2	S_3^1	S_3^2	E

Table 4.3 Multiplication table for a group generated by an improper axis of order four

S_4	E	$S_4{}^1$	$S_4{}^3$	$C_2{}^1$
E	E	$S_4{}^1$	$S_4{}^3$	$C_2{}^1$
$S_4{}^1$	$S_4{}^1$	$C_2{}^1$	E	$S_4{}^3$
$S_4{}^3$	$S_4{}^3$	E	$C_2{}^1$	$S_4{}^1$
$C_2{}^1$	$C_2{}^1$	$S_4{}^3$	$S_4{}^1$	E

2. The collection of elements generated by a proper-rotation axis of any order is a group given the symbol C_n (n). As in the S_n groups, each operation in a C_n group commutes with every other element and is in a class by itself. Refer to Table 4.4 for the multiplication table for group C_4.

3. The next type of group is generated by the addition of a vertical mirror plane to a proper axis. In Sec. 2.7 (and in Prob. 2.6) we saw that the combination of a C_n axis and one vertical mirror—a plane containing the rotation axis—requires a total of n such mirror planes. Hence such a group possesses $2n$ operations and is given the symbol C_{nv} (see Tables 4.10 and 4.11 for the Hermann-Mauguin symbols). The multiplication table for group C_{4v} is given in Table 4.5; for C_{3v} see Sec. 6.3.

Table 4.4 Multiplication table for group C_4

C_4	E	$C_4{}^1$	$C_4{}^3$	$C_2{}^1$
E	E	$C_4{}^1$	$C_4{}^3$	$C_2{}^1$
$C_4{}^1$	$C_4{}^1$	$C_2{}^1$	E	$C_4{}^3$
$C_4{}^3$	$C_4{}^3$	E	$C_2{}^1$	$C_4{}^1$
$C_2{}^1$	$C_2{}^1$	$C_4{}^3$	$C_4{}^1$	E

Table 4.5 Multiplication table for group C_{4v}

C_{4v}	E	$C_4{}^1$	$C_4{}^3$	$C_2{}^1$	σ_v	σ_v'	σ_d	σ_d'
E	E	$C_4{}^1$	$C_4{}^3$	$C_2{}^1$	σ_v	σ_v'	σ_d	σ_d'
$C_4{}^1$	$C_4{}^1$	$C_2{}^1$	E	$C_4{}^3$	σ_d	σ_d'	σ_v'	σ_v
$C_4{}^3$	$C_4{}^3$	E	$C_2{}^1$	$C_4{}^1$	σ_d'	σ_d	σ_v	σ_v'
$C_2{}^1$	$C_2{}^1$	$C_4{}^3$	$C_4{}^1$	E	σ_v'	σ_v	σ_d'	σ_d
σ_v	σ_v	σ_d'	σ_d	σ_v'	E	$C_2{}^1$	$C_4{}^3$	$C_4{}^1$
σ_v'	σ_v'	σ_d	σ_d'	σ_v	$C_2{}^1$	E	$C_4{}^1$	$C_4{}^3$
σ_d	σ_d	σ_v	σ_v'	σ_d'	$C_4{}^1$	$C_4{}^3$	E	$C_2{}^1$
σ_d'	σ_d'	σ_v'	σ_v	σ_d	$C_4{}^3$	$C_4{}^1$	$C_2{}^1$	E

Table 4.6   Multiplication table for group D_3

D_3	E	C_3^1	C_3^2	C_2	C_2'	C_2''
E	E	C_3^1	C_3^2	C_2	C_2'	C_2''
C_3^1	C_3^1	C_3^2	E	C_2''	C_2	C_2'
C_3^2	C_3^2	E	C_3^1	C_2'	C_2''	C_2
C_2	C_2	C_2'	C_2''	E	C_3^1	C_3^2
C_2'	C_2'	C_2''	C_2	C_3^2	E	C_3^1
C_2''	C_2''	C_2	C_2'	C_3^1	C_3^2	E

Each rotation and its inverse, $C_n{}^m$ and $C_n{}^{n-m}$, belong to the same class. When n is odd, all reflections belong to the same class, but when n is even, the reflections fall into two classes, vertical and dihedral mirror planes. Classes of operations will be considered more fully in Sec. 4.5.

4. Another set of groups is obtained when a horizontal mirror is added to a proper axis of order n. The total of $2n$ operations includes $n - 1$ proper rotations, n improper rotations, and the identity. Each element is in a class by itself since all elements commute with each other. The symbol for this group is C_{nh} (n/m). The multiplication table for group C_{3h} is shown in Table 4.2.

5. The D (dihedral) groups are produced by the addition of n twofold axes perpendicular to a proper-rotation axis. The group consisting of the $n - 1$ proper rotations, the n twofold rotations, and the identity is given the symbol D_n $(n22)$. As in the C_{nv} groups, each rotation (generated by the C_n axis) and its inverse form a class, and the twofold rotations form one class when n is odd but two classes when n is even (see the multiplication table for D_3 in Table 4.6).

Table 4.7   Multiplication table for group D_{3h}

D_{3h}	E	C_3^1	C_3^2	S_3^1	S_3^2	σ_v	σ_v'	σ_v''	C_2	C_2'	C_2''	σ_h
E	E	C_3^1	C_3^2	S_3^1	S_3^2	σ_v	σ_v'	σ_v''	C_2	C_2'	C_2''	σ_h
C_3^1	C_3^1	C_3^2	E	S_3^2	σ_h	σ_v'	σ_v''	σ_v	C_2''	C_2	C_2'	S_3^1
C_3^2	C_3^2	E	C_3^1	σ_h	S_3	σ_v''	σ_v'	σ_v	C_2'	C_2''	C_2	S_3^2
S_3^1	S_3^1	S_3^2	σ_h	C_3^2	E	C_2''	C_2	C_2'	σ_v''	σ_v	σ_v'	C_3^1
S_3^2	S_3^2	σ_h	S_3^1	E	C_3^1	C_2'	C_2''	σ_h	σ_v'	σ_v''	σ_v	C_3^2
σ_v	σ_v	σ_v'	σ_v''	C_2'	C_2''	E	C_3^1	C_3^2	σ_h	S_3^1	S_3^2	C_2
σ_v'	σ_v'	σ_v''	σ_v	C_2''	C_2	C_3^2	E	C_3^1	S_3^2	σ_h	S_3^1	C_2'
σ_v''	σ_v''	σ_v	σ_v'	C_2	C_2'	C_3^1	C_3^2	E	S_3^1	S_3^2	σ_h	C_2''
C_2	C_2	C_2'	C_2''	σ_v'	σ_v''	σ_h	S_3^1	S_3^2	E	C_3^1	C_3^2	σ_v
C_2'	C_2'	C_2''	C_2	σ_v''	σ_v	S_3^2	σ_h	S_3^1	C_3^2	E	C_3^1	σ_v'
C_2''	C_2''	C_2	C_2'	σ_v	σ_v'	S_3^1	S_3^2	σ_h	C_3^1	C_3^2	E	σ_v''
σ_h	σ_h	S_3^1	S_3^2	C_3^1	C_3^2	C_2	C_2'	C_2''	σ_v	σ_v'	σ_v''	E

6. When a horizontal mirror plane is added to the D_n groups, the D_{nh} groups are produced (see Tables 4.10 and 4.11 for the Hermann-Mauguin symbols). When the procedure outlined in Sec. 2.7 is pursued for such combination operations as $\sigma_h C_2'$, it is discovered that n vertical mirror planes are generated. Hence, D_{nh} groups contain $n - 1$ proper rotations, $n - 1$ improper rotations, n vertical-mirror-plane reflections, n twofold rotations, the horizontal-mirror-plane reflection, and the identity, for a total of $4n$ operations. As in D_n groups, each rotation (generated by the C_n axis) and its inverse form a class, as do each improper rotation and its inverse. The horizontal mirror and the identity are in classes by themselves. Both the n twofold rotations and the n vertical mirror planes fall into one class each for odd n and into two classes each for even n. Table 4.7 contains the multiplication table for group D_{3h}.

TYPE III POINT GROUPS: LINEAR AND HIGH SYMMETRY

1. Point groups based on linear structures may occur in one of two groups, $D_{\infty h}$ and $C_{\infty v}$. Since rotation through any angle about the linear axis is a symmetry operation, the order of that rotation axis is infinite. The symbol for such an infinite axis is C_∞. As in type II point groups, the distinguishing feature between the C and D group is the presence of twofold axes perpendicular to the principal axis. When the twofold axes are present, so also is a horizontal mirror plane, perpendicular to the principal axis. Hence, the more symmetrical linear group is given the Schoenflies symbol $D_{\infty h}$, whereas the less symmetrical point-group symbol is $C_{\infty v}$. Because infinitefold axes are not permitted in crystallographic lattices, there are no Hermann-Mauguin symbols for linear point groups.

Examples of molecules whose structures possess $D_{\infty h}$ point-group symmetry are CO_2, C_3O_2, and C_2H_2; OCS, DCCH, and HCl belong to the point group $C_{\infty v}$.

2. The point-group classification scheme outlined so far cannot handle the presence of rotation axes and mirror planes which are not perpendicular to the principal axis. Thus, such cases will be treated as special cases. Such treatment is, however, appropriate because the high-symmetry point groups are related to the geometrically regular solids, the tetrahedron, cube, octahedron, dodecahedron, and icosahedron. There are seven point groups related to regular solids, and they can be placed into three divisions: tetrahedral, T, T_d, T_h; octahedral, O, O_h; and icosahedral, I, I_h.

The lowest symmetry group in each case is a group containing only rotations, and the other groups are obtained by addition of mirror planes to the rotation groups.

Tetrahedral point groups. The rotation axes of the T groups are conveniently discussed in relation to a cube, since certain of the symmetry elements of the cube may be related to those of a tetrahedron. Figure 4.6

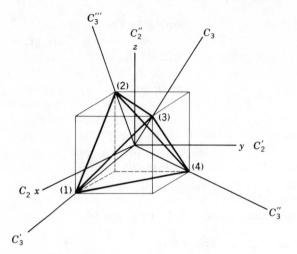

Fig. 4.6   The relative orientation of the rotation axes of the tetrahedron (and cube).

shows a tetrahedron inscribed in a cube such that the threefold axes of both solids coincide—a body diagonal of the cube lies along the line which joins the tetrahedron center with one of the tetrahedron vertices.   There are, of course, four such cube body diagonals and, hence, four threefold axes.

Now observe the combined action of a rotation of 120° around C_3 followed by a 120° rotation around C_3' (see Fig. 4.6).   The procedure can be illustrated by operation on point 1, a vertex of the tetrahedron:

$$C_3{}^1 \, (1) \rightarrow (2)$$
$$C_3'{}^1 \, (2) \rightarrow (3)$$

or

$$C_3'{}^1 C_3{}^1 \, (1) \rightarrow (3)$$

The result, however, is equivalent to a twofold rotation around the x axis.

$$C_3'{}^1 C_3{}^1 = C_2$$

Hence, three C_2 axes along the x, y, and z directions must be included in the list of rotations of a tetrahedron in order that the collection of symmetry operations be closed and form a group.   This group is given the Schoenflies symbol T (23)

$$T \left\{ \begin{array}{l} 4 \, C_3 \\ 3 \, C_2 \end{array} \right.$$

A higher symmetry group can be obtained by the addition of mirror planes. Group T_d is produced by adding six mirror planes, each of which contains two of the four threefold axes. Thus, each mirror plane contains one of the twofold axes and one of the six edges of the tetrahedron, bisecting the opposite edge. In addition, three fourfold improper axes are generated (collinear with the twofold axes) by the combination of reflection followed by a twofold rotation. Consider points 1 and 2 in Fig. 4.6. Let us use the label σ_{111} for the mirror plane which contains C_3 and C_3''' (as well as C_2''). Then

$$\sigma_{111}(1) \to (4)$$
$$C_3(4) \to (2)$$

or

$$C_3\sigma_{111}(1) \to (2)$$

However,

$$S_4{}^1(1) \to (2) \quad \text{and} \quad C_3\sigma_{111} = S_4{}^1$$

Hence, the list of group elements must also include the improper rotations generated by the three fourfold improper axes. The Hermann-Mauguin symbol for this group is $\bar{4}3m$.

$$T_d \begin{cases} 4\,C_3 \\ 3\,C_2 \\ 6\,S_4 \\ 6\,\sigma_d \end{cases}$$

Another group can be generated from T by the addition of three mirror planes, each of which contains two of the twofold axes. Each mirror plane is then perpendicular to the third twofold axis. Because of the perpendicular intersection of these mirror planes, a center of inversion is generated. This group is usually referred to as a cubic group and is not frequently encountered in chemistry. The symbol is T_h $(m3)$.

$$T_h \begin{cases} 4\,C_3 \\ 3\,C_2 \\ 3\,\sigma \\ 3\,S_4 \\ i \end{cases}$$

Octahedral point groups. The group of the rotations of an octahedron is called O (432). Figure 4.7 shows an octahedron inscribed in a cube which is set in a cartesian coordinate system such that the fourfold axes

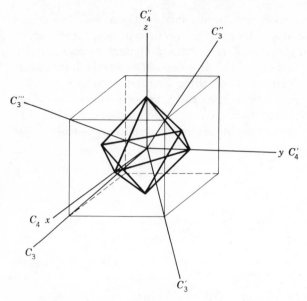

Fig. 4.7   The relative orientation of the three- and fourfold rotation axes of the octahedron.

of the octahedron coincide with the cartesian x, y, and z axes.   Consecu-
tive rotations of 90° about any two fourfold axes is equivalent to a threefold rotation about an axis perpendicular to an octahedral face.   Hence,
four threefold axes are generated perpendicular to the triangular faces of
the octahedron.   Further, a rotation of 90° about one fourfold axis followed by 180° rotation about another fourfold axis is equivalent to one of
yet another set of rotations: six twofold axes which emerge through the
midpoint of each edge.   Hence, the rotation group of the octahedron
contains 13 proper axes:

$$O \begin{cases} 3\ C_4 \\ 4\ C_3 \\ 6\ C_2 \end{cases}$$

The only higher symmetry octahedral group also possesses the full
symmetry of the cube: O_h $(m3m)$. O_h is obtained by adding to O the
six mirror planes σ_d (each of which contains two threefold axes and one
twofold axis) and the three mirror planes σ_h (each of which contains two
twofold axes and bisects the angle between two threefold axes).   The
introduction of mirror planes perpendicular to axes also generates improper
axes: four sixfold and three fourfold improper axes.   Finally, the group
also possesses a center of inversion.

$$O_h \begin{cases} 3\ C_4 \\ 4\ C_3 \\ 6\ C_2 \\ 4\ S_6 \\ 3\ S_4 \\ 6\ \sigma_d \\ 3\ \sigma_h \\ i \end{cases}$$

Icosahedral point groups. Group I is the rotation group of the icosahedron and possesses 12 fivefold axes, 20 threefold axes, and 15 twofold axes. Figure 4.8 shows the relative orientation of some of these axes.

The group of the full symmetry of the icosahedron I_h is generated by the following symmetry elements:

$$I_h \begin{cases} 12\ C_5 \\ 20\ C_3 \\ 15\ C_2 \\ 12\ S_{10} \\ 20\ S_6 \\ 15\ \sigma \\ i \end{cases}$$

These symmetry elements generate a total of 120 symmetry operations.

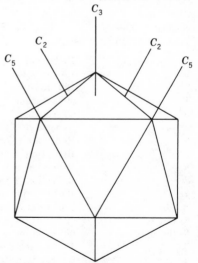

Fig. 4.8 The relative orientation of a representative selection of some of the rotation axes of the icosahedron.

The fact that there are no point groups of high symmetry (type III) possessing rotation axes of order greater than 5 is related to the fact that the icosahedron is the regular geometric solid of highest symmetry.

4.3 POINT-GROUP SYMBOLISM

The reader may object to learning two quite different schemes of point-group symbols; however, both systems are widely used, and the reader will probably encounter both. Each system has its advantages and disadvantages. The Schoenflies scheme is more systematic in applying a symbol to a collection of the symmetry elements of an isolated molecule. Therefore, one can proceed in a more straightforward and systematic manner to deduce the Schoenflies symbol for a particular structure. The reader may observe this feature in the point-group-symbol correlation table (Table 4.10) and in the flow-chart scheme of point-group identification (Table 4.11) presented in the next section.

The Schoenflies system, however, is not adequate in the description of crystallographic space groups in which both lattice type and spatial orientation must be indicated. The Hermann-Mauguin system (or International system) was established for just this purpose. The space-group symbol consists of two parts: a capital letter which identifies the lattice type and a collection of lowercase letters and numbers which signify both

Table 4.8 Space-group symmetry-operation symbols

Symbol	Operation	Translation-free symbol
m	Reflection	m
2	180° rotation	2
3	120° rotation	3
4	90° rotation	4
6	60° rotation	6
a	Reflection + translation $\parallel a\,\ddagger$	m
b	Reflection + translation $\parallel b$	m
c	Reflection + translation $\parallel c$	m
n	Reflection + translation $\parallel$ face diagonal	m
d	Reflection + translation $\parallel$ body diagonal	m
2_1	180° rotation + translation $a/2$ or $b/2$ or $c/2$	2
3_1 (3_2)	120° rotation + translation $c/3$	3
4_1 $(4_2, 4_3)$	90° rotation + translation $a/4$ or $c/4$	4
6_1 $(6_2, 6_3, 6_4, 6_5)$	60° rotation + translation $c/6$	6
$\bar{3}$	120° rotation + inversion	3
$\bar{4}$	90° rotation + inversion	4
$\bar{6}$	60° rotation + inversion	6

$\ddagger$ Means "parallel to the a direction."

the crystallographic symmetry elements and their spatial orientation. We shall not discuss here the details of the determination of a space-group symbol. We shall show how to convert a space-group symbol to a point-group symbol with the aid of Table 4.8.

Table 4.9 Lattice type symbols

Symbol	Type
P	Primitive
A	Centered on the A face
B	Centered on the B face
C	Centered on the C face
F	Centered on all faces
I	Body-centered
R	Rhombohedral
H	Hexagonal

There are two steps in the conversion from space-group to point-group symbol: (1) remove the lattice type symbol and (2) convert all space-group symmetry symbols to their translation-free symbols (see Table 4.8), as in the following four examples:

Space group				Point group
$P2_1/c$	→	$2_1/c$	→	$2/m$
$Pnma$	→	nma	→	mmm
$I\bar{4}\,2_1c$	→	$\bar{4}\,2_1c$	→	$42m$
$Fm3c$	→	$m3c$	→	$m3m$

The reader is cautioned here. In general the point group of a molecule or ion cannot be inferred from the point group derived from the space-group symbol. A knowledge of the details of the crystal structure is necessary for determination of the symmetry of the molecules or ions of which the crystal is constituted.

Table 4.10 is the point-group-symbol correlation table and is useful in the conversion of a symbol from one system to another. (The reader must remember that in crystals rotation axes whose order is 5 or greater than 6 are not allowed.)

4.4 SYSTEMATIC IDENTIFICATION OF POINT GROUPS

Now that a scheme for point-group classification has been established, we must pass on to the more important but more difficult problems involved in the correct identification of the point group of a molecular

Table 4.10   Point-group-symbol correlation table

	Schoenflies	*Hermann-Mauguin*
1	C_1	1
2	C_2	2
3	$C_3 \quad \} \, C_n$	$3 \quad \} \, n$
4	C_4	4
5	C_6	6
6	$C_i \,(= S_2)$	$\bar{1}$
7	$C_s \,(= S_1)$	$\bar{2}$ or m
8	$S_6 \;\}\, S_n$	$\bar{3} \quad\quad \} \, \bar{n}$
9	S_4	$\bar{4}$
10	$---C_{3h}$	$\bar{6}$ or $3/m$
11	D_2	222
12	$D_3 \quad \} \, D_n$	$32 \quad\quad \} \, n22$
13	D_4	422
14	D_6	622
15	T	23
16	O	432
17	C_{2h}	$2/m$
18	$\rightarrow C_{4h} \quad \} \, C_{nh}$	$4/m \quad \} \, n/m$
19	C_{6h}	$6/m$
20	C_{2v}	$mm2$
21	$C_{3v} \quad \} \, C_{nv}$	$3m \quad\quad \} \, nmm$
22	C_{4v}	$4mm$
23	C_{6v}	$6mm$
24	D_{2h}	mmm
25	$D_{3h} \quad \} \, D_{nh}$	$\bar{6}m2$
26	D_{4h}	$4/mmm$
27	D_{6h}	$6/mmm$
28	$D_{2d} \;\}\, D_{nd}$	$\bar{4}2m$
29	D_{3d}	$\bar{3}m$
30	T_h	$m3$
31	T_d	$\bar{4}3m$
32	O_h	$m3m$
	$C_{\infty v}$	
	$D_{\infty h} \;\}$ not allowed in crystal	
	$I \quad\quad$ lattices	
	I_h	

structure. We shall develop here a systematic procedure using a flow-chart scheme as an aid.

The most critical step in any point-group identification procedure is the correct recognition of the symmetry elements present in the molecular structure. There is no substitute for working directly with models of the structure under investigation. As one familiarizes oneself with the system, one should also draw several accurate views of the structure. For any but the simplest of structures such a procedure should always be a preliminary step to final point-group identification.

The systematic scheme presented here, reinforced by the flow chart, will tend to develop a sharper eye in the frequent user. In the final analysis, however, experience—repeated point-group identification—is the best teacher of this subject.

The procedure developed below consists of a series of questions concerning the presence or absence of symmetry elements. The chart flows into various branches depending on the answer to each question.

PROCEDURE FOR POINT-GROUP IDENTIFICATION

Step 1. *Is the structure of the linear or high-symmetry type, type III?* If yes, go to step 13; otherwise, proceed to step 2.

Step 2. *Does the structure possess a proper rotation axis?* If yes, go to step 4. If no, the group is type I; go to step 3.

Step 3. (a) If the structure possesses one and *only* one mirror plane, the point group is C_s (m or $\bar{2}$).

(b) If the structure possesses an inversion center, the point group is C_i ($\bar{1}$).

(c) If the structure possesses no symmetry elements other than the identity, the point group is C_1 (1).

Step 4. A choice must now be made. If the structure possesses more than one rotation axis, one of them must be singled out as the principal axis. If axes of several orders are present, the axis of highest order is used. If there are several axes of the highest order, there may be one which is unique in a symmetry sense (in a different symmetry class) or unique with reference to the molecular structure: along the main backbone of the molecule or perpendicular to a molecular plane. In some very rare instances an arbitrary choice may be necessary. The principal axis is called C_n, where n is its order.

Step 5. *Is there an improper axis collinear with the principal axis?* If no, proceed to step 8.

Step 6. *Is the order of the improper axis even?* If no, go to step 8.

Step 7. *In addition to the principal axis and the improper axis, are there symmetry elements present other than a center of inversion, e.g., mirror planes, twofold axes perpendicular to the principal axis?* If no, the point group is S_n ($\bar{n}$). Otherwise, proceed to step 8.

Step 8. *Are there n twofold axes perpendicular to C_n?* If yes, the group is a D group; go to step 11. If no, the group is a C group; proceed to step 9.

Step 9. *Is there a mirror plane perpendicular to C_n?* If yes, the point group is C_{nh} (n/m). If no, proceed to step 10.

Step 10. *Are there n vertical mirror planes (σ_v or σ_d mirror planes) which contain the principal axis C_n?* If yes, the point group is C_{nv} (see Table 4.10). If no, the group is C_n (n).

Step 11. *Is there a mirror plane perpendicular to C_n?* If yes, the point group is D_{nh} (see Table 4.10). If no, proceed to step 12.

Step 12. *Are there n dihedral mirror planes (σ_d mirror planes) which contain the principal axis C_n and bisect the angles between the n C_2 axes which are perpendicular to C_n?* If yes, the point group is D_{nd} (see Table 4.10). If no, the point group is D_n ($n22$).

Step 13. *Is the structure linear?* If no, the structure is related to one of the regular geometric solids: go to step 15. If yes, proceed to step 14.

Step 14. *Is there a mirror plane perpendicular to the principal (molecular) axis?* If yes, the point group is $D_{\infty h}$ (see Table 4.10). If no, the point group is $C_{\infty v}$ (see Table 4.10).

Step 15. The structure must be examined *carefully* to determine whether it is truly of the high-symmetry type! *Is the structure tetrahedral?* If no, go to step 16. If yes, it is one of the three point groups.

(a) *Does the structure possess only two- and threefold rotations?* If yes, the point group is T (23).

(b) *Does the structure possess six mirror planes in addition to the two- and threefold rotations?* If yes, the point group is T_d ($\overline{4}3m$).

(c) *Does the structure possess three mirror planes in addition to the two- and threefold rotations?* If yes, the point group is T_h ($m3$).

Step 16. *Is the structure octahedral?* If no, go to step 17. If yes, the structure belongs to one of two point groups:

(a) *Does the structure possess only rotations of order 2, 3, and 4?* If yes, the point group is O (432).

(b) *Does the structure possess six dihedral mirror planes (σ_d) and three horizontal mirror planes (σ_h) (as well as other elements) in addition to the rotation axes?* If yes, the point group is O_h ($m3m$).

Step 17. *Is the structure icosahedral (or dodecahedral)?* If yes, the point group is one of the following two:

(a) *Does the structure possess only rotations of order 5, 3, and 2?* If yes, the point group is I (see Table 4.10).

(b) *Does the structure possess 15 mirror planes and improper six- and tenfold rotation axes in addition to the proper rotation axes?* If yes, the point group is I_h (see Table 4.10).

It cannot be overstressed that a structure thought to be of high symmetry must be examined in detail to make sure that no irregularity (departure from high symmetry) exists. It should be pointed out further that symmetry is a mathematical quality here; the existence of a particular symmetry element depends on the exact equality or mathematical relation between certain coordinates, i.e., coordinates of those atoms supposed to be related by symmetry. Structures which do not quite meet the rigid specifications for a high-symmetry group may, however, be described as being approximately of a particular high symmetry. Such is often the case with complexes of transition metals. A complex may be viewed as an idealized structure, a structure in which the distortions are small or less than experimental error.

Table 4.11 is the flow chart for point-group identification which is based on the scheme developed above. With a little practice in the determination of point groups, the reader can commit the flow chart to memory, at least in its gross features. Once the material of this chapter is understood, the flow chart is the only feature of this chapter necessary for rapid and accurate point-group identification.

4.5 CLASSES OF SYMMETRY OPERATIONS

In Sec. 3.4 we discussed the concept of classes of group elements: a collection of group elements which are conjugate to each other forms a class. By systematically developing all the possible similarity transformations on a group of elements, one can determine all the classes. Such a procedure was used for the point group of ammonia, C_{3v}.

In Chap. 6 we shall see that the use of the class concept allows a simplification in some of the equations developed there for use in the succeeding chapters. The class concept is an important one. The reader by now has observed that systematic exhaustion of all possible similarity transformations in a group may lead to exhaustion on the part of the reader before all the classes are discovered. In group D_{3h} one must consider 144 transformations of the 12 group elements, which means that a total of 432 group-element multiplications must be performed!

In this section we shall develop a simple technique for the assignment of symmetry operations to classes. It will be seen that the use of this technique will improve the user's ability to identify point groups of molecular structures.

In Sec. 3.4 the group C_{3v} was shown to contain three classes: the three reflections in vertical mirror planes σ_v, the two threefold rotations, and the identity. This example, taken together with the results of Prob. 3.11, suggests a straightforward division of symmetry elements into

Table 4.11   Flow-chart scheme for point-group identification

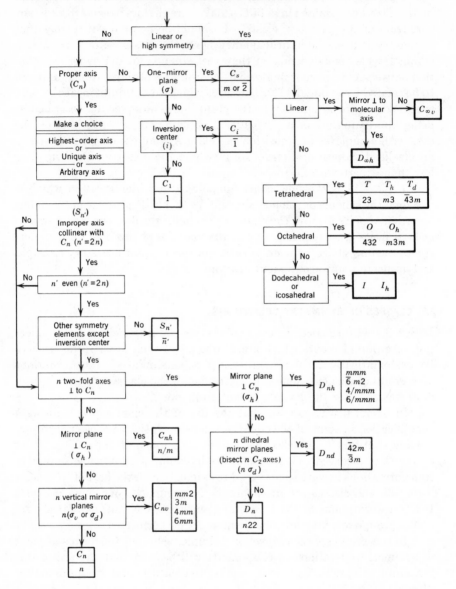

classes: all those operations in a given class perform a similar symmetry operation. (Note the use of the word similar.) We may, then, set forth the following set of rules:

1. The identity is always in a class by itself.
2. The inversion operation is always in a class by itself because it commutes with all other symmetry operations.
3. The rotation about a proper axis $C_n{}^k$ and its inverse $C_n{}^{-k}$ ($C_n{}^{n-k}$) will belong to the same class under two conditions:
   (a) There are n vertical mirror planes (σ_v or σ_d) present.
   (b) There are n twofold axes (C_2) perpendicular to the rotation axis.

   When neither the vertical mirror planes nor twofold axes are present, $C_n{}^k$ and $C_n{}^{-k}$ are in separate classes by themselves.

4. Rule 3 holds for improper rotations.
5. Two reflections will belong to the same class when there exists in the group an operation which interchanges all the points on the corresponding mirror planes. Hence, in C_{nv} groups all the σ_v operations belong to the same class because the $C_n{}^k$ operations will interchange the mirrors, but in D_{nh} groups the σ_v and σ_d reflections belong to separate groups. Likewise, reflection across a horizontal mirror plane σ_h is always in a class by itself.
6. As in Rule 5, two rotations $C_n{}^k$ and $C'_n{}^k$ about two different rotation axes are in the same class when there exists in the group an operation which interchanges all the points on the two axes. Hence, in D_{nd} groups all the C'_2 axes (perpendicular to the principal axis) are in the same class but not so in D_{nh} groups.
7. Rule 6 holds for improper rotations.

   These rules may be summarized as follows: two operations will be in the same class when (1) the two operations are of the same kind (rotation, reflection, etc.) and (2) there exists in the group another operation which interchanges the two operations in question. For example, in the group C_6 all the operations of rotation are in separate classes. In C_{6v}, however, reflection in a vertical mirror plane interchanges the effect of 60° and 300° rotations. Hence, $C_6{}^1$ and $C_6{}^5$ ($= C_6{}^{-1}$) belong to the same class. The same can be said of the effect of the twofold rotations in the group D_4.

4.6 EQUIVALENT AND SPECIAL POSITIONS

We shall borrow two terms from crystallographic space-group terminology, equivalent positions and special positions. *Equivalent position* refers to various locations throughout the crystal which are related by space-group symmetry operations and, hence, are equivalent. An observer standing at any equivalent position could not distinguish one position from another. A *special position* is any position located on a symmetry element. Any object, i.e., a molecule or ion, located in the special position must possess the symmetry of the symmetry element on which it is located. If a molecule is located on a fourfold axis, it must possess a fourfold rotation symmetry.

We shall refer to the stereographic projection for the discussion of equivalent positions. Each point (open or closed circle) in a stereographic projection is an equivalent position of the point group. (Such positions are also called *general positions*.) The multiplicity of the point group is, then, the number of equivalent (general) positions in the stereographic projection. The multiplicity is 12 for D_{3h}, 6 for C_{3h}, and 44 for O_h.

Special positions are obtained when the stereographic projection is made by placing the "first" point on a symmetry element, e.g., a mirror or rotation axis, etc. When such a procedure is pursued, fewer total points than the point-group multiplicity are produced. The number of such points is called the *multiplicity* of the special position. Figure 4.9 shows some examples of special positions in point groups.

In C_{3h} the multiplicity of the special position on σ_h is 3 and on position C_3 it is 2. In D_{4h} the multiplicity for the position on a vertical mirror but not on the horizontal mirror is 8, the same as halfway between vertical mirror planes (Fig. 4.9e and d).

The importance of this concept lies in its relation to molecular structure. The multiplicity of both equivalent general and special positions is related to the number of atoms possible in a structure and to their chemical equivalence. The number of atoms of one chemical type (atoms which are equivalent) must be a multiple of the point-group multiplicities. For example, in H_2O (in point group C_{2v}) the two hydrogen atoms occupy equivalent positions of multiplicity 2. Not all hydrogen atoms in a molecule need be equivalent. Consider pyridine, also of point group C_{2v} (see Fig. 4.10). The plane of the molecule is one mirror plane, and a plane perpendicular to the molecular plane—through the nitrogen atom and C_5—is the second mirror plane. Neither all the hydrogen atoms nor all the carbon atoms are chemically equivalent. However, those atoms related by symmetry are chemically equivalent! H_1 is equivalent to H_2, C_3 to C_4, and so forth. H_5 occupies a special position—on σ_v—of multiplicity 1 and, hence, is chemically unique. Any chemical or physical phenomenon dependent upon chemical equivalence would reflect these symmetry differences and likenesses. Such effects play an important role in understanding such important chemical measurements as nuclear-magnetic-resonance spectra.

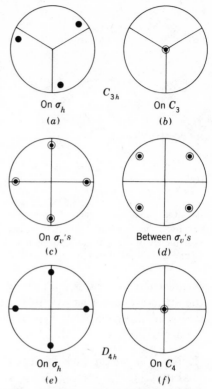

Fig. 4.9 Stereographic projections showing some special equivalent positions in the point groups C_{3h} and D_{4h}. Special positions generated (a) by the horizontal mirror σ_h; (b) by the three-fold axis C_3; (c) by the vertical mirrors σ_v; (d) halfway between the vertical mirrors; (e) on both the horizontal mirror σ_h and the vertical mirrors; and (f) on the fourfold axis C_4.

By the same token if a molecule is known to possess three equivalent atoms and only three of these atoms, the structure cannot possess a four-fold rotation axis. Such considerations are useful in experimental determinations of molecular structure and in discussing the possible conformations or structures a particular molecule might assume.

4.7 EXAMPLES OF POINT-GROUP IDENTIFICATION

In order to demonstrate the application of techniques developed in this chapter, let us consider several examples of the point-group identification

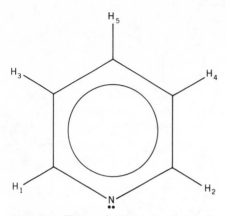

Fig. 4.10 The molecular structure of pyridine showing the symmetry non-equivalence of some of the hydrogen and carbon atoms (see text).

of molecular structures. The reader is urged to make or obtain models of the structures used as examples here. In each case, the reader should verify the presence or absence of the various symmetry elements. There is no substitute for building and handling structural models.

1. NH_3, *ammonia* (also NF_3, PH_3, and Cl_3PO), trigonal pyramid (see Fig. 4.11).

(*a*) NH_3 is not a type III (high-symmetry or linear) molecule.

(*b*) The molecule does possess a threefold axis passing through the nitrogen atom. C_3 is the only rotation axis.

(*c*) There is no sixfold improper axis, S_6.

(*d*) It may be observed that no C_2 axes exist perpendicular to C_3; hence, the point group is of the C type.

(*e*) There is no mirror plane σ_h perpendicular to C_3.

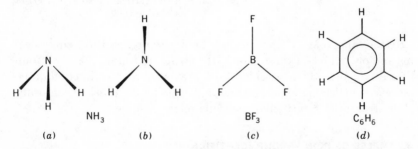

Fig. 4.11 The molecular structures of (*a*) ammonia, showing its pyramidal structure; (*b*) ammonia with a view down the threefold axis; (*c*) boron trifluoride; (*d*) benzene.

(f) Each of the three hydrogen atoms lies on a vertical mirror plane σ_v. Hence, the point group is C_{3v} ($3m$).

2. BF$_3$, *boron trifluoride* (also NO$_3^-$ and 1,3,5-trifluorobenzene), trigonal planar (see Fig. 4.11).

(a) BF$_3$ is not a type III (high-symmetry or linear) molecule.

(b) It may be observed that the structure possesses a threefold axis perpendicular to the molecular plane through the boron atom as well as three twofold axes, one along each B—F bond. C_3 is the principal axis.

(c) There is an S_6 axis collinear with C_3, but there are other elements present.

(d) We have already observed the presence of the ($n = 3$) C_2 axes perpendicular to C_3. The point group then is of the D type.

(e) The plane of the molecule is a mirror plane σ_h which is perpendicular to C_3.

Hence, the point group is D_{3h} ($\bar{6}m2$).

3. C$_6$H$_6$, *benzene*, hexagonal planar (see Fig. 4.11).

(a) Benzene is not a type III (high-symmetry or linear) molecule.

(b) The structure possesses several proper rotation axes. The principal axis is the sixfold axis C_6, which is perpendicular to the molecular plane and passes through the molecular center.

(c) The structure does not possess an S_{12} improper axis, although it possesses both S_6 and S_3 axes.

(d) There are six ($n = 6$) C_2 axes perpendicular to C_6, three along C—H bonds and three through C—C bond midpoints, all in the molecular plane. Thus, the point group is of the D type.

(e) The molecular plane is a horizontal mirror plane σ_h.

Hence, the point group is D_{6h} ($6/mmm$).

4. B(OH)$_3$, *boric acid* (see Fig. 4.12). There are at least two conformations possible for isolated B(OH)$_3$ molecules. We shall consider two. *Planar*.

(a) B(OH)$_3$ is not a type III structure.

(b) The structure possesses a threefold rotation axis through the boron atom. C_3 is the only axis present.

(c) There are no improper rotation axes except S_3 along C_3.

(d) There are no C_2 axes perpendicular to C_3.

(e) The molecular plane is a horizontal mirror plane σ_h perpendicular to C_3.

Hence the point group is C_{3h} ($3/m$).

Nonplanar, hydrogen atoms all above the plane. (The angle the O—H bonds make with the BO$_3$ plane is not 0 or 90°.) The point group analysis is the same as for the planar configuration in steps (a) to (d).

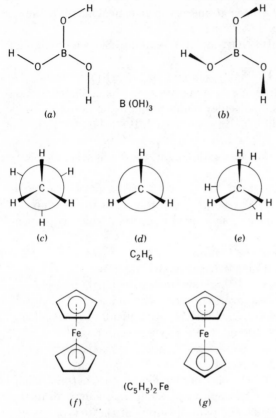

Fig. 4.12 The molecular structures of (a) boric acid (planar); (b) boric acid (nonplanar); (c) ethane (staggered); (d) ethane (eclipsed); (e) ethane (neither staggered nor eclipsed); (f) ferrocene (eclipsed); (g) ferrocene (staggered).

    (e) There is no longer a mirror plane perpendicular to C_3.

    (f) No vertical mirror planes exist.

Hence, the point group is C_3 (3).

5. C_2H_6, *ethane* (see Fig. 4.12). We shall consider three possible conformations of ethane made possible because of the free rotation about the C—C bond.

Staggered (trigonal antiprism).

    (a) Ethane (staggered) is not a type III structure.

    (b) The highest-order axis present is the threefold rotation axis C_3 along the C—C bond.

    (c) There is an S_6 improper axis collinear with C_3. However, the point group is not S_6 because of the presence of C_2 axes perpendicular to C_3.

(d) The C_2 axes perpendicular to C_3 pass through the midpoint of the C—C bond and when viewed down the C_3 axis, the C_2 axes lie between the C—H bonds attached to the two different carbon atoms. Thus, the group is a D type.

(e) There is no mirror plane perpendicular to C_3.

(f) There are three ($n = 3$) vertical mirror planes σ_v, each containing two trans C—H bonds (one from each carbon atom).

Hence, the point group is D_{3d} ($\overline{3}m$).

Eclipsed (trigonal prism). The analysis is the same as for the staggered configuration down to step (e).

(e) There does exist a horizontal mirror plane σ_h perpendicular to C_3. Hence, the point group is D_{3h} ($\overline{6}m2$).

Between staggered and eclipsed. The analysis is the same down to step (e) as for the eclipsed configuration.

(e) There is no mirror plane perpendicular C_3.

(f) There are no vertical mirror planes.

Hence, the point group is D_{2d} (222).

6. $(C_5H_5)_2Fe$, *ferrocene* (see Fig. 4.12). *Staggered configuration* (pentagonal antiprism).

(a) Ferrocene (staggered) is not a type III structure.

(b) The structure possesses several rotation axes. The principal axis is a fivefold axis C_5 perpendicular to the cyclopentadiene rings, through the iron atom.

(c) There is an S_{10} axis present, but there also are present several other symmetry elements. Thus, the point group is not S_{10}.

(d) There are five ($n = 5$) C_2 axes perpendicular to C_5. Thus, the point group is a D type.

(e) There is no mirror plane perpendicular to C_5.

(f) There are five ($n = 5$) vertical mirror planes σ_v each containing a C—H bond and bisecting the opposite C—C midpoint in each plane.

Hence, the point group is D_{5d}.

Eclipsed configuration (pentagonal prism). The analysis is the same as for the staggered configuration down to step (e).

(e) There is a horizontal mirror plane σ_h perpendicular to C_5 through the iron atom.

Hence the point group is D_{5h}.

7. $ClFCH_2$, *chlorofluoromethane* (see Fig. 4.13).

(a) $ClFCH_2$ is not a type III structure.

(b) The structure possesses no proper rotation axes. Thus, the structure is type I.

(c) There exists only one mirror plane containing the chlorine, fluorine, and carbon atoms and bisecting the H—C—H angle.
Hence, the point group is C_s (m or $\bar{2}$).

8. CF_4, *carbon tetrafluoride*, tetrahedral (see Fig. 4.13).

(a) Because of its apparent high symmetry, the structure should be examined for the requisite rotation axes.

(b) There are four threefold axes (along the C—F bonds) which are not mutually perpendicular. There are also three twofold axes, each bisecting an F—C—F angle. Thus, the group is tetrahedral.

(c) There are six mirror planes σ_d, each of which contains two threefold axes and one twofold axis. There is no center of symmetry and no other set of mirror planes.

Hence, the point group is T_d ($\bar{4}3m$).

9. C_2H_2, *acetylene*, and C_2HD, *monodeuteroacetylene*, linear (see Fig. 4.13).
Acetylene.

(a) Acetylene is linear (type III).

(b) There is a mirror plane perpendicular to the linear axis through the midpoint of the C—C bond.

Hence, the point group is $D_{\infty h}$.

Monodeuteroacetylene.

(a) The molecule is linear (type III).

(b) There is no mirror plane perpendicular to the linear axis because of the difference between hydrogen and deuterium.

Hence, the point group is $C_{\infty v}$.

10. $FeF_6{}^{3-}$, *hexafluoroferrate(III) ion*, octahedral (see Fig. 4.14).

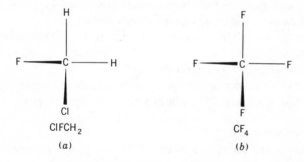

Fig. 4.13 The molecular structures of (a) chlorofluoromethane;
(b) carbon tetrafluoride; (c) acetylene; (d) monodeuteroacetylene.

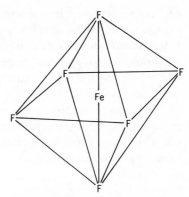

Fig. 4.14 The molecular structure of the octahedral hexafluoroferrate-(III) ion.

(a) Because of its apparent high symmetry the structure should be examined for the requisite rotation axes.

(b) Each F—Fe—F direction defines a fourfold axis, making a total of three C_4 axes. The bisector of each F—Fe—F angle is a twofold axis, six in total. The line connecting the iron atom with the midpoint of each geometric face (defined by three fluorine atoms) is a threefold axis, of which there are four. Thus, the structure is octahedral.

(c) The structure also possesses six dihedral mirror planes and three horizontal mirror planes plus a center of inversion.

Hence, the point group is O_h ($m3m$).

PROBLEMS

4.1. List the operations in the group D_6 (622). Show that this collection of operations is a group by constructing its multiplication table.

4.2. Draw the stereographic projections for the following point groups and show that each is a group by examination of these diagrams: C_{2h} ($2/m$), D_{2d} ($\overline{4}2m$), and D_{6h} ($6/mmm$).

4.3. Using Fig. 4.1, construct the multiplication table for the point group D_{4h} ($4/mmm$).

4.4. (a) Make a drawing of a tetrahedron with a view down one of the threefold axes. Draw the other threefold axes and the twofold axes and observe their relative orientation.

(b) Repeat with a view down a twofold axis. The improper fourfold axis can now be observed clearly.

4.5. Make a sketch of an octahedron with a view down a threefold axis. How else might an octahedron be described in this perspective?

4.6. We have shown in the text that the collection of the rotations of such regular solids as the tetrahedron form a group in the mathematical sense. What about the collection of reflections? (What is the product of two reflections across different mirror planes?)

4.7. (a) Show that the symmetry operation inversion commutes with all other operations.

(b) Show that the commutation property demonstrated for inversion in part (a) guarantees that inversion will always be in a class by itself.

4.8. Using the rules developed in Sec. 4.5, determine the classes in the following point groups:

(a) D_5

(b) C_{4v}

(c) C_{4h}

(d) D_{3h}

(e) T_h

(f) S_6

4.9. Show that in D_{nh} groups the σ_v mirror reflections are not in the same class as the σ_d mirror reflections.

4.10. (a) What is the multiplicity of the general positions in point group D_{4h}; D_{2d}; C_{6h}?

(b) List all the special positions in the point groups in part (a) and determine their multiplicities.

4.11. Determine both the Schoenflies and Hermann-Mauguin symbols for the following molecules and ions:

(a) CH_4, CH_3Cl, CH_2Cl_2, $CHCl_3$, CCl_4

(b) $H_2C{=}C{=}CH_2$, allene

(c) CBrClFH, bromochlorofluoromethane

(d) Anthracene and phenanthrene

(e) Bis(norbornadiene)nickel

(f) Cyclohexane, chair and boat form

(g) $Fe(CN)_6^{3-}$

(h) $Co(NH_3)_6^{++}$

4.12. Determine the point group of each of the following molecules or ions. (Write both point-group symbols.)

(a) Butadiene, cis and trans

(b) Dibenzenechromium

(c) Coronene

(d) Thalocyanine

(e) Cyclobutadiene

(f) Biacetylene

4.13. Determine the point groups of each of the following conformations of aniline, $C_6H_5NH_2$:

(a) Planar NH_2 group coplanar with the benzene ring

(b) Planar NH_2 group perpendicular to the benzene ring

(c) Nonplanar NH_2 group with both amino hydrogens below or above the plane of the benzene ring

(d) Nonplanar NH_2 group with one amino hydrogen above and one below the plane of the benzene ring

4.14. Consider the triphenylmethyl radical. Find the point group of each of the following structures:

(a) A totally planar radical

(b) Same as (a) but with the phenyl rings rotated 90° out of the plane

(c) Same as (b) but with rotation angle between 0 and 90°

(d) Same as (b) but nonplanar, pyramidal

4.15. There are three possible conformations of biphenyl: (a) two phenyl rings coplanar, (b) the two rings perpendicular, and (c) the two rings between coplanar and perpendicular. What is the point group of each conformation?

4.16. List the point group of each distinct conformation of n-propane. Sketch each conformation and show the various symmetry elements.

4.17. What is the point group of the possible conformations of toluene, considering rotation about the phenyl-methyl bond?

4.18. Determine the point group, including both symbols, for each of the following:

(a) Benzene

(b) Chlorobenzene

(c) o-Dichlorobenzene

(d) m-Dichlorobenzene

(e) p-Dichlorobenzene

(f) 1,3,5-Trichlorobenzene

4.19. It has been reported that in bromobenzene the bromine atom crowds adjacent hydrogen atoms out of the plane of the benzene ring. How does this affect the point-group symmetry?

4.20. A recent report on the electron diffraction study of gaseous ferrocene states that the hydrogen atoms are not in the plane of the cyclopentadiene rings but are uniformly displaced toward the iron atom so that the C—H bonds each make an angle of 5° with the cyclopentadiene rings. How does this affect the point group?

4.21. It is generally stated that a molecular species is optically active (able to rotate the plane of polarized light) if its mirror image is not superimposable upon the original structure. A more universally applicable test is for the presence of an improper rotation axis. When an improper axis (S_1, S_2, S_3, S_4, S_5, S_6, etc.) is present, the structure is optically *inactive*. Using this criterion determine whether the following substances are optically active:

(a) *trans*-1,2-Dichlorocyclopropane

(b) Spirane

(c) Ethane (neither staggered nor eclipsed)

(d) Chlorofluorobromomethane

(e) Hexaphenylbenzene (nonplanar)

(f) Biphenyl (angle θ between planes: $0° < \theta < 90°$)

4.22. Name the point group of each of the following structures of hydrogen peroxide, H_2O_2:

(a) Planar, trans

(b) Planar, cis

(c) Nonplanar, angle between H—O—O and O—O—H is 90°

4.23. What is the point group of each of the following?

(a) PF_5

(b) SF_6

(c) CO—$Mn(CO)_4$—$Mn(CO)_4$—CO

(d) $Cr(CO)_6$

(e) UOF_5^{3-}

4.24. What is the point group of the following compounds?

(a) B_2H_6, diborane

(b) Spiropentane

(c) Thiophene

(d) Formic acid (planar)

(e) Ketene

(f) The carbon skeleton of adamantane

(g) Ethylene oxide

(h) Nickeltetracarbonyl

(i) P_4O_{10}, P_4O_6, and P_4

(j) I_3^- (linear)

(k) trans-$Co(NH_3)_4Cl_2$

(l) cis-$Co(NH_3)_4Cl_2$

4.25. Following the pattern of the discussion in Sec. 4.2 on tetrahedral point groups show that:

(a) In the octahedral point group O (432) the presence of three mutually perpendicular fourfold axes implies the presence of four threefold axes.

(b) Six twofold axes must also be present.

4.26. The following molecular structures are related to the icosahedron and dodecahedron. Determine the point-group symbol of each molecule:

(a) $B_{12}H_{12}^{--}$

(b) $C_2B_{10}H_{12}$ (ortho conformation of carbon atoms)

(c) $C_2B_{10}H_{12}$ (meta conformation of carbon atoms)

(d) $C_2B_{10}H_{12}$ (para conformation of carbon atoms)

(e) $B_{10}H_{10}^{--}$

(f) $B_{10}H_{14}$

5

matrices, vectors and representations

Thus far in our discussions of group theory and molecular symmetry we have not made any connection between symmetry properties and group-theoretical arguments. The connection will now be established by considering matrices as representations of molecular symmetry point groups. It will be found that certain properties of matrices lend themselves well to the expression of group-theoretical ideas.

First, let us discuss the various properties of matrices which will be found useful. A matrix is an array (of numbers or symbols) which is rectangular in its general form. A matrix, which is related to a mathematical operation, is not to be confused with a determinant, which is a number written in the form of an array.

5.1 MATRIX DEFINITIONS

Let us denote a matrix either by a capital letter, such as U, or by a double subscripted lowercase letter in brackets, such as $[u_{ij}]$. For example, in the matrix U below, u_{23} is -2.

$$U = \begin{bmatrix} 1 & -1 & 0 \\ 0 & 2 & -2 \\ 3 & 0 & 1 \end{bmatrix}$$

The subscripts refer to the number of the row and column, respectively, which locate the element in the array. Although a matrix may be rectangular in general, we shall consider only square matrices, i.e., matrices in which the number of rows is equal to the number of columns.

We shall find the following definitions useful in later discussions.

1. *Identity matrix.* The identity, or unit, matrix is usually given one of the following symbols: E, I, or $\mathbb{1}$. The diagonal elements u_{ii} are all equal to 1 and the off-diagonal elements are zero. Thus, the elements of the identity matrix may be represented by the Kronecker delta

$$u_{ij} = \delta_{ij} = \begin{cases} 0 & i \neq j \\ 1 & i = j \end{cases}$$

2. *Diagonal matrix.* A diagonal matrix is similar to a unit matrix; the off-diagonal elements are zero, but the diagonal elements are not necessarily equal.

3. *Symmetric matrix.* A symmetric matrix is one in which matrix elements related by reflection across the diagonal are equal:

$$u_{ij} = u_{ji}$$

4. *Transpose of a matrix.* The transpose of a matrix is obtained by interchanging elements across the diagonal. The transpose of a matrix is symbolized by a tilde over the matrix symbol.

$$\tilde{u}_{ij} = u_{ji}$$

5. *Hermitian adjoint.* The hermitian adjoint of U is obtained by taking the complex conjugate of the transpose of U. The hermitian adjoint of U is symbolized as $U^\dagger$.

$$U^\dagger = \tilde{U}^*$$
$$[u_{ij}]^\dagger = [u_{ji}^*]$$

6. *Hermitian matrix.* A hermitian matrix is one which is equal to its hermitian adjoint.

$$u_{ij}^\dagger = u_{ji}^*$$
$$U = U^\dagger$$

7. *Unitary matrix.* A unitary matrix is one for which the inverse of the matrix is equal to the hermitian adjoint of the matrix.

$$U^{-1} = U^\dagger$$

The definition of the inverse of a matrix is discussed in the appendix to this chapter.

In order to understand the use of matrices one must understand the methods of combination of matrices. Matrices may be combined by addition, subtraction, multiplication, and in a special manner by division.

1. *Addition.* Two matrices can be combined under addition or subtraction only when they are of identical dimensions. When of equal dimensions, the elements of a matrix U given by the sum or difference of A and B are

$$u_{ij} = a_{ij} \pm b_{ij}$$

Two matrices A and B which are equal are identical element by element:

$$A = B$$
$$a_{ij} = b_{ij} \quad \text{all } i \text{ and } j$$

2. *Multiplication.* Two matrices can be multiplied if they are conformable: when considering the product $BA = U$, the matrices can be multiplied only if the number of columns of B is equal to the number of rows of A. Thus, matrix B of dimension $m \times n$ multiplied times A of dimension $n \times p$ produces matrix U of dimension $m \times p$. Each element u_{ij} of U is given as follows:

$$u_{ij} = \sum_{k=1}^{n} b_{ik} a_{kj}$$

3. *Division.* Division of matrices is accomplished in a manner analogous to one method of multiplication of numbers. Division is accomplished as multiplication by the reciprocal or inverse of a matrix. The indicated division $U = B/A$ is rewritten as the multiplication by the reciprocal or inverse of A, A^{-1}:

$$U = BA^{-1}$$

The elements of B and of A^{-1} are combined as in multiplication, as outlined above. The definition of the inverse matrix and the calculation of its elements are discussed in the appendix to this chapter.

Since we shall use only square matrices in the study of the applications of group theory, the following examples use only square matrices. Consider the matrices P and R:

$$P = \begin{bmatrix} 1 & 2 \\ -2 & 3 \end{bmatrix} \quad \text{and} \quad R = \begin{bmatrix} 1 & 0 \\ 2 & 1 \end{bmatrix}$$

$$Q = P + R = \begin{bmatrix} 1 & 2 \\ -2 & 3 \end{bmatrix} + \begin{bmatrix} 1 & 0 \\ 2 & 1 \end{bmatrix} = \begin{bmatrix} 2 & 2 \\ 0 & 4 \end{bmatrix}$$

$$S = PR = \begin{bmatrix} 1 & 2 \\ -2 & 3 \end{bmatrix}\begin{bmatrix} 1 & 0 \\ 2 & 1 \end{bmatrix} = \begin{bmatrix} 5 & 2 \\ 4 & 3 \end{bmatrix}$$

$$T = RP = \begin{bmatrix} 1 & 0 \\ 2 & 1 \end{bmatrix}\begin{bmatrix} 1 & 2 \\ -2 & 3 \end{bmatrix} = \begin{bmatrix} 1 & 2 \\ 0 & 7 \end{bmatrix}$$

Note that matrix multiplication is not commutative in general: $PR \neq RP$.

Let $V = \begin{bmatrix} 1 & 2 \\ 2 & 1 \end{bmatrix}$

Then

$$W = (PR)V = SV = \begin{bmatrix} 5 & 2 \\ 4 & 3 \end{bmatrix}\begin{bmatrix} 1 & 2 \\ 2 & 1 \end{bmatrix} = \begin{bmatrix} 9 & 12 \\ 10 & 11 \end{bmatrix}$$

$$X = P(RV) = P\begin{bmatrix} 1 & 0 \\ 2 & 1 \end{bmatrix}\begin{bmatrix} 1 & 2 \\ 2 & 1 \end{bmatrix} = P\begin{bmatrix} 1 & 2 \\ 4 & 5 \end{bmatrix}$$

$$\begin{bmatrix} 1 & 2 \\ -2 & 3 \end{bmatrix}\begin{bmatrix} 1 & 2 \\ 4 & 5 \end{bmatrix} = \begin{bmatrix} 9 & 12 \\ 10 & 11 \end{bmatrix}$$

Note that matrix multiplication obeys the associative law, as can be seen from $W = (PR)V = P(RV) = X$.

5.2 MATRICES AS REPRESENTATIONS OF OPERATIONS

In the description of symmetry operations matrices are found to be quite useful. We shall now develop matrices for the various point-group operations. We shall consider matrices for the operations of rotation, reflection, inversion, improper rotation, and also the identity matrix by considering the action of the operations on the components of a two-dimensional vector.

ROTATION C_n

Consider the two-dimensional vector $\mathbf{r}$ shown in the two-dimensional coordinate system in Fig. 5.1. The vector $\mathbf{r}$ may be expressed in terms of its components x and y and the unit vectors $\hat{\imath}$ and $\hat{\jmath}$

$$\mathbf{r} = x\hat{\imath} + y\hat{\jmath}$$

Vector $\mathbf{r}$ may also be expressed as a column matrix of rank 2

$$\mathbf{r} = \begin{bmatrix} x \\ y \end{bmatrix}$$

Consider the rotation of $\mathbf{r}$ through the angle ϕ. The rotation operation may be expressed symbolically as

$$C_n \cdot \mathbf{r} = \mathbf{r}'$$

The symbol C_n refers to rotation about an axis, where $n = 2\pi/\phi$, the fraction of 2π radians through which rotation occurs. The vector $\mathbf{r}$ may also be expressed in terms of the components x' and y'

$$\mathbf{r} = x'\hat{\imath} + y'\hat{\jmath}$$

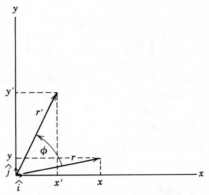

Fig. 5.1 A two-dimensional coordinate system defined by unit vectors $\hat{\imath}$ directed along the x axis and $\hat{\jmath}$ directed along the y axis. The system is used to demonstrate the rotation (in the plane) of vector $\mathbf{r}$ through angle ϕ.

The components of $\mathbf{r'}$ may in turn be expressed in terms of the components of $\mathbf{r}$. When one considers the rotation of the components x and y into x' and y', the following equations may be written:

$$x' = x \cos \phi + y \sin \phi$$
$$y' = -x \sin \phi + y \cos \phi$$

This set of equations may also be formulated in matrix notation:

$$\mathbf{r'} = C\mathbf{r}$$

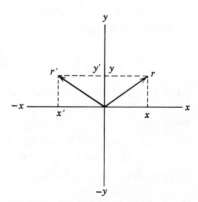

Fig. 5.2 A two-dimensional coordinate system used to demonstrate the reflection of vector $\mathbf{r}$ across the y axis.

or

$$\begin{bmatrix} x' \\ y' \end{bmatrix} = \begin{bmatrix} \cos \phi & \sin \phi \\ -\sin \phi & \cos \phi \end{bmatrix} \begin{bmatrix} x \\ y \end{bmatrix}$$

Thus, the matrix C represents the rotation of a two-dimensional vector through an angle ϕ.

REFLECTION R

Consider again the vector $\mathbf{r}$ and the operation of reflecting $\mathbf{r}$ across the y axis (across the yz plane), as shown in Fig. 5.2:

$$\sigma_{yz}\mathbf{r} = \mathbf{r}''$$

which may also be written in component notation

$$\sigma_{yz} \begin{bmatrix} x \\ y \end{bmatrix} = \begin{bmatrix} x'' \\ y'' \end{bmatrix}$$

The components of $\mathbf{r}''$ may be written in terms of the components of $\mathbf{r}$. The equations can be determined by simply observing the action of reflection on the components x and y:

$$x'' = -1 \cdot x + 0 \cdot y$$
$$y'' = 0 \cdot x + 1 \cdot y$$

In matrix notation these equations can be combined

$$\mathbf{r} = \begin{bmatrix} x'' \\ y'' \end{bmatrix} = \begin{bmatrix} -1 & 0 \\ 0 & 1 \end{bmatrix} \begin{bmatrix} x \\ y \end{bmatrix} = R\mathbf{r}$$

Thus, the matrix R represents the reflection of a two-dimensional vector across the y axis. Further inspection will reveal that the matrix R' represents reflection across the x axis

$$R' = \begin{bmatrix} 1 & 0 \\ 0 & -1 \end{bmatrix}$$

Note the similarity of R and R'.

INVERSION

By considering the action of the inversion operation on $\mathbf{r}$ in a manner similar to the above examples, the matrix I_2, which represents inversion (in two dimensions), is obtained.

$$i \cdot \mathbf{r} = \mathbf{r}'''$$

$$\mathbf{r}''' = i \cdot \mathbf{r} = \begin{bmatrix} -1 & 0 \\ 0 & -1 \end{bmatrix} \begin{bmatrix} x \\ y \end{bmatrix} = I_2 \mathbf{r}$$

The preceding considerations can easily be extended to three dimensions. First let us consider rotation. Although implicitly we have considered rotation in the xy plane, i.e., rotation around z, the above considerations may readily be applied to rotation about x and y. The vector component corresponding to the axis about which rotation takes place is unchanged. Thus, the matrix C_z, which represents rotation about z, is written

$$C_z = \begin{bmatrix} \cos\phi & \sin\phi & 0 \\ -\sin\phi & \cos\phi & 0 \\ 0 & 0 & 1 \end{bmatrix}$$

Likewise reflection across the xy plane is represented by R_{xy}:

$$R_{xy} = \begin{bmatrix} 1 & 0 & 0 \\ 0 & 1 & 0 \\ 0 & 0 & -1 \end{bmatrix}$$

Inversion in three dimensions is given by I:

$$I = \begin{bmatrix} -1 & 0 & 0 \\ 0 & -1 & 0 \\ 0 & 0 & -1 \end{bmatrix}$$

IMPROPER ROTATION S_n

The application of successive symmetry operations may be represented by the product of the two matrices which represent the two operations:

$$S = CR$$
$$S = \begin{bmatrix} \cos\phi & \sin\phi & 0 \\ -\sin\phi & \cos\phi & 0 \\ 0 & 0 & 1 \end{bmatrix} \begin{bmatrix} 1 & 0 & 0 \\ 0 & 1 & 0 \\ 0 & 0 & -1 \end{bmatrix}$$

and

$$S = \begin{bmatrix} \cos\phi & \sin\phi & 0 \\ -\sin\phi & \cos\phi & 0 \\ 0 & 0 & -1 \end{bmatrix}$$

Thus, the matrix S represents an improper rotation about the z axis.

IDENTITY

The identity operation may be termed the leave-it-alone operation. Although it may appear trivial, it plays an essential role in group theory. It is necessary for the definition of both the group and the inverse of an operation. When we consider the components of a vector, we can see that the identity operation must leave each component unchanged: the operation must not mix the components. We can then write the following three equations which represent the action of the identity operation on vector $\mathbf{r}$:

$$x' = 1 \cdot x + 0 \cdot y + 0 \cdot z$$
$$y' = 0 \cdot x + 1 \cdot y + 0 \cdot z$$
$$z' = 0 \cdot x + 0 \cdot y + 1 \cdot z$$

The set of equations may again be written in vector and matrix notation.

$$\mathbf{r}' = E\mathbf{r} = \begin{bmatrix} 1 & 0 & 0 \\ 0 & 1 & 0 \\ 0 & 0 & 1 \end{bmatrix} \begin{bmatrix} x \\ y \\ z \end{bmatrix}$$

5.3 MATRICES AS GROUP REPRESENTATIONS

It is now clear that we can obtain a collection of matrices each of which represents a specific symmetry operation of a point group. In order to show that a collection of matrices is a representation of a group, we must also show that the collection of matrices obeys the definition of a group. Let us consider the group C_{2h} as a specific example. The multiplication table for the group C_{2h} is

C_{2h}	E	C_2	i	σ_h
E	E	C_2	i	σ_h
C_2	C_2	E	σ_h	i
i	i	σ_h	E	C_2
σ_h	σ_h	i	C_2	E

We can obtain a set of 3×3 matrices using a vector, i.e., its three cartesian components, as a basis set.

$$E = \begin{bmatrix} 1 & 0 & 0 \\ 0 & 1 & 0 \\ 0 & 0 & 1 \end{bmatrix} \qquad C_2 = \begin{bmatrix} -1 & 0 & 0 \\ 0 & -1 & 0 \\ 0 & 0 & 1 \end{bmatrix}$$

$$i = \begin{bmatrix} -1 & 0 & 0 \\ 0 & -1 & 0 \\ 0 & 0 & -1 \end{bmatrix} \qquad \sigma_h = \begin{bmatrix} 1 & 0 & 0 \\ 0 & 1 & 0 \\ 0 & 0 & -1 \end{bmatrix}$$

Let us consider the four rules for the definition of a group found in Chap. 3:

1. The product of any two group elements must also be an element of the group.

Let us consider the product $iC_2 = \sigma_h$:

$$\begin{bmatrix} -1 & 0 & 0 \\ 0 & -1 & 0 \\ 0 & 0 & -1 \end{bmatrix} \begin{bmatrix} -1 & 0 & 0 \\ 0 & -1 & 0 \\ 0 & 0 & 1 \end{bmatrix} = \begin{bmatrix} 1 & 0 & 0 \\ 0 & 1 & 0 \\ 0 & 0 & -1 \end{bmatrix}$$

The product of the two matrices is the matrix which represents the operation σ_h. Likewise for the product $C_2\sigma_h = i$:

$$\begin{bmatrix} -1 & 0 & 0 \\ 0 & -1 & 0 \\ 0 & 0 & 1 \end{bmatrix} \begin{bmatrix} 1 & 0 & 0 \\ 0 & 1 & 0 \\ 0 & 0 & -1 \end{bmatrix} = \begin{bmatrix} -1 & 0 & 0 \\ 0 & -1 & 0 \\ 0 & 0 & -1 \end{bmatrix}$$

The reader may check the other products. The result is that this collection of matrices obeys rule 1. Now, consider the other rules.

2. One element in the group must leave all the elements unchanged and be commutative.

The very nature of the identity matrix guarantees compliance with rule 2.

3. The associative law must hold.

We have shown earlier that matrix multiplication obeys the associative law.

4. Every element of the group must have a reciprocal which is also a member of the group.

The definition of a reciprocal provides that the multiplication of an element times its reciprocal yields the identity. In the group C_{2h} each element is its own reciprocal. We can check this by determining the products of the elements with themselves.

$C_2 \cdot C_2 = E$

$$\begin{bmatrix} -1 & 0 & 0 \\ 0 & -1 & 0 \\ 0 & 0 & 1 \end{bmatrix} \begin{bmatrix} -1 & 0 & 0 \\ 0 & -1 & 0 \\ 0 & 0 & 1 \end{bmatrix} = \begin{bmatrix} 1 & 0 & 0 \\ 0 & 1 & 0 \\ 0 & 0 & 1 \end{bmatrix}$$

$i \cdot i = E$

$$\begin{bmatrix} -1 & 0 & 0 \\ 0 & -1 & 0 \\ 0 & 0 & -1 \end{bmatrix} \begin{bmatrix} -1 & 0 & 0 \\ 0 & -1 & 0 \\ 0 & 0 & -1 \end{bmatrix} = \begin{bmatrix} 1 & 0 & 0 \\ 0 & 1 & 0 \\ 0 & 0 & 1 \end{bmatrix}$$

$\sigma_h \cdot \sigma_h = E$

$$\begin{bmatrix} 1 & 0 & 0 \\ 0 & 1 & 0 \\ 0 & 0 & -1 \end{bmatrix} \begin{bmatrix} 1 & 0 & 0 \\ 0 & 1 & 0 \\ 0 & 0 & -1 \end{bmatrix} = \begin{bmatrix} 1 & 0 & 0 \\ 0 & 1 & 0 \\ 0 & 0 & 1 \end{bmatrix}$$

Thus, the collection of the above matrices does represent the group C_{2h}.

We might now ask how many representations are there for group C_{2h}. We obtained the above representation by using a vector (in three dimensions) as a basis function. We might just as well use a collection of vectors or a single cartesian component. We would then obtain representations of dimension other than three. In fact the number of representations appears to be limited only by our ingenuity in constructing representations. We shall return to this important question in Chap. 6.

5.4 VECTORS AND VECTOR SPACES

Consider a collection of vectors α_j: α_1, α_2, . . . , α_N.
These vectors are linearly independent if for the equation

$$c_1\alpha_1 + c_2\alpha_2 + c_3\alpha_3 + \cdots + c_N\alpha_N = 0 = \Sigma c_i\alpha_i$$

there is only one solution: all $c_i = 0$ for $\alpha_i \neq 0$.

In order for a set of n nonzero vectors to be linearly dependent, it is necessary and sufficient that one vector be a linear combination of the others.   Consider the set

$$\alpha_1, \ \alpha_2, \ \alpha_3, \ . . . , \ \alpha_i, \ . . . \ ; \ \alpha_N$$

where

$$\alpha_i = d_1\alpha_1 + d_2\alpha_2 + d_3\alpha_3 + \cdots + d_{i-1}\alpha_{i-1}$$

Then

$$d_1\alpha_1 + d_2\alpha_2 + d_3\alpha_3 + \cdots - 1\alpha_i = 0$$

Therefore, at least one of the coefficients is nonzero.   Write out the whole set.

$$d_1\alpha_1 + d_2\alpha_2 + d_3\alpha_3 + \cdots + d_i\alpha_i + \cdots + d_N\alpha_N = 0$$

Say d_i is the last nonvanishing coefficient.   All others vanish; so that

$$\alpha_i = -\sum_{j=1}^{i-1} \frac{d_j\alpha_j}{d_i} = \sum_{j=1}^{i-1} (-d_j d_i^{-1})\alpha_j = \sum_{j=1}^{i-1} c_j\alpha_j$$

Thus, α_i is a linear combination of the other vectors in the set.   The collection of all vectors in a space is said to span the space.   A smaller number of vectors can also be found which also span the space.   A basis set is a set of linearly independent vectors that span the space.   The dimensionality of the space is the number of basis vectors required to span the space.

5.5 VECTOR TRANSFORMATIONS

Consider a basis set α_j: α_1, α_2, α_3, . . . , α_N.   These can be written in terms of the unit vectors ε_j.

$$\varepsilon_1 = [1 \ \ 0 \ \ 0 \ \cdots \ 0]$$
$$\varepsilon_2 = [0 \ \ 1 \ \ 0 \ \cdots \ 0]$$
$$\varepsilon_3 = [0 \ \ 0 \ \ 1 \ \cdots \ 0]$$
$$\varepsilon_N = [0 \ \ 0 \ \ 0 \ \cdots \ 1]$$

So that

$$\alpha_j = \alpha_j\varepsilon_j$$

Then, the coefficients α_j can be written as the components of a vector **A**.

$$\mathbf{A} = [\alpha_1 \quad \alpha_2 \quad \alpha_3 \quad \cdots \quad \alpha_N]$$

By a linear transformation this basis set can be transformed into a new basis set $\boldsymbol{\alpha}'_j$. Again we can write the $\boldsymbol{\alpha}'_j$ as

$$\boldsymbol{\alpha}'_j = \alpha'_j \boldsymbol{\varepsilon}_j$$
$$A' = [\alpha'_1 \quad \alpha'_2 \quad \alpha'_3 \quad \cdots \quad \alpha'_N]$$

Any vector in a space may be written as a linear combination of the basis vectors. Let us write the $\boldsymbol{\alpha}'_j$ as linear combinations of the original basis set.

$$\alpha'_1 = t_{11}\alpha_1 + t_{12}\alpha_2 + t_{13}\alpha_3 + \cdots$$
$$\alpha'_2 = t_{21}\alpha_1 + t_{22}\alpha_2 + t_{23}\alpha_3 + \cdots$$

Or in matrix notation

$$\mathbf{A}' = T\mathbf{A}$$

and

$$\alpha'_1 = \sum_{i=1}^{N} t_{1i}\alpha_i$$

or in general

$$\boldsymbol{\alpha}'_j = \sum_{i=1}^{N} t_{ji}\alpha_i \boldsymbol{\varepsilon}_i$$

Now, consider a vector **r** which in basis **A** has components x_j: x_1, x_2, x_3, . . . , x_N; or

$$\mathbf{r} = x_1\boldsymbol{\alpha}_1 + x_2\boldsymbol{\alpha}_2 + x_3\boldsymbol{\alpha}_3 + \cdots + x_N\boldsymbol{\alpha}_N = \sum_{j=1}^{N} x_j\boldsymbol{\alpha}_j$$

or

$$\mathbf{r} = \sum_{j=1}^{N} x_j\alpha_j \boldsymbol{\varepsilon}_j$$

In basis A' the vector **r** will have different components x'_j.

$$\mathbf{r}' = \sum_{j=1}^{N} x'_j\boldsymbol{\alpha}_j = \sum_{j=1}^{N} x'_j\alpha'_j \boldsymbol{\varepsilon}_j$$

We know the transformation which takes **A** into **A**', but what is the transformation which takes **r** into **r**'?

What is M such that

$$X' = MX \qquad X = [x_1 \quad x_2 \quad x_3 \quad \cdots \quad x_N]$$

when

$$\mathbf{A}' = T\mathbf{A}$$

From above we can write

$$\mathbf{r} = \sum_{i=1}^{N} x_i \alpha_i = \sum_{j=1}^{N} x_j' \alpha_j' = \sum_{j=1}^{N} x_j \sum_{i} t_{ji} \alpha_i$$

Interchange the order of summation

$$\mathbf{r} = \sum_{i} \left(\sum_{j} x_j' \right) t_{ji} \alpha_i \qquad \text{but} \qquad \mathbf{r} = \sum_{i=1}^{N} x_i \alpha_i$$

so that

$$x_i = \sum_{j} x_j' t_{ji} = \sum_{j} t_{ji} x_j'$$

By transposing T we find

$$x_i = \sum_{j} \tilde{t}_{ij} x_j'$$

In matrix notation we write

$$X = \tilde{T} X'$$

or

$$\mathbf{X}' = \tilde{T}^{-1} \mathbf{X}$$

Thus

$$M = \tilde{T}^{-1} = (T^\dagger)^{-1} \qquad \text{if } T \text{ is complex}$$

But

$$\mathbf{A}' = T\mathbf{A}$$

Therefore the inverse of the hermitian conjugate of the matrix which transforms the basis set is the matrix which transforms vectors in that space.

Remember that if T is unitary, $T = (T^\dagger)^{-1}$. Thus, if

$$P\mathbf{X} = \mathbf{Y} \qquad \text{in } \mathbf{A}$$

and

$$QX' = Y' \qquad \text{in } \mathbf{A}'$$

where

$$\mathbf{A}' = T\mathbf{A}$$

then

$$P = T^{-1}QT$$

5.6 EIGENVECTORS AND EIGENVALUES

Eigenvalues are sometimes referred to as characteristic values of a transformation.

$$T\mathbf{u}_j = t_j\mathbf{u}_j$$

where t_j = scalars
$\quad\mathbf{u}_j$ = vectors
$\quad T$ = matrix

Theorem one: If the eigenvectors of a matrix A span the space V, then A is similar to a diagonal matrix D and the entries (diagonal elements) in D are the eigenvalues of A.

Consider a matrix D which is similar to A. We can always find such a matrix. Consider the unit vectors $\boldsymbol{\varepsilon}_j = [0 \quad 0 \quad 0 \quad \cdots \quad 1 \quad \cdots \quad 0]$. These unit vectors are eigenvectors of D. Consider eigenvector number 1.

$$D\boldsymbol{\varepsilon}_1 = \begin{bmatrix} d_1 & 0 & 0 & \cdots & 0 \\ 0 & d_2 & 0 & \cdots & 0 \\ 0 & 0 & d_3 & \cdots & 0 \\ \multicolumn{5}{c}{\cdots\cdots\cdots\cdots\cdots} \\ 0 & 0 & 0 & \cdots & d_N \end{bmatrix} \begin{bmatrix} 1 \\ 0 \\ 0 \\ . \\ . \\ . \\ 0 \end{bmatrix} = d_1 \begin{bmatrix} 1 \\ 0 \\ 0 \\ . \\ . \\ . \\ 0 \end{bmatrix} = d_1\boldsymbol{\varepsilon}_1$$

Thus, the nonzero (diagonal) elements or entries in D are its eigenvalues. But A is similar to D, and so these are also the eigenvalues of A. Furthermore, these are the only eigenvectors of D.

Take $\mathbf{S}$, any other eigenvector. Write it as a linear combination of the unit vectors of the space.

$$\mathbf{S} = S_1\boldsymbol{\varepsilon}_1 + S_2\boldsymbol{\varepsilon}_2 + S_3\boldsymbol{\varepsilon}_3 + \cdots$$

If $\mathbf{S}$ is an eigenvector of D, then in the three-dimensional case

$$D\mathbf{S} = C\mathbf{S}$$
$$\begin{bmatrix} d_1 & 0 & 0 \\ 0 & d_2 & 0 \\ 0 & 0 & d_3 \end{bmatrix} \begin{bmatrix} S_1 \\ S_2 \\ S_3 \end{bmatrix} = \begin{bmatrix} d_1S_1 \\ d_2S_2 \\ d_3S_3 \end{bmatrix} = \begin{bmatrix} CS_1 \\ CS_2 \\ CS_3 \end{bmatrix}$$

Since at least one $S_j \neq 0$, we can write for the one nonzero S_j

$$d_jS_j = CS_j$$

or $C = d_j$, an eigenvalue of D.

Converse of theorem one: If the eigenvectors of A span the space V, then we can take a linearly independent set to form a basis set β_j. In terms of this *new* basis set A will be diagonal.

$$A\beta_j = b_j\beta_j \qquad \text{where } \beta_j = \beta_j\varepsilon_j'$$

Now we want to find the diagonalizing matrix.

What is the matrix T which transforms matrix A by a similarity transformation into a diagonal matrix D? Construct a matrix T by making the eigenvectors of A the columns of T.

$$T = \begin{bmatrix} \beta_{11} & \beta_{12} & \beta_{13} & \cdots & \beta_{1N} \\ \beta_{21} & \beta_{22} & \beta_{23} & \cdots & \beta_{2N} \\ \beta_{31} & \beta_{32} & \beta_{33} & \cdots & \beta_{3N} \\ \cdots & \cdots & \cdots & \cdots & \cdots \\ \beta_{N1} & \beta_{N2} & \beta_{N3} & \cdots & \beta_{NN} \end{bmatrix}$$

$$\begin{array}{cccc} \uparrow & \uparrow & \uparrow & \uparrow \\ \text{1st} & \text{2nd} & \text{3rd} & N\text{th} \end{array}$$

$$\text{eigenvector}$$

Then, we can show that

$$AT = TD$$

Take 3×3 matrices as an example.

$$\begin{bmatrix} a_{11} & a_{12} & a_{13} \\ a_{21} & a_{22} & a_{23} \\ a_{31} & a_{32} & a_{33} \end{bmatrix} \begin{bmatrix} \beta_{11} & \beta_{12} & \beta_{13} \\ \beta_{21} & \beta_{22} & \beta_{23} \\ \beta_{31} & \beta_{32} & \beta_{33} \end{bmatrix}$$

$$= \begin{bmatrix} (a_{11}\beta_{11} + a_{12}\beta_{21} + a_{13}\beta_{31}) & (a_{11}\beta_{12} + a_{12}\beta_{22} + a_{13}\beta_{32}) & \cdots \\ (a_{21}\beta_{11} + a_{22}\beta_{21} + a_{23}\beta_{31}) & \cdots & \cdots \\ (a_{31}\beta_{11} + a_{32}\beta_{21} + a_{33}\beta_{31}) & \cdots & \cdots \end{bmatrix}$$

$$= [A\beta_1 \quad A\beta_2 \quad A\beta_3] \qquad \text{but } A\beta_j = b_j\beta_j$$

$$= \begin{bmatrix} b_1\beta_{11} & b_2\beta_{12} & b_3\beta_{13} \\ b_1\beta_{21} & b_2\beta_{32} & b_3\beta_{23} \\ b_1\beta_{31} & b_2\beta_{32} & b_3\beta_{33} \end{bmatrix}$$

$$= \begin{bmatrix} \beta_{11} & \beta_{12} & \beta_{13} \\ \beta_{21} & \beta_{22} & \beta_{23} \\ \beta_{31} & \beta_{32} & \beta_{33} \end{bmatrix} \begin{bmatrix} b_1 & 0 & 0 \\ 0 & b_2 & 0 \\ 0 & 0 & b_3 \end{bmatrix} = TD \qquad \text{Q.E.D.}$$

Therefore

$$AT = TD$$

Now we shall right-multiply by T^{-1}, which we shall symbolize by

$$T^{-1} \,\S \qquad AT = TD$$

getting

$$T^{-1}AT = D$$

So that the matrix of eigenvectors (as columns) is the matrix which diagonalizes A, and the diagonal elements of D are the eigenvalues of A appearing in the same order as the ordering of the eigenvectors (as columns) in T.

T is nonsingular because all the rows are independent!

Consider the statement of the eigenvalue equation.

$$A\beta_j = b_j\beta_j = b_jE\beta_j$$
$$A\beta_j - b_jE\beta_j = 0$$
$$\{A - b_jE\} \cdot \beta_j = 0 \qquad \beta_j \neq 0$$

This is another statement of the eigenvalue problem as shown below in expanded form for a 3×3 case.

$$\begin{bmatrix} a_{11} - b_j & a_{12} & a_{13} \\ a_{21} & a_{22} - b_j & a_{23} \\ a_{31} & a_{32} & a_{33} - b_j \end{bmatrix} \begin{bmatrix} \beta_{1j} \\ \beta_{2j} \\ \beta_{3j} \end{bmatrix} = 0$$

The only nontrivial solution to this problem, that is, $\beta_{ij} \neq 0$ for all i and j, is that the determinant of the coefficients be identically zero.

$$\{A - b_jE\} \cdot \beta_j = 0$$
$$|A - b_jE| \equiv 0$$

5.7 EXAMPLE SOLUTION OF THE EIGENVALUES OF A MATRIX

Let

$$A = \begin{bmatrix} 1 & 2 \\ 2 & 1 \end{bmatrix}$$

Then

$$\begin{vmatrix} 1 - b & 2 \\ 2 & 1 - b \end{vmatrix} = 0$$
$$(1 - b)^2 - 4 = 0$$
$$b^2 - 2b - 3 = 0$$

$$\boxed{\begin{aligned} b_1 &= -1 \\ b_2 &= 3 \end{aligned}} \qquad \text{eigenvalues}$$

To obtain eigenvectors substitute each eigenvalue into the equation $(A - b_jE) \cdot \beta_j = 0$ and solve for ratio of coefficients. Note that absolute values of coefficients cannot be obtained in this manner.

$$\begin{bmatrix} 1 - b_1 & 2 \\ 2 & 1 - b_1 \end{bmatrix} \begin{bmatrix} \beta_{11} \\ \beta_{21} \end{bmatrix} = 0 \qquad \beta_1 = \begin{bmatrix} \beta_1' \\ \beta_2' \end{bmatrix} = \begin{bmatrix} \beta_{11} \\ \beta_{21} \end{bmatrix}$$

$$\begin{bmatrix} 1 - (-1) & 2 \\ 2 & 1 - (-1) \end{bmatrix} \begin{bmatrix} \beta_{11} \\ \beta_{21} \end{bmatrix} = \begin{bmatrix} 2 & 2 \\ 2 & 2 \end{bmatrix} \begin{bmatrix} \beta_{11} \\ \beta_{21} \end{bmatrix} = 0$$

$$\begin{bmatrix} 2\beta_{11} + 2\beta_{21} \\ 2\beta_{11} + 2\beta_{21} \end{bmatrix} = 0 = \begin{bmatrix} 0 \\ 0 \end{bmatrix}$$

$$2\beta_{11} + 2\beta_{21} = 0$$

or

$$\boxed{\beta_{11} = -\beta_{21}}$$

Now substitute the second eigenvalue b_2.

$$\begin{bmatrix} 1 - b_2 & 2 \\ 2 & 1 - b_2 \end{bmatrix} \begin{bmatrix} \beta_{12} \\ \beta_{22} \end{bmatrix} = \begin{bmatrix} -2 & 2 \\ 2 & -2 \end{bmatrix} \begin{bmatrix} \beta_{12} \\ \beta_{22} \end{bmatrix} = 0$$

$$-2\beta_{12} + 2\beta_{22} = 0$$

$$\boxed{\beta_{12} = \beta_{22}}$$

Therefore if we let

$$|\beta_{11}| = |\beta_{21}| = |\beta_{12}| = |\beta_{22}| = \beta$$

the eigenvectors are

$$\beta_1 = \beta \begin{bmatrix} 1 \\ -1 \end{bmatrix} = \begin{bmatrix} \beta \\ -\beta \end{bmatrix}$$

$$\beta_2 = \beta \begin{bmatrix} 1 \\ 1 \end{bmatrix} = \begin{bmatrix} \beta \\ \beta \end{bmatrix}$$

We could normalize these vectors, i.e., require them to be of unit length

$$\beta_j{}^2 = \sum_{i=1}^{N} \beta_{ij}{}^2 = 1$$

so that in both cases we obtain the same equation $\beta^2 + \beta^2 = 1$, or

$$2\beta^2 = 1$$

$$\beta = \frac{1}{\sqrt{2}}$$

So that the normalized eigenvectors are

$$\beta_1 = \frac{1}{\sqrt{2}} \begin{bmatrix} 1 \\ -1 \end{bmatrix} \qquad \beta_2 = \frac{1}{\sqrt{2}} \begin{bmatrix} 1 \\ 1 \end{bmatrix}$$

$$b_1 = -1 \qquad\qquad b_2 = 3$$

Construct the matrix T from the eigenvectors as follows:

$$T = [\beta_j] = \begin{bmatrix} \dfrac{1}{\sqrt{2}} & \dfrac{1}{\sqrt{2}} \\ \dfrac{-1}{\sqrt{2}} & \dfrac{1}{\sqrt{2}} \end{bmatrix}$$

Show the following as an exercise:

$$T^{-1}AT = D = \begin{bmatrix} 3 & 0 \\ 0 & -1 \end{bmatrix}$$

5.8 BLOCK DIAGONALIZATION IN THE EIGENVALUE PROBLEM

In later chapters we shall find that the order of the matrices involved in certain chemical eigenvalue problems becomes quite large. If one wishes to use extended Hückel theory to study pyridine, the matrix is of order 28. Even if simple Hückel theory were used, the matrix would be 6×6. The polynomials from these two secular determinants would then, also, be of orders 28 and 6, respectively. There are no general methods available for solving polynomials of orders greater than 4 (except approximation techniques appropriate for high-speed digital computers). Hence, the labor involved in solving such problems is enormous, if not prohibitive. One obvious solution is the use of digital computers, which will be discussed in a later chapter.

There is, however, a procedure for reducing the order of the matrix by the production of several smaller matrices from the one large matrix. The heart of Chap. 6 deals with the development of such general techniques. Let us here simply allude to the basic principle upon which Chap. 6 and subsequent chapters are built.

It may be possible to operate on the matrix—in the sense of matrix multiplication—so as to block-diagonalize the matrix. The matrix operation is the similarity operation, as shown here. Let matrix A be the original matrix of order $N \times N$ and B the block-diagonalized matrix. The appropriate similarity transformation (under matrix T in this example) produces matrix B, in which the nonzero elements are collected in small blocks along the principal diagonal of B.

$$T^{-1}AT = B$$

$$B = \begin{bmatrix} B_1 & & & 0 \\ & B_2 & & \\ & & B_3 & \\ 0 & & & B_4 \end{bmatrix}$$

(Of course, the secret lies in obtaining matrix T. Chapter 6 shows how T is obtained.) Because of its special structure, the determinant of B may then be written as follows:

$$\det B = |B| = |B_1|\,|B_2|\,|B_3|\,|B_4|$$

Since in the eigenvalue problem det B is set equal to zero in order to obtain nontrivial solutions, we may obtain the desired result:

$$|B_1| = 0$$
$$|B_2| = 0$$
$$|B_3| = 0$$
$$|B_4| = 0$$

The solution to the original $N \times N$ eigenvalue problem can now be accomplished by the solution of several $n \times n$ eigenvalue problems in which $n \ll N$.

In typical cases such as simple Hückel theory applied to naphthalene the problem is reduced from the solution of a 10×10 determinant to two 3×3 and two 2×2 determinants and in benzene from a 6×6 to two 1×1 and two 2×2 determinants. In pyridine the reduction is from 6×6 to one 4×4 and one 2×2. The higher the symmetry the greater the degree of reduction of the eigenvalue problem.

APPENDIX TO CHAPTER 5: THE INVERSE OF A MATRIX

The properties of the inverse (or reciprocal) of a matrix are summarized by

$$AA^{-1} = A^{-1}A = E$$

in which A^{-1} represents the inverse of A. In this appendix we shall discuss the definition of the elements of the inverse matrix and show how to obtain the inverse of a given matrix.

By definition, the inverse of a matrix is the transposed matrix of the cofactors of the given matrix divided by the determinant of the given matrix. Any element of the inverse matrix is a fraction having for its denominator the determinant of the given matrix and for its numerator the cofactor of the term in the direct matrix which is symmetrical with itself across the principal diagonal.

In order to understand the meaning of this complex definition consider a system of linear homogeneous equations, such as the transformation

$$x' = a_1x + b_1y + c_1z$$
$$y' = a_2x + b_2y + c_2z$$
$$z' = a_3x + b_3y + c_3z$$

We can put these equations in matrix form

$$\mathbf{R}' = T\mathbf{R}$$

or

$$\begin{bmatrix} x' \\ y' \\ z' \end{bmatrix} = \begin{bmatrix} a_1 & b_1 & c_1 \\ a_2 & b_2 & c_2 \\ a_3 & b_3 & c_3 \end{bmatrix} \begin{bmatrix} x \\ y \\ z \end{bmatrix}$$

If we wish to know the unprimed variables x, y, z in terms of the primed variables x', y', z', we can use the inverse of the transformation matrix T as follows:

$$\mathbf{R} = T^{-1}\mathbf{R}'$$

or

$$\begin{bmatrix} x \\ y \\ z \end{bmatrix} = \begin{bmatrix} a_1' & b_1' & c_1' \\ a_2' & b_2' & c_2' \\ a_3' & b_3' & c_3' \end{bmatrix} \begin{bmatrix} x' \\ y' \\ z' \end{bmatrix}$$

The x, y, z can be obtained by a direct elimination procedure, but the use of determinants will provide a compact statement of the solution which leads to the generalized statement in matrix notation involving the inverse matrix as shown above. The determinantal method also directly yields the definition of the elements of the inverse matrix.

We can apply Cramer's rule to the solution of the system of equations. Hence, the solution is given in terms of the cofactors (defined below) of the elements of the transformation matrix.

$$x = \frac{1}{|T|}\left(a_1 T^{11} + b_1 T^{21} + c_1 T^{31}\right)$$

$$y = \frac{1}{|T|}\left(a_2 T^{12} + b_2 T^{22} + c_2 T^{32}\right)$$

$$z = \frac{1}{|T|}\left(a_3 T^{13} + b_3 T^{23} + c_3 T^{33}\right)$$

where $|T|$ means the determinant of matrix T and T^{ij} means the cofactor of element ij of T. Let us write the solution in the more compact determinantal form.

$$x = \frac{\begin{vmatrix} x' & b_1 & c_1 \\ y' & b_2 & c_2 \\ z' & b_3 & c_3 \end{vmatrix}}{|T|}$$

$$y = \frac{\begin{vmatrix} a_1 & x' & c_1 \\ a_2 & y' & c_2 \\ a_3 & z' & c_3 \end{vmatrix}}{|T|}$$

$$z = \frac{\begin{vmatrix} a_1 & b_1 & x' \\ a_2 & b_2 & y' \\ a_3 & b_3 & z' \end{vmatrix}}{|T|}$$

Each of the determinants in the numerator can now be expanded in the Laplace development (expansion by minors).

$$x = \frac{\begin{vmatrix} b_2 & c_2 \\ b_3 & c_3 \end{vmatrix}}{|T|} x' - \frac{\begin{vmatrix} b_1 & c_1 \\ b_3 & c_3 \end{vmatrix}}{|T|} y' + \frac{\begin{vmatrix} b_1 & c_1 \\ b_2 & c_2 \end{vmatrix}}{|T|} z'$$

$$y = - \frac{\begin{vmatrix} a_2 & c_2 \\ a_3 & c_3 \end{vmatrix}}{|T|} x' + \frac{\begin{vmatrix} a_1 & c_1 \\ a_3 & c_3 \end{vmatrix}}{|T|} y' - \frac{\begin{vmatrix} a_1 & c_1 \\ a_2 & c_2 \end{vmatrix}}{|T|} z'$$

$$z = \frac{\begin{vmatrix} a_2 & b_2 \\ a_3 & b_3 \end{vmatrix}}{|T|} x' - \frac{\begin{vmatrix} a_1 & b_1 \\ a_3 & b_3 \end{vmatrix}}{|T|} y' + \frac{\begin{vmatrix} a_1 & b_1 \\ a_2 & b_2 \end{vmatrix}}{|T|} z'$$

The set of equations is now in the same form as the original set of equations, a transformation. The only difference is that the primed and unprimed quantities are in an inverted relation. Hence, the matrix of this transformation is quite properly called the *inverse* of matrix T.

$$T^{-1} = \begin{bmatrix} \dfrac{\begin{vmatrix} b_2 & c_2 \\ b_3 & c_3 \end{vmatrix}}{|T|} & -\dfrac{\begin{vmatrix} b_1 & c_1 \\ b_3 & c_3 \end{vmatrix}}{|T|} & \dfrac{\begin{vmatrix} b_1 & c_1 \\ b_2 & c_2 \end{vmatrix}}{|T|} \\[3ex] -\dfrac{\begin{vmatrix} a_2 & c_2 \\ a_3 & c_3 \end{vmatrix}}{|T|} & \dfrac{\begin{vmatrix} a_1 & c_1 \\ a_3 & c_3 \end{vmatrix}}{|T|} & -\dfrac{\begin{vmatrix} a_1 & c_1 \\ a_2 & c_2 \end{vmatrix}}{|T|} \\[3ex] \dfrac{\begin{vmatrix} a_2 & b_2 \\ a_3 & b_3 \end{vmatrix}}{|T|} & -\dfrac{\begin{vmatrix} a_1 & b_1 \\ a_3 & b_3 \end{vmatrix}}{|T|} & \dfrac{\begin{vmatrix} a_1 & b_1 \\ a_2 & b_2 \end{vmatrix}}{|T|} \end{bmatrix}$$

We can now obtain the definition of a *cofactor:* the cofactor of element ij of matrix T is the minor of element ij multiplied by $(-1)^{i+j}$. The minor of element ij is the determinant obtained by striking out row i and column j in matrix T. The symbol T^{ij} thus stands for the cofactor of element ij. Thus, the inverse of T might be symbolized as

$$T_{ij}^{-1} = \frac{(-1)^{i+j}\tilde{T}ij}{|T|} = \frac{\tilde{T}^{ij}}{|T|}$$

where $\mathbb{T}ij$ represents the minor of element ij.

Because of the division by the determinant of T, the inverse of T is not defined when its determinant is zero. Such matrices are known as *singular* matrices. Hence, only square matrices have inverses.

OBTAINING THE INVERSE: AN EXAMPLE

Consider the matrix T

$$T = \begin{bmatrix} 1 & 1 & 0 \\ 1 & 1 & -1 \\ 0 & -1 & 1 \end{bmatrix}$$

$$|T| = \begin{vmatrix} 1 & 1 & 0 \\ 1 & 1 & -1 \\ 0 & -1 & 1 \end{vmatrix} = +1 \begin{vmatrix} 1 & -1 \\ -1 & 1 \end{vmatrix} - 1 \begin{vmatrix} 1 & -1 \\ 0 & 1 \end{vmatrix}$$

$$= (1 - 1) - 1(1 - 0)$$

$$= -1$$

The matrix of cofactors may then be written as

$$\begin{bmatrix} +1\underline{\begin{vmatrix} 1 & -1 \\ -1 & 1 \end{vmatrix}} & -1\underline{\begin{vmatrix} 1 & -1 \\ 0 & 1 \end{vmatrix}} & +1\underline{\begin{vmatrix} 1 & 1 \\ 0 & -1 \end{vmatrix}} \\ -1 & -1 & -1 \\ -1\underline{\begin{vmatrix} 1 & 0 \\ -1 & 1 \end{vmatrix}} & +1\underline{\begin{vmatrix} 1 & 0 \\ 0 & 1 \end{vmatrix}} & -1\underline{\begin{vmatrix} 1 & 1 \\ 0 & -1 \end{vmatrix}} \\ -1 & -1 & -1 \\ +1\underline{\begin{vmatrix} 1 & 0 \\ 1 & -1 \end{vmatrix}} & -1\underline{\begin{vmatrix} 1 & 0 \\ 1 & -1 \end{vmatrix}} & +1\underline{\begin{vmatrix} 1 & 1 \\ 1 & 1 \end{vmatrix}} \\ -1 & -1 & -1 \end{bmatrix}$$

Evaluation of the determinants leads to

$$\begin{bmatrix} 0 & 1 & 1 \\ 1 & -1 & -1 \\ 1 & -1 & 0 \end{bmatrix}$$

This matrix is symmetric (it is equal to its transpose), and it is equal to the inverse of T.

$$T^{-1} = \begin{bmatrix} 0 & 1 & 1 \\ 1 & -1 & -1 \\ 1 & -1 & 0 \end{bmatrix}$$

That this matrix is the inverse of T can be shown by demonstrating that the following matrix equations hold.

$$TT^{-1} = T^{-1}T = E$$

$$\begin{bmatrix} 1 & 1 & 0 \\ 1 & 1 & -1 \\ 0 & -1 & 1 \end{bmatrix} \begin{bmatrix} 0 & 1 & 1 \\ 1 & -1 & -1 \\ 1 & -1 & 0 \end{bmatrix} = \begin{bmatrix} 1 & 0 & 0 \\ 0 & 1 & 0 \\ 0 & 0 & 1 \end{bmatrix}$$

and

$$\begin{bmatrix} 0 & 1 & 1 \\ 1 & -1 & -1 \\ 1 & -1 & 0 \end{bmatrix} \begin{bmatrix} 1 & 1 & 0 \\ 1 & 1 & -1 \\ 0 & -1 & 1 \end{bmatrix} = \begin{bmatrix} 1 & 0 & 0 \\ 0 & 1 & 0 \\ 0 & 0 & 1 \end{bmatrix}$$

PROBLEMS

5.1. Find the matrix which performs a rotation through angle θ in the reverse direction of the matrix constructed in Sec. 5.2. What is the relation of these two matrices?

5.2. Construct a cube with its body center at the origin of a cartesian coordinate system and the x, y, z, axes along the edges as in Fig. 4.6.

(a) Find the matrix corresponding to a rotation of $2\pi/3$ radians about the body diagonal of the cube (by considering the transformation equations for the cartesian components).

(b) Show that this matrix is equal to the product of two rotation matrices with rotation angles of 90° about any two cartesian axes (see Fig. 8.6).

5.3. Show by matrix multiplication that rotation of 180° successively about z, y, and then x is equivalent to an identity operation.

5.4. Write vectors in (cartesian) component form for the following lines:

(a) The body diagonal which intersects the origin of the cube in Prob. 5.2

(b) Three face diagonals which intersect

(c) The line which bisects the angle between the body diagonal of part (a) and the face diagonal which lies in the xz plane

5.5. By consideration of the definition of the dot product of two vectors $(\mathbf{r}_1 \cdot \mathbf{r}_2 = |\mathbf{r}_1|\,|\mathbf{r}_2|\cos\theta)$ find the angle between the following vectors:

(a) The body diagonal of part (a) of Prob. 5.4 and the face diagonal which lies in the yz plane

(b) The angle between any two face diagonals of the cube

(c) The angle between the body diagonal and the z axis

5.6. As in Prob. 5.5, determine the tetrahedral angle. *Hint:* Construct a tetrahedron inside a cube and take the origin of the cartesian system as the center of the cube. Find expressions for the vectors defining the lines from the tetrahedron center to the vertices.

5.7. Diagonalize the rotation matrix C_n:

$$C_n = \begin{bmatrix} \cos\theta & \sin\theta & 0 \\ -\sin\theta & \cos\theta & 0 \\ 0 & 0 & 1 \end{bmatrix}$$

(a) Find the eigenvalues and normalized eigenvectors.

(b) Diagonalize C_n by a similarity transformation.

(c) Compare the sum of the diagonal elements of C_n with the sum for the diagonal matrix.

5.8. Show that a matrix whose columns are a set of n orthogonal and normalized vectors is a unitary matrix.

5.9. Find the matrix which represents rotation through angle θ around the x axis; around the y axis.

5.10. (a) Prove that the product of two diagonal matrices is also a diagonal matrix.

(b) Prove that the product of two unitary matrices is also a unitary matrix.

5.11. Prove that a matrix equation is still true if every matrix in the equation is subjected to the same similarity transformation; i.e., use the equations $AB = C$ and $D + F = G$.

5.12. (a) Find the eigenvalues of

$$
A = \begin{bmatrix}
\dfrac{11}{9} & -\dfrac{\sqrt{6}}{6} & -\dfrac{\sqrt{2}}{18} \\[2ex]
-\dfrac{\sqrt{6}}{6} & \dfrac{21}{12} & \dfrac{\sqrt{3}}{12} \\[2ex]
-\dfrac{\sqrt{2}}{18} & \dfrac{\sqrt{3}}{12} & \dfrac{37}{36}
\end{bmatrix}
$$

This matrix represents the equation of the ellipsoid

$$
\frac{11}{9} x^2 - \frac{\sqrt{6}}{3} xy + \frac{21}{12} y^2 - \frac{\sqrt{2}}{9} xz + \frac{\sqrt{3}}{6} yz + \frac{37}{36} z^2 = 1
$$

when written in bilinear form:

$$
\begin{bmatrix} x & y & z \end{bmatrix} A \begin{bmatrix} x \\ y \\ z \end{bmatrix} = 1
$$

(b) Find the matrix which will diagonalize A (a rotation matrix which rotates the ellipsoid so that its major axes line up with the cartesian axes) by obtaining the matrix of eigenvectors of A. *Hint:* Since there is a degeneracy in the eigenvalues, *some* degree of arbitrariness may be introduced in the determination of the eigenvectors. Remember about the eigenvectors of a hermitian matrix. Is A hermitian?

5.13. The eigenvectors of matrix P represent the normal modes of vibration for a linear triatomic molecule AX_2 of $D_{\infty h}$ symmetry when the motion is constrained to lie solely along the molecular axis. The eigenvalues are proportional to the squares of the frequencies of the modes of motion.

$$P = \begin{bmatrix} \dfrac{k}{m} & -\dfrac{k}{\sqrt{mM}} & 0 \\[2ex] -\dfrac{k}{\sqrt{mM}} & \dfrac{2k}{M} & -\dfrac{k}{\sqrt{mM}} \\[2ex] 0 & -\dfrac{k}{\sqrt{mM}} & \dfrac{k}{m} \end{bmatrix}$$

where k = force constant associated with bond A—X

m = mass of atom X

M = mass of atom A

(a) Find the eigenvalues, and hence the frequencies, by using the substitution that

$$\omega^2 = k\lambda$$

Then, the determinant may be written

$$|P - \omega^2 E| = |P - k\lambda E| = 0$$

(b) Find the eigenvectors.

(c) Sketch the modes of motion. Are they all genuine normal modes of vibration?

5.14. Show that diagonal matrices commute.

5.15. For all values of a, b, c, and d show that $AB = BA$ when

$$A = \begin{bmatrix} a & b \\ -b & a \end{bmatrix} \qquad B = \begin{bmatrix} c & d \\ -d & c \end{bmatrix}$$

5.16. Two matrices are said to be *anticommutative* when $AB = -BA$. The following 2×2 matrices are known as the *Pauli spin matrices*. Show that all pairs of these matrices are anticommutative.

$$\sigma_x = \begin{bmatrix} 0 & 1 \\ 1 & 0 \end{bmatrix} \qquad \sigma_y = \begin{bmatrix} 0 & -i \\ i & 0 \end{bmatrix} \qquad \sigma_z = \begin{bmatrix} 1 & 0 \\ 0 & -1 \end{bmatrix}$$

where $i = \sqrt{-1}$.

5.17. The matrix $AB - BA$ is called the commutator of A and B. Show that the commutators of the Pauli spin matrices σ_x, σ_y, and σ_z are $2i\sigma_z$, $2i\sigma_x$, and $2i\sigma_y$, respectively.

5.18. The character, or trace, of a matrix is the sum of the diagonal elements of the matrix:

$$\chi_A = \operatorname{tr} A = \Sigma a_{ii}$$

(a) For matrix C of order $m \times n$ and matrix G of order $n \times m$ prove that

$$\operatorname{tr} CG = \operatorname{tr} GC$$

(b) For two matrices A and B of the same order show

$$\operatorname{tr} (A + B) = \operatorname{tr} A + \operatorname{tr} B$$

5.19. Find the inverse of the following matrices

(a) $\begin{bmatrix} 1 & 0 & 0 \\ 0 & 1 & 0 \\ 0 & 0 & 1 \end{bmatrix}$

(b) $\begin{bmatrix} 0 & 0 & a_3 \\ 0 & a_2 & 0 \\ a_1 & 0 & 0 \end{bmatrix}$

(c) $\begin{bmatrix} a & -b \\ b & a \end{bmatrix}$

(d) $\begin{bmatrix} 0 & -i \\ i & 0 \end{bmatrix}$

5.20. Evaluate the squares of the Pauli spin matrices.

5.21. A square matrix A is skew hermitian if $A = -A^\dagger$, that is, $a_{ij} = -a_{ji}^*$. Show that any square matrix may be written as the sum of a hermitian and a skew hermitian matrix.

5.22. Show that every hermitian matrix H may be written as

$$H = A + iB$$

where A is a real symmetric matrix, B is a skew hermitian matrix, and $i = \sqrt{-1}$.

5.23. Find all the eigenvalues and eigenvectors of the following matrices. Normalize the eigenvectors. Where appropriate show that the eigenvectors of the matrix form an orthonormal set.

(a) The Pauli spin matrices

(b) $A = \begin{bmatrix} a & -b \\ b & a \end{bmatrix}$

(c) $M = \begin{bmatrix} 4 & -1 & 0 \\ -1 & 4 & -1 \\ 0 & -1 & 4 \end{bmatrix}$

(d) $N = \begin{bmatrix} 1 & 0 & 0 \\ 0 & 0 & \omega^2 \\ 0 & \omega & 0 \end{bmatrix}$ $\qquad \omega = e^{\frac{2\pi i}{3}}$

5.24. By obtaining the set of eigenvectors and then performing a similarity transformation diagonalize the following matrices:

(a) $\begin{bmatrix} 5 & 2 & 0 & 0 \\ 2 & 5 & 0 & 0 \\ 0 & 0 & 5 & -2 \\ 0 & 0 & -2 & 5 \end{bmatrix}$

(b) $\begin{bmatrix} 1 & -1 & 0 \\ -1 & 1 & 0 \\ 0 & 0 & 1 \end{bmatrix}$

(c) $\begin{bmatrix} 0 & 2 & 4 \\ 2 & 0 & 8 \\ 4 & 8 & 0 \end{bmatrix}$

5.25. Show that all the eigenvalues of matrix H are nonnegative if $H = A^{\dagger}A$.

5.26. Show that all the eigenvalues of a unitary matrix have an absolute value of unity.

5.27. Show by matrix multiplication and by the use of trigonometric identities that two successive rotations about the z axis through angle α followed by angle β are represented by the matrix equation

$$\begin{bmatrix} \cos \beta & \sin \beta & 0 \\ -\sin \beta & \cos \beta & 0 \\ 0 & 0 & 1 \end{bmatrix} \begin{bmatrix} \cos \alpha & \sin \alpha & 0 \\ -\sin \alpha & \cos \alpha & 0 \\ 0 & 0 & 1 \end{bmatrix}$$
$$= \begin{bmatrix} \cos (\alpha + \beta) & \sin (\alpha + \beta) & 0 \\ -\sin (\alpha + \beta) & \cos (\alpha + \beta) & 0 \\ 0 & 0 & 1 \end{bmatrix}$$

5.28. Find the inverse, $R(\theta)^{-1}$, of the matrix for rotation through angle θ about the z axis.

$$R(\theta) = \begin{bmatrix} \cos \theta & \sin \theta & 0 \\ -\sin \theta & \cos \theta & 0 \\ 0 & 0 & 1 \end{bmatrix}$$

Physically, the inverse of $R(\theta)$ represents a rotation in the reverse direction. Construct a matrix $R(-\theta)$ by simply replacing θ with $-\theta$ in $R(\theta)$. Compare $R(-\theta)$ with $R(\theta)^{-1}$.

REFERENCES

Aitken, A. C.: "Determinants and Matrices," Oliver & Boyd, Ltd., Edinburgh, 1964.

Hammermesh, M.: "Group Theory and Its Applications to Physical Problems," Addison-Wesley Publishing Company, Inc., Reading, Mass., 1962.

Hohn, Franz: "Elementary Matrix Algebra," The Macmillan Company, New York, 1965.

Margenau, H., and G. M. Murphy: "The Mathematics of Physics and Chemistry," chap. 10, D. Van Nostrand Company, Inc., Princeton, N.J., 1956.

Owen, G. E.: "Fundamentals of Scientific Mathematics," The Johns Hopkins Press, Baltimore, 1961.

Tinkham, M.: "Group Theory and Quantum Mechanics," McGraw-Hill Book Company, New York, 1964.

Wilf, H. S.: "Mathematics for the Physical Sciences," chap. 1, John Wiley & Sons, Inc., New York, 1962.

6
reducibility
and
irreducibility
of
representations

We have considered the various ways in which one can build up representations of the symmetry groups of interest to chemists. The use of matrices has facilitated the construction of certain representations. We see, however, that the matrix representations may be quite large and unwieldy. The $3N \times 3N$ representations for large molecules based on cartesian coordinate systems may indeed become exceedingly large.

Perhaps by now we have developed the feeling that such a complete matrix is not needed to describe the molecular system adequately. After all, even if decaborane 14 has 24 atoms (making the cartesian-type matrix representations of order 72×72), its point group C_{2v} has only four irreducible representations; the molecule also possesses only four chemically nonequivalent boron atoms and five chemically nonequivalent hydrogen atoms.

Let us now consider the possibility that a large representation may be reduced to a group of smaller representations. We shall find not only that it is possible to reduce the large representations but also that the process is accomplished easily.

In Sec. 6.2 we use a rather rigorous approach to this problem. Theorems are not given without proof. Although the proofs are often detailed and abstract, we find that the exercise they provide puts us on a firm footing to proceed further. In addition, the resulting equations are simple and easily used.

6.1 THE REDUCED FORM

Consider a matrix representation $\Gamma^{(R)}$, that is, a collection of matrices.[1] If by a similarity transformation S

$$\Gamma'^{(R)} = S^{-1}\Gamma^{(R)}S \qquad \text{for all } R \in G \tag{6.1}$$

all the matrices of $\Gamma^{(R)}$ can simultaneously be put into the form

$$\Gamma'^{(R)} = \left[\begin{array}{c|c} \Gamma_1^{(R)} & Q^{(R)} \\ \hline 0 & \Gamma_2^{(R)} \end{array} \right] \tag{6.2}$$

The representation $\Gamma^{(R)}$ is said to be *reducible*, and $\Gamma'^{(R)}$ is said to be the *reduced form* of $\Gamma^{(R)}$. Note that

$$\left. \begin{array}{l} \Gamma_1^{(R)} \text{ is an } n_1 \times n_1 \text{ matrix} \\ \Gamma_2^{(R)} \text{ is an } n_2 \times n_2 \text{ matrix} \end{array} \right\} \quad n_1 + n_2 = N$$
$$Q^{(R)} \text{ is an } n_1 \times n_2 \text{ matrix}$$

If all the matrices of a representation cannot simultaneously be put into a reduced form, the representation is said to be completely reduced. That is, $\Gamma_1^{(R)}$ and $\Gamma_2^{(R)}$ may or may not be reducible. However, if $\Gamma_1^{(R)}$ and $\Gamma_2^{(R)}$ are irreducible, then $\Gamma'^{(R)}$ is completely reduced.

If $\Gamma'^{(R)}$ is unitary then, $Q^{(R)} \equiv 0$, as shown as follows because of the definition of a unitary matrix.

$$(\Gamma'^{(R)})^{-1} = \Gamma'^{(R)\dagger} \tag{6.3}$$

But

$$\Gamma'^{(R)\dagger} = \left[\begin{array}{c|c} \Gamma_1^{(R)\dagger} & 0 \\ \hline Q^{(R)\dagger} & \Gamma_2^{(R)\dagger} \end{array} \right] \tag{6.4}$$

but $R^{-1} \in G$ and $(\Gamma^{(R)})^{-1} \in \Gamma^{(R)}$ of G. Therefore $\Gamma'^{(R)\dagger}$ must also be in reduced form. Thus

$$\Gamma'^{(R)\dagger} = \left[\begin{array}{c|c} \Gamma_1^{(R)\dagger} & 0 \\ \hline Q^{(R)\dagger} & \Gamma_2^{(R)\dagger} \end{array} \right] = \left[\begin{array}{c|c} \Gamma_1^{(R)\dagger} & Q^{(R)\dagger} \\ \hline 0 & \Gamma_2^{(R)\dagger} \end{array} \right]$$

---

[1] The reader's attention is called to the glossary of symbols at the end of this chapter.

so that $Q^{(R)\dagger} = 0 = Q^{(R)\dagger}$ when $\Gamma'^{(R)}$ is unitary. Thus, for a reduced unitary representation

$$\Gamma'^{(R)} = \left[\begin{array}{c|c} \Gamma_1^{(R)} & 0 \\ \hline 0 & \Gamma_2^{(R)} \end{array} \right] \tag{6.5}$$

which is often written as the *direct sum:*

$$\Gamma'^{(R)} = \Gamma_1^{(R)} + \Gamma_2^{(R)} \tag{6.6}$$

Note that $\Gamma_1^{(R)}$ and $\Gamma_2^{(R)}$ are both representations of the group G.

6.2 REDUCIBILITY OF REPRESENTATIONS

Theorem one: Any representation by square, nonsingular matrices can be transformed into a unitary representation by a similarity transformation.

U is a unitary matrix if $U^{-1} = U^\dagger = \tilde{U}^*$.   Consider a representation $\Gamma^{(R)}$ which consists of square, nonsingular matrices.   Form the matrix H.

$$H = \sum_R \Gamma^{(R)} \Gamma^{(R)\dagger} \tag{6.7}$$

H is hermitian, that is, $H = H^\dagger$, as shown by

$$H^\dagger = \left(\sum_R \Gamma^{(R)} \Gamma^{(R)\dagger} \right)^\dagger = \sum_R \Gamma^{(R)\dagger\dagger} \Gamma^{(R)\dagger} = \sum_R \Gamma^{(R)} \Gamma^{(R)\dagger} = H$$

Any hermitian matrix can be diagonalized in a similarity transformation with a unitary matrix.

That is, if U is unitary, $U^{-1}HU = D$, where D is diagonal.   The eigenvalues of D are the eigenvalues of H and are *real* and positive (see Prob. 5.25).   We may write the diagonal elements as

$$D_{jj} = \sum_i \sum_k U_{ji}^{-1} H_{ik} U_{kj} \tag{6.8}$$

Form the matrix $D^{\frac{1}{2}}$, taking the positive roots.

$$(D^{\frac{1}{2}})_{jj} = +(D_{jj})^{\frac{1}{2}} \tag{6.9}$$

Let us now find a relation between $\Gamma^{(R)}$, U, and D.   Substitute for H in the diagonalization expression, $U^{-1}HU = D$.

$$U^{-1} \left(\sum_R \Gamma^{(R)} \Gamma^{(R)\dagger} \right) U = D \tag{6.10}$$

Take U under the summation.

$$\sum_R U^{-1}\Gamma^{(R)}\Gamma^{(R)\dagger}U = D \qquad U \neq U(R)$$

Insert the identity matrix, $\mathbb{1} = UU^{-1}$, in the center:

$$\sum_R U^{-1}\Gamma^{(R)}(UU^{-1})\Gamma^{(R)\dagger}U = D \tag{6.11}$$

But

$$U^{-1}\Gamma^{(R)\dagger}U = (U^\dagger\Gamma^{(R)\dagger\dagger}U^{-1\dagger})^\dagger$$
$$= (U^{-1}\Gamma^{(R)}U)^\dagger \qquad U^{-1} = U^\dagger$$

and so

$$\sum_R (U^{-1}\Gamma^{(R)}U)(U^{-1}\Gamma^{(R)}U)^\dagger = D \tag{6.12}$$

Let

$$\Gamma'^{(R)} = U^{-1}\Gamma^{(R)}U \tag{6.13}$$

Then

$$\sum_R \Gamma'^{(R)}\Gamma'^{(R)\dagger} = D \tag{6.14}$$

Define $\Gamma''^{(R)}$ and show that $\Gamma''^{(R)}$ is similar to $\Gamma^{(R)}$

$$\Gamma''^{(R)} = D^{-\frac{1}{2}}\Gamma'^{(R)}D^{\frac{1}{2}} \tag{6.15}$$

Then

$$\Gamma''^{(R)} = D^{-\frac{1}{2}}(U^{-1}\Gamma^{(R)}U)D^{\frac{1}{2}}$$

or

$$\Gamma''^{(R)} = (UD^{\frac{1}{2}})^{-1}\Gamma^{(R)}(UD^{\frac{1}{2}}) \tag{6.16}$$

Show that $\Gamma''^{(R)}$ is unitary by showing the identity

$$\Gamma''^{(R)}\Gamma''^{(R)\dagger} = \Gamma''^{(R)}\Gamma''^{(R)-1} = \mathbb{1} \tag{6.17}$$

First, substitute for $\Gamma''^{(R)}$ in Eq. (6.17), $\Gamma''^{(R)} = D^{-\frac{1}{2}}\Gamma'^{(R)}D^{\frac{1}{2}}$, and insert the identity as $\mathbb{1} = D^{-\frac{1}{2}}DD^{-\frac{1}{2}}$. (Note that $D^{\frac{1}{2}\dagger} = D^{\frac{1}{2}}$.)

$$(D^{-\frac{1}{2}}\Gamma'^{(R)}D^{\frac{1}{2}})(D^{-\frac{1}{2}}DD^{-\frac{1}{2}})(D^{\frac{1}{2}}\Gamma'^{(R)\dagger}D^{-\frac{1}{2}}) = \Gamma''^{(R)}\Gamma''^{(R)-1} \tag{6.18}$$

But $D^{\frac{1}{2}}D^{-\frac{1}{2}} = D^{-\frac{1}{2}}D^{\frac{1}{2}} = \mathbb{1}$ and we may substitute for D,

$$D = U^{-1}\left[\sum_{R'}\Gamma^{(R')}\Gamma^{(R')\dagger}\right]U$$

to give

$$(D^{-\frac{1}{2}}\Gamma'^{(R)})U^{-1}\left(\sum_{R'}\Gamma^{(R')}\Gamma^{(R')\dagger}\right)U(\Gamma'^{(R)\dagger}D^{-\frac{1}{2}}) = \Gamma''^{(R)}\Gamma''^{(R)-1} \qquad (6.19)$$

But $\Gamma'^{(R)} = U^{-1}\Gamma^{(R)}U$, and Eq. (6.19) becomes

$$(D^{-\frac{1}{2}}U^{-1}\Gamma^{(R)}U)U^{-1}\left(\sum_{R'}\Gamma^{(R')}\Gamma^{(R')\dagger}\right)U(U^{-1}\Gamma^{(R)\dagger}UD^{-\frac{1}{2}})$$
$$= \Gamma''^{(R)}\Gamma''^{(R)-1} \qquad (6.20)$$

Now, $UU^{-1} = \mathbb{1}$, and $\Gamma^{(R)}$ may be taken under the sum over R'.

$$D^{-\frac{1}{2}}\left(U^{-1}\sum_{R'}\Gamma^{(R)}\Gamma^{(R')}\Gamma^{(R')\dagger}\Gamma^{(R)\dagger}U\right)D^{-\frac{1}{2}} = \Gamma''^{(R)}\Gamma''^{(R)-1} \qquad (6.21)$$

Notice that $\Gamma^{(R)}\Gamma^{(R')} = \Gamma^{(RR')} = \Gamma^{(R)}$, $RR' \in G$.

$$D^{-\frac{1}{2}}\left(U^{-1}\sum_{R}\Gamma^{(R)}\Gamma^{(R)\dagger}U\right)D^{-\frac{1}{2}} = \Gamma''^{(R)}\Gamma''^{(R)-1} \qquad (6.22)$$

But $U^{-1}\sum_{R}\Gamma^{(R)}\Gamma^{(R)\dagger}U = D$ from Eq. (6.10).

Therefore,

$$D^{-\frac{1}{2}}DD^{-\frac{1}{2}} = \mathbb{1}$$

and

$$\Gamma''^{(R)}\Gamma''^{(R)\dagger} = \mathbb{1} \qquad \text{Q.E.D.}$$

Thus, the matrix which transforms any (square, nonsingular) representation into a unitary representation is $UD^{\frac{1}{2}}$, where U is the matrix of eigenvectors of H, where

$$H = \sum_{R}\Gamma^{(R)}\Gamma^{(R)\dagger}$$

and where $D^{\frac{1}{2}}$ is the diagonal matrix whose elements are the square roots of the eigenvalues of H.

Theorem two: The only matrix which commutes with all the matrices of an irreducible representation is a constant matrix, a constant times the unit matrix.

To show that $C = cE$ if $C\Gamma^{(R)} = \Gamma^{(R)}C$, let $\Gamma^{(R)}$ be unitary by assumption or transformation. Consider

$$C\Gamma^{(R)} = \Gamma^{(R)}C \qquad (6.23)$$

Write the adjoint (conjugate transpose) of Eq. (6.23).

$$\Gamma^{(R)\dagger}C^{\dagger} = C^{\dagger}\Gamma^{(R)\dagger} \qquad (6.24)$$

But

$$\Gamma^{(R)\dagger} = \Gamma^{-1(R)} = \Gamma^{(R-1)} \rightarrow \Gamma^{(R)}$$

because all $R^{-1} \in G$; so that $C^{\dagger}\Gamma^{(R)} = \Gamma^{(R)}C^{\dagger}$ and $C^{\dagger}$ also commutes. Note that if C and $C^{\dagger}$ commute, so does $C' = C + C^{\dagger}$. C' is hermitian

$$C'^{\dagger} = (C + C^{\dagger})^{\dagger} = C^{\dagger} + C = C + C^{\dagger} = C'$$

We therefore continue the proof for a hermitian C'. C' can be diagonalized by a unitary transformation.

$$U^{-1}C'U = D \tag{6.25}$$

Use U to transform $\Gamma^{(R)}$

$$\Gamma'^{(R)} = U^{-1}\Gamma^{(R)}U \tag{6.26}$$

But D also commutes with $\Gamma'^{(R)}$.

$$\Gamma'^{(R)}D - D\Gamma'^{(R)} = U^{-1}\Gamma^{(R)}UD - DU^{-1}\Gamma^{(R)}U \tag{6.27}$$

or

$$U^{-1}\Gamma^{(R)}U(U^{-1}C'U) - (U^{-1}C'U)U^{-1}\Gamma^{(R)}U$$
$$= U^{-1}\Gamma^{(R)}C'U - U^{-1}C'\Gamma^{(R)}U \tag{6.28}$$

But $\Gamma^{(R)}C' = C'\Gamma^{(R)}$ from Eq. (6.23). So that

$$U^{-1}C'\Gamma^{(R)}U - U^{-1}C'\Gamma^{(R)}U \equiv 0 \tag{6.29}$$

and D commutes with $\Gamma'^{(R)}$.

Let us now say that D at least has two elements different from the rest. We can show that this assumption forces U to diagonalize $\Gamma^{(R)}$, which is contrary to our hypothesis that $\Gamma^{(R)}$ is irreducible. Consider

$$\Gamma'^{(R)}D = D\Gamma'^{(R)} \tag{6.30}$$

or as matrix elements

$$\sum_k \Gamma'^{(R)}_{ik}D_{kl} = \sum_k D_{ik}\Gamma'^{(R)}_{kl} \tag{6.31}$$

But since D is diagonal: $D_{kl} = 0$, $k \neq l$, the sums are reduced to single terms of the form

$$\Gamma'^{(R)}_{il}D_{ll} = D_{ii}\Gamma'^{(R)}_{il}$$

or

$$\Gamma'^{(R)}_{il}(D_{ll} - D_{ii}) = 0 \tag{6.32}$$

Thus

$$\Gamma'^{(R)} = \begin{bmatrix} n \times n & 0 \\ \hline 0 & \end{bmatrix}$$

This is because we chose the first n D_{jj} to be different from the remaining diagonal elements. That is,

$$\Gamma'^{(R)}_{il} = 0 \qquad i, l < n \tag{6.33}$$

but for $i, l > n$, $\Gamma'^{(R)}_{il} = 0$. Therefore, $\Gamma'^{(R)}$ is in reduced form. However, $\Gamma^{(R)}$ was irreducible by hypothesis. In order to prevent $\Gamma^{(R)}$ from being reduced, all the diagonal elements of D must be equal, i.e.,

$$D = dE \tag{6.34}$$

Thus

$$C = U^{-1}DU = U^{-1}(dE)U = dU^{-1}EU = dE$$

or

$$C = dE \qquad \text{Q.E.D.}$$

Corollary to theorem two: If the only matrix which commutes with all the matrices of a representation is a constant matrix, then the representation is irreducible.

Theorem three: If an $n \times m$ matrix A is formed such that

$$A\Gamma_1^{(R)} = \Gamma_2^{(R)}A$$

for $\Gamma_1^{(R)}$ of dimension $m \times m$ and $\Gamma_2^{(R)}$ of dimension $n \times n$ all irreducible, then either A is a null matrix or A is square and nonsingular and $\Gamma_1^{(R)}$ and $\Gamma_2^{(R)}$ are equivalent.

Assume the $\Gamma^{(R)}$ are unitary. Take the conjugate transpose of

$$\begin{aligned} A\Gamma_1^{(R)} &= \Gamma_2^{(R)}A \\ \Gamma_1^{(R)\dagger}A^\dagger &= A^\dagger\Gamma_2^{(R)\dagger} \end{aligned} \tag{6.35}$$

But

$$\Gamma_1^{(R)\dagger} = \Gamma_1^{(R)^{-1}} = \Gamma_1^{(R^{-1})} = \Gamma_1^{(R)} \qquad R^{-1} \in G$$

So that

$$\begin{aligned} \Gamma_1^{(R)}A^\dagger &= A^\dagger\Gamma_2^{(R)} \quad \S\, A \quad &\text{(right-multiply by } A) \tag{6.36} \\ A^\dagger\, \S \quad A_1\Gamma_1^{(R)} &= \Gamma_2^{(R)}A \quad &\text{(left-multiply by } A^\dagger) \end{aligned}$$

To obtain the following two equations

$$\Gamma^{(R)}A^\dagger A = A^\dagger\Gamma^{(R)}A$$
$$A^\dagger A\Gamma^{(R)} = A^\dagger\Gamma^{(R)}A$$

By subtracting these two equations we obtain

$$A^\dagger A\Gamma^{(R)} = \Gamma^{(R)}A^\dagger A \qquad (6.37)$$

So that by the previous theorem, $A^\dagger A = cE$.

Case I Suppose $c = 0$, $n = m$. Then

$$A^\dagger A = 0$$

or in matrix elements

$$\sum_i A^\dagger_{hi}A_{ij} = 0$$

but $A^\dagger A$ is diagonal, and so all terms $h \neq j$ are zero.

$$\sum_i A^\dagger_{hi}A_{ih} = 0 \qquad (6.38)$$

But $A^\dagger_{hi} = A^*_{ih}$, and so

$$\sum_i A^*_{ih}A_{ih} = \sum_i |A_{ih}|^2 = 0 \qquad \text{element by element}$$

Therefore each $A_{ih} = 0$, and thus, A *is a null matrix.*

Case II Suppose $c \neq 0$, $n = m$. Then

$$A^\dagger A \neq 0 \qquad cE \neq 0$$
$$|A^\dagger A| \neq 0 \qquad |cE| \neq 0$$

and

$$|A^\dagger|\,|A| \neq 0$$

and

$$|A| \neq 0$$

Therefore A is nonsingular and has an inverse, and

$$A^{-1}\,\S \qquad A\Gamma_1^{(R)} = \Gamma_2^{(R)}A \qquad (6.39)$$
$$\Gamma_1^{(R)} = A^{-1}\Gamma_2^{(R)}A \qquad (6.40)$$

$\Gamma_1^{(R)}$ and $\Gamma_2^{(R)}$ are similar.

Case III What if $n \neq m$? Then, by the definition of a nonsquare determinant

$$|A| = 0$$

and

$$|A^\dagger|\,|A| = 0$$

and

$$|A^\dagger A| = 0$$

but

$$A^\dagger A = cE$$

and

$$|A^\dagger A| = |cE| = 0$$

that is,

$$c = 0$$

and so A is a null matrix.

The previous theorem is known as *Schur's lemma*. We shall use it to prove an orthogonality condition on the matrix elements of irreducible representations.

Theorem four

$$\sum_R [\Gamma_\alpha{}^{(R)}]_{ij}[\Gamma_\beta{}^{(R)}]_{kl}^* = \frac{g}{\sqrt{n_\alpha}\sqrt{n_\beta}}\,\delta_{\alpha\beta}\delta_{ik}\delta_{jl} \tag{6.41}$$

where n is the dimension of the αth irreducible representation and g is the order of the group.

Construct a matrix A, where X is an arbitrary matrix.

$$A = \sum_{R'} \Gamma_\alpha{}^{(R')} X \Gamma_\beta{}^{(R')^{-1}} \tag{6.42}$$

We can show

$$\Gamma_\alpha{}^{(R)} A = A \Gamma_\beta{}^{(R)} \tag{6.43}$$

Substitute for A in Eq. (6.43) and right-multiply by $\Gamma_\beta{}^{(R)^{-1}}\Gamma_\beta{}^{(R)}$.

$$\Gamma_\alpha{}^{(R)} A = \Gamma_\alpha{}^{(R)} \sum_{R'} \Gamma_\alpha{}^{(R')} X \Gamma_\beta{}^{(R')^{-1}} = \S \underbrace{\Gamma_\beta{}^{(R)^{-1}}\Gamma_\beta{}^{(R)}}_{E} \tag{6.44}$$

$$\Gamma_\alpha{}^{(R)} \sum_{R'} \Gamma_\alpha{}^{(R')} X \Gamma_\beta{}^{(R')} \Gamma_\beta{}^{(R)^{-1}}\Gamma_\beta{}^{(R)}$$

$$= \left[\sum_{R'} \Gamma_\alpha{}^{(R'R)} X \Gamma_\beta{}^{(RR')^{-1}}\right] \Gamma_\beta{}^{(R)} = A\Gamma_\beta{}^{(R)} \tag{6.45}$$

The quantity in brackets is equal to A.

Thus, by Schur's lemma A must either be a null matrix or square and nonsingular, and $\Gamma_\alpha^{(R)}$ is equivalent to $\Gamma_\beta^{(R)}$.

Case I Take $\Gamma_\alpha^{(R)}$ and $\Gamma_\beta^{(R)}$ *not* equivalent, so that $A = 0$.

$$A_{ij} = 0 = \sum_R \sum_j \sum_i [\Gamma_\alpha^{(R)}]_{ij} X_{jl} [\Gamma_\beta^{(R)}]_{lk}^{-1} = 0 \tag{6.46}$$

This equation is independent of X, and so, for some kl let $X_{kl} \neq 0$ and

$$\sum_R [\Gamma_\alpha^{(R)}]_{ij} [\Gamma_\beta^{(R)}]_{lk}^{-1} = 0 \tag{6.47}$$

For unitary representations $\Gamma^{-1} = \Gamma^\dagger = \tilde{\Gamma}^*$, so that

$$\sum_R [\Gamma_\alpha^{(R)}]_{ij} [\Gamma_\beta^{(R)}]_{kl}^* = 0 \tag{6.48}$$

When $\alpha = \beta$, the sum has some nonzero value in general.

Case II Now let us consider the case in which α and β are equal, that is, $\Gamma_\beta = E^{-1}\Gamma_\alpha E$ (similar under the identity matrix). Then

$$A = cE \qquad \text{or} \qquad A_{ij} = c\delta_{ij}$$

and

$$A_{ij} = \sum_R \sum_k \sum_l [\Gamma_\alpha^{(R)}]_{ik} X_{kl} [\Gamma_\alpha^{(R)}]_{lj}^{-1} = c\delta_{ij} \tag{6.49}$$

To determine c, let $i = j$ then for arbitrary X

$$\sum_R \sum_k \sum_l [\Gamma_\alpha^{(R)}]_{ik} X_{kl} [\Gamma_\alpha^{(R)}]_{li}^{-1} = c \cdot 1 \tag{6.50}$$

Since X is arbitrary, the following must be true:

$$\sum_R [\Gamma_\alpha^{(R)}]_{ik} [\Gamma_\alpha^{(R)}]_{li}^{-1} = c$$

i.e., let $X_{kl} = 1$ as in one of the following matrices:

$$\begin{bmatrix} 0 & 0 & 1 & 0 \\ 0 & 0 & 0 & 0 \\ 0 & 0 & 0 & 0 \\ 0 & 0 & 0 & 0 \end{bmatrix} \quad \begin{bmatrix} 0 & 0 & 0 & 0 \\ 0 & 0 & 0 & 0 \\ 0 & 1 & 0 & 0 \\ 0 & 0 & 0 & 0 \end{bmatrix} \quad \begin{bmatrix} 0 & 0 & 0 & 0 \\ 0 & 0 & 0 & 0 \\ 0 & 0 & 0 & 0 \\ 0 & 0 & 0 & 1 \end{bmatrix}$$

Also, $AA^{-1} = A^{-1}A$. Therefore

$$\sum_R [\Gamma_\alpha^{(R)}]_{li}^{-1} [\Gamma_\alpha^{(R)}]_{ik} = c \tag{6.51}$$

Let us sum over i from 1 to n_α.

$$\sum_{i=1}^{n_\alpha} \sum_R [\Gamma_\alpha^{(R)}]_{li}^{-1} [\Gamma_\alpha^{(R)}]_{ik} = \sum_{i=1}^{n_\alpha} c = n_\alpha c \tag{6.52}$$

or

$$\sum_R \left(\sum_{i=1}^{n_\alpha} [\Gamma_\alpha^{(R)}]_{li}^{-1} [\Gamma_\alpha^{(R)}]_{ik} \right) = n_\alpha c$$

But $\Gamma_\alpha^{-1}\Gamma_\alpha = E$, which may be written as a sum

$$\sum_{i=1}^{n_\alpha} [\Gamma_\alpha^{(R)}]_{li}^{-1} [\Gamma_\alpha^{(R)}]_{ik} = \delta_{lk} \tag{6.53}$$

Then Eq. (6.52) becomes

$$\sum_{R=1}^{g} \delta_{lk} = n_\alpha c$$

$$g\delta_{lk} = n_\alpha c$$

so that

$$c = \frac{g\delta_{lk}}{n_\alpha} \tag{6.54}$$

Thus

$$A_{ij} = \sum_R [\Gamma_\alpha^{(R)}]_{ik}[\Gamma_\alpha^{(R)}]_{lj}^{-1} = c\delta_{ij}$$

or

$$\sum_R [\Gamma_\alpha^{(R)}]_{ik}[\Gamma_\alpha^{(R)}]_{lj}^{-1} = \frac{g}{n_\alpha}\delta_{ij}\delta_{lk} \tag{6.55}$$

Note that $[\Gamma_\alpha^{(R)}]_{lj}^{-1} = \Gamma^{(R)\dagger} = [\Gamma_\alpha^{(R)}]_{jl}^*$ if Γ_α is unitary; so that

$$\sum_R [\Gamma_\alpha^{(R)}]_{ik}[\Gamma_\alpha^{(R)}]_{jl}^* = \frac{g}{n_\alpha}\delta_{ij}\delta_{lk} \tag{6.56}$$

Let us now combine this result from case II with the result from case I (which places a restriction on α and β).

$$\sum_R [\Gamma_\alpha^{(R)}]_{ik}[\Gamma_\beta^{(R)}]_{jl}^* = \frac{g}{\sqrt{n_\alpha n_\beta}}\delta_{ij}\delta_{lk}\delta_{\alpha\beta} \tag{6.57}$$

Theorem five: Character systems of equivalent representations are identical.

For

$$\Gamma'^{(R)} = S^{-1}\Gamma^{(R)}S \tag{6.58}$$

and the character $\chi^{(R)}$ is defined

$$\chi^{(R)} = \sum_i \Gamma_{ii}^{(R)}$$

to show that

$$\chi^{(R)} = \sum_j \Gamma_{jj}'^{(R)}$$

$$\chi^{(R)} = \sum_j \Gamma_{jj}'^{(R)} = \sum_j \sum_i \sum_k S_{ji}^{-1} \Gamma_{ik}^{(R)} S_{kj} \tag{6.59}$$

interchange order of summations twice.

$$\chi^{(R)} = \sum_j \sum_k \sum_i S_{ji}^{-1} S_{kj} \Gamma_{ik}^{(R)} \tag{6.60}$$

$$= \sum_k \sum_i \underbrace{\left(\sum_j S_{kj} S_{ji}^{-1} \right)}_{\delta_{ki}} \Gamma_{ik}^{(R)}$$

$$= \sum_k \sum_i \delta_{ki} \Gamma_{ik}^{(R)}$$

$$\chi^{(R)} = \sum_k \Gamma_{kk}^{(R)} \qquad \text{Q.E.D.} \tag{6.61}$$

Since symmetry operations in the same class are related by similarity transformations, all the matrices in the same class have the same character.

We can use the orthogonality condition and the definition of character to obtain a relation between group order g and characters. Let

$$\chi_\alpha^{(R)} = \sum_i [\Gamma_\alpha^{(R)}]_{ii}$$

(This defines the character corresponding to element R in the αth irreducible representation.) Consider

$$\sum_R [\Gamma_\alpha^{(R)}]_{ij} [\Gamma_\beta^{(R)}]_{kl}^* = \frac{g}{\sqrt{n_\alpha n_\beta}} \delta_{\alpha\beta} \delta_{ik} \delta_{jl} \tag{6.62}$$

We must sum over i and k when $j = i$ and $l = k$; so that

$$\sum_i \sum_k \sum_R [\Gamma_\alpha^{(R)}]_{ii} [\Gamma_\beta^{(R)}]_{kk}^* = \sum_i \sum_k \frac{g}{\sqrt{n_\alpha n_\beta}} \delta_{\alpha\beta} \delta_{ik} \delta_{ik} \tag{6.63}$$

Note that

$$\sum_R \left(\sum_i [\Gamma_\alpha^{(R)}]_{ii} \right) \left(\sum_k [\Gamma_\beta^{(R)}]_{kk}^* \right) = \sum_R \chi_\alpha^{(R)} \chi_\beta^{(R)*}$$

and so we sum the right side over k and then over i.

$$\sum_{i=1}^{n_\alpha} \frac{g}{\sqrt{n_\alpha n_\beta}} \delta_{\alpha\beta} \sum_{k=1}^{n_\alpha} \delta_{ik}\delta_{ik} = \sum_{i=1}^{n_\alpha} \frac{g}{\sqrt{n_\alpha n_\beta}} \delta_{\alpha\beta}\delta_{ii}$$

$$= \frac{g}{\sqrt{n_\alpha n_\beta}} \delta_{\alpha\beta} \sum_{i=1}^{n_\alpha} \delta_{ii} = \frac{g}{\sqrt{n_\alpha n_\beta}} \delta_{\alpha\beta} n_\alpha \quad (6.64)$$

Therefore

$$\boxed{\sum_R \chi_\alpha^{(R)}\chi_\beta^{(R)*} = \frac{g}{\sqrt{n_\alpha n_\beta}} n_\alpha \delta_{\alpha\beta} = g} \qquad (6.65)$$

or

$$\sum_{R=1}^{g} \chi_\alpha^{(R)} \sqrt{\frac{1}{g}} \chi_\beta^{(R)*} \sqrt{\frac{1}{g}} = \delta_{\alpha\beta} \qquad (6.66)$$

Let $\alpha = \beta$. Then

$$\boxed{\sum_R |\chi_\alpha^{(R)}|^2 = g} \qquad (6.67)$$

or

$$\sum_{l=1}^{N_c} \chi_\alpha^{(\mathfrak{e}_l)} \sqrt{\frac{h_l}{g}} \chi_\beta^{(\mathfrak{e}_l)*} \sqrt{\frac{h_l}{g}} = \delta_{\alpha\beta} \qquad (6.68)$$

where h_l is the number of elements in the lth class and N_c is the number of classes. Since there exist only N inequivalent orthogonal (character) vectors, there can be at most N such vectors. *Thus, the number of irreducible representations is equal to the number of classes.*

Let us consider the direct sum of a reduced representation.

$$\Gamma'^{(R)} = \begin{bmatrix} \Gamma_1^{(R)} & & & 0 \\ & \Gamma_2^{(R)} & & \\ & & \Gamma_3^{(R)} & \\ 0 & & & \Gamma_1^{(R)} \end{bmatrix} \rightarrow \text{irreducible representations}$$

or

$$\Gamma'^{(R)} = 2\Gamma_1^{(R)} + \Gamma_2^{(R)} + \Gamma_3^{(R)}$$

or

$$\Gamma'^{(R)} = \sum_\alpha m_\alpha \Gamma_\alpha^{(R)} \qquad m_\alpha = \text{number of times } \Gamma_\alpha \text{ appears}$$

Let $\chi^{(R)} = \sum_\alpha m_\alpha \chi_\alpha^{(R)}$ and right-multiply by $\sum_R \chi_{\alpha'}^{(R)*}$.

$$\sum_R \chi_{\alpha'}^{(R)*} \S \quad \chi^{(R)} = m_1\chi_1^{(R)} + m_2\chi_2^{(R)} + \cdots + m_{\alpha'}\chi_{\alpha'}^{(R)} + \cdots$$

$$\sum_R \chi_{\alpha'}^{(R)*}\chi^{(R)} = \underbrace{\sum_R m_1\chi_{\alpha'}^{(R)*}\chi_1^{(R)}}_{=0} + \cdots + \underbrace{\sum_R m_{\alpha'}\chi_{\alpha'}^{(R)}\chi_{\alpha'}^{(R)*}}_{=m_{\alpha'}} \quad (6.69)$$

So that

$$\sum_R \chi_{\alpha'}^{(R)*}\chi^{(R)} = m_{\alpha'}g$$

and we obtain the general reduction equation

$$\boxed{m_\alpha = \frac{1}{g}\sum_R \chi^{(R)}\chi_\alpha^{(R)*}} \qquad (6.70)$$

Again

$$\sum_R \chi^{(R)*} \S \quad \chi^{(R)} = \sum_\alpha m_\alpha \chi_\alpha^{(R)} \qquad (6.71)$$

$$\sum_R \chi^{(R)}\chi^{(R)*} = \sum_\alpha \sum_R m_\alpha \chi_\alpha^{(R)}\chi^{(R)*}$$

Using the above relation for $\sum_R \chi^{(R)}\chi_\alpha^{(R)*}$, we find $\sum_\alpha m_\alpha m_\alpha g$ so that

$$\sum_R |\chi^{(R)}|^2 = g\sum_\alpha m_\alpha^2 \qquad (6.72)$$

Let $\chi^{(R)}$ refer to an irreducible representation. Then $m_\alpha = 1$, and there is only one term on the right.

$$g = \sum_R |\chi_\alpha^{(R)}|^2 \qquad (6.73)$$

Further it can be shown that for any group

$$\boxed{g = \sum_\alpha n_\alpha^2} \qquad (6.74)$$

This result suggests that the irreducible representations are a property of the group (see Prob. 6.10).

There are as many irreducible representations as there are classes.

6.3 CHARACTER TABLES

Now we can consider the problem of constructing the character table for a group, i.e., the character of each class for each irreducible representation.

Classes Irreducible representations	$\mathcal{C}_1$	$\mathcal{C}_2$	$\mathcal{C}_3$	$\mathcal{C}_4$
Γ_1	$\chi_1^{(\mathcal{C}_1)}$	$\chi_1^{(\mathcal{C}_2)}$	$\chi_1^{(\mathcal{C}_3)}$	$\chi_1^{(\mathcal{C}_4)}$
Γ_2	$\chi_2^{(\mathcal{C}_1)}$	$\chi_2^{(\mathcal{C}_2)}$	$\chi_2^{(\mathcal{C}_3)}$	$\chi_2^{(\mathcal{C}_4)}$
Γ_3	$\chi_3^{(\mathcal{C}_1)}$	$\chi_3^{(\mathcal{C}_2)}$	$\chi_3^{(\mathcal{C}_3)}$	$\chi_3^{(\mathcal{C}_4)}$
Γ_4	$\chi_4^{(\mathcal{C}_1)}$	$\chi_4^{(\mathcal{C}_2)}$	$\chi_4^{(\mathcal{C}_3)}$	$\chi_4^{(\mathcal{C}_4)}$

By a class we mean all the elements of a group which obey the relation

$$a^{-1}\mathcal{C}_i a = \mathcal{C}_i$$

Because of this relation all elements of a class possess the same character. For example, consider the group C_{3v}

C_{3v}	E	$2C_3 \begin{cases} C_3^1 \\ C_3^2 \end{cases}$	$3\sigma \begin{cases} \sigma_v \\ \sigma_v' \\ \sigma_v'' \end{cases}$
Γ_1	1	1	1
Γ_2	1	1	-1
Γ_3	2	-1	0

Note that the character of the irreducible representation is independent of the basis. Consider the multiplication table for C_{3v}.

C_{3v}	E	C_3^1	C_3^2	σ_v	σ_v'	σ_v''
E	E	C_3^1	C_3^2	σ_v	σ_v'	σ_v''
C_3^1	C_3^1	C_3^2	E	σ_v'	σ_v''	σ_v
C_3^2	C_3^2	E	C_3^1	σ_v''	σ_v	σ_v'
σ_v	σ_v	σ_v''	σ_v'	E	C_3^2	C_3^1
σ_v'	σ_v'	σ_v	σ_v''	C_3^1	E	C_3^2
σ_v''	σ_v''	σ_v'	σ_v	C_3^2	C_3^1	E

The table indicates that when products are formed between whole classes, the results are whole classes, not parts of classes. That is,

$$\mathcal{C}_i\mathcal{C}_j = \sum_l^{N_c} c_{ij,l}\mathcal{C}_l \qquad c_{ij,l} \text{ is integral}$$

The $c_{ij,l}$ are determined directly from the table.

$$
\begin{array}{llll}
\mathcal{C}_1\mathcal{C}_1 = \mathcal{C}_2 & c_{11,1} = 0 & c_{11,2} = 1 & c_{11,3} = 0 \\
\mathcal{C}_1\mathcal{C}_2 = \mathcal{C}_1 & c_{12,1} = 1 & c_{12,2} = 0 & c_{12,3} = 0 \\
\mathcal{C}_2\mathcal{C}_2 = 2\mathcal{C}_1 + \mathcal{C}_2 & c_{22,1} = 2 & c_{22,2} = 1 & c_{22,3} = 0 \\
\mathcal{C}_3\mathcal{C}_3 = 3\mathcal{C}_1 + 3\mathcal{C}_2 & c_{33,1} = 3 & c_{33,2} = 3 & c_{33,3} = 0 \\
\mathcal{C}_2\mathcal{C}_3 = 2\mathcal{C}_3 & c_{23,1} = 0 & c_{23,2} = 0 & c_{23,3} = 2 \\
\mathcal{C}_1\mathcal{C}_3 = \mathcal{C}_3 & c_{13,1} = 0 & c_{13,2} = 0 & c_{13,3} = 1
\end{array}
\qquad (6.75)
$$

Write a matrix for a class

$$\Gamma_\alpha^{(e_i)} = \sum_{j=1}^{h_i} \Gamma_\alpha^{(R_j)} \qquad (6.76)$$

For example,

$$\Gamma_\alpha^{(e_2)} = \Gamma_\alpha^{(C_3^1)} + \Gamma_\alpha^{(C_3^2)}$$

For any $R \in G$

$$\Gamma_\alpha^{(R)}\Gamma_\alpha^{(e_i)}\Gamma_\alpha^{(R)^{-1}} = \Gamma_\alpha^{(e_i)} \qquad (6.77)$$

or

$$a\mathcal{C}_i a^{-1} = \mathcal{C}_i$$

Right-multiply Eq. (6.77) by $\Gamma_\alpha^{(R)}$

$$\Gamma_\alpha^{(R)}\Gamma_\alpha^{(e_i)} = \Gamma_\alpha^{(e_i)}\Gamma_\alpha^{(R)} \qquad (6.78)$$

Thus, by Theorem two, $\Gamma^{(e_i)}$ is a constant matrix. That is,

$$\Gamma_\alpha^{(e_i)} = \eta_\alpha^i E = \begin{bmatrix} \eta_\alpha^i & 0 & 0 & 0 \\ 0 & \eta_\alpha^i & 0 & 0 \\ 0 & 0 & \eta_\alpha^i & 0 \\ 0 & 0 & 0 & \eta_\alpha^i \end{bmatrix} \qquad (6.79)$$

Then, the character of $\Gamma_\alpha^{(e_i)}$ is given as

$$\text{tr } \Gamma_\alpha^{(e_i)} = \eta_\alpha^i n_\alpha$$

But from the definition of $\Gamma_\alpha^{(e_i)}$

$$\text{tr } \Gamma_\alpha^{(e_i)} = h_i \chi_\alpha^{(e_i)} \tag{6.80}$$

Thus

$$\eta_\alpha{}^i = \frac{h_i \chi_\alpha^{(e_i)}}{n_\alpha}$$

But

$$e_i e_j = \sum_l c_{ij,l} e_l$$

and

$$\Gamma_\alpha^{(e_i)} \Gamma_\alpha^{(e_j)} = \sum_l c_{ij,l} \Gamma_\alpha^{(e_l)}$$

$$\eta_\alpha{}^i E \eta_\alpha{}^j E = \sum_l c_{ij,l} \eta_\alpha{}^l E$$

or

$$\eta_\alpha{}^i \eta_\alpha{}^j = \sum_l c_{ij,l} \eta_\alpha{}^l \tag{6.81}$$

Substituting from above,

$$\frac{h_i \chi_\alpha^{(e_i)}}{n_\alpha} \frac{h_j \chi_\alpha^{(e_j)}}{n_\alpha} = \sum_l c_{ij,l} \frac{h_l \chi_\alpha^{(e_l)}}{n_\alpha}$$

Finally

$$\boxed{h_i h_j \chi_\alpha^{(e_i)} \chi_\alpha^{(e_j)} = n_\alpha \sum_l c_{ij,l} h_l \chi_\alpha^{(e_l)}} \tag{6.82}$$

A set of simultaneous equations to determine the χ_α is obtained. From the multiplication table we get h_i, h_j, h_l, and $c_{ij,l}$. We obtain n_α from the relation

$$g = \sum_\alpha n_\alpha{}^2$$

Since we need know only the characters of the reducible and irreducible representations, we can reduce any reducible representation without knowing the transformation matrix. We need know only Eq. (6.70)

$$m_\alpha = \frac{1}{g} \sum_R \chi^{(R)} \chi_\alpha^{(R)*}$$

which expresses the number of times the αth irreducible representation appears in the totally reduced form.

$$\Gamma'^{(R)} = S^{-1}\Gamma^{(R)}S \rightarrow \chi^{(R)}$$

that is,

$$\Gamma'^{(R)} = \sum_\alpha m_\alpha \Gamma_\alpha{}^{(R)} \rightarrow \chi_\alpha{}^{(R)}$$

Let us consider an example containing two reducible representations in the group C_{3v}. The only information we need to know about the reducible representations Γ_A and Γ_B is their character system.

C_{3v}	E	$2C_3$	3σ
Γ_1	1	1	1
Γ_2	1	1	-1
Γ_3	2	-1	0
Γ_A	2	2	0
Γ_B	4	1	0

Using the above expression, we find the m_α.

$$m_1{}^A = \tfrac{1}{6}(1 \cdot 2 \cdot 1 + 1 \cdot 2 \cdot 2 + 1 \cdot 0 \cdot 3) = \tfrac{1}{6}(6) = 1$$
$$m_2{}^A = \tfrac{1}{6}[1 \cdot 2 \cdot 1 + 1 \cdot 2 \cdot 2 + (-1) \cdot 0 \cdot 3] = \tfrac{1}{6}(6) = 1$$
$$m_3{}^A = \tfrac{1}{6}[2 \cdot 2 \cdot 1 + (-1) \cdot 2 \cdot 2 + 0 \cdot 0 \cdot 3] = \tfrac{1}{6}(0) = 0$$

Thus,

$$\Gamma_A = \Gamma_1 + \Gamma_2$$

Similarly for Γ_B:

$$m_1{}^B = \tfrac{1}{6}(1 \cdot 4 \cdot 1 + 1 \cdot 1 \cdot 2 + 1 \cdot 0 \cdot 3) = \tfrac{1}{6}(6) = 1$$
$$m_2{}^B = \tfrac{1}{6}[1 \cdot 4 \cdot 1 + 1 \cdot 1 \cdot 2 + (-1) \cdot 0 \cdot 3] = \tfrac{1}{6}(6) = 1$$
$$m_3{}^B = \tfrac{1}{6}[2 \cdot 4 \cdot 1 + (-1) \cdot 1 \cdot 2 + 0 \cdot 0 \cdot 3] = \tfrac{1}{6}(6) = 1$$

Thus,

$$\Gamma_B = \Gamma_1 + \Gamma_2 + \Gamma_3$$

The reader will find that the direct products similar to Γ_B are very important in determining spectral-transition selection rules.

Special symbols suggested by R. S. Mulliken, are often used to designate the irreducible representations.

Symbol	Dimension
A,B	1
E	2
$T(F)$	3

Symmetry	Symbol			
	Rotation C_n	$C_2 \perp C_n$ or σ_v (σ_d)	$\sigma \perp C_n$ σ_h	Inversion center i
Symmetric	A	1	$'$	g
Antisymmetric	B	2	$''$	u

The following example uses the Mulliken symbols.

C_{3v}	E	$2C_3$	3σ	
A_1	1	1	1	z, $x^2 + y^2$, z^2
A_2	1	1	-1	R_z
E	2	-1	0	(x, y), (R_x, R_y), $(x^2 - y^2, xy)$, (xz, yz)

There are several special basis sets as follows:

1. Cartesian coordinates x, y, $z(T_x, T_y, T_z)$
2. Rotations about cartesian axes R_x, R_y, R_z
3. Binary cartesian products xy, xz, yz (α_{xy} etc.); $x^2 + y^2$, $x^2 - y^2$; x^2, y^2, z^2

An irreducible representation is said to have the symmetry of one of these basis sets when it transforms in the same manner, i.e., has the same character system.

We shall see that various types of basis sets can be used as a basis for a representation:

1. N cartesian axis sets centered on the N atoms of a molecule
2. Vectors directed along the various bonds of a molecule
3. A general cartesian point
4. The wave functions of a molecule

Consider the atomic orbitals p_x, p_y, and p_z as a basis for C_{3v}.   We find

P_z	E	C_3	σ	A_1
	[1]	[1]	[1]	

$$P_x, P_y \quad \begin{bmatrix} 1 & 0 \\ 0 & 1 \end{bmatrix} \quad \begin{bmatrix} -\dfrac{1}{2} & -\dfrac{\sqrt{3}}{2} \\ \dfrac{\sqrt{3}}{2} & -\dfrac{1}{2} \end{bmatrix} \quad \begin{bmatrix} 1 & 0 \\ 0 & -1 \end{bmatrix} \quad E$$

6.4 DIRECT PRODUCTS OF REPRESENTATIONS

As we shall see in Sec. 6.5 and in succeeding chapters, products of the matrices of representations are important.   Since in applications of group theory we need know only the characters of the matrices, let us consider an important property of direct-product representations.

Consider an operation $R \in G$ and two sets of basis functions which form bases for two representations, $\mathbf{A}$ $(A_1, \ldots, A_M)$ and $\mathbf{B}$ $(B_1, \ldots, B_N)$.   Since the operation on one basis function in a set in general produces a linear combination of the other functions, we can write

$$RA_k = \sum_{l=1}^{M} a_{lk}A_l \tag{6.83}$$

and

$$RB_i = \sum_{j=1}^{N} b_{ji}B_j \tag{6.84}$$

R on all B produces matrix $B^{(R)} = [b_{ji}{}^{(R)}]$; the set of $B^{(R)}$ matrices make up the representation.   Further, we may write

$$RA_iB_k = \sum_{j=1}^{M} \sum_{l=1}^{N} a_{ji}b_{lk}A_jB_l = \sum_j \sum_l c_{ji,lk}A_jB_l \tag{6.85}$$

Thus, the set of product functions A_iB_k also form a basis for a representation of the group G.   The matrices $C^{(R)} = [c_{jl,ik}{}^{(R)}]$ are of order $MN \times MN$.   Let us now prove the important theorem concerning the characters of direct-product representations.

Theorem six: The characters of the representation of a direct product are equal to the products of the characters of the representations based on the individual sets of functions.

$$\chi_c{}^{(R)} = \sum_j \sum_l c_{jl,jl} = \sum_j \sum_l b_{jj}a_{ll} = \chi_b{}^{(R)}\chi_a{}^{(R)} \qquad \text{Q.E.D.} \tag{6.86}$$

The importance of the product representation will become obvious in Sec. 6.5 and in Chaps. 7 and 8. Let us consider the point group D_{3h} and some product representations of the irreducible representations of D_{3h} as shown in the following table.

D_{3h}	E	$2C_3$	$3C_2$	σ_h	$2S_3$	$3\sigma_v$
A_1'	1	1	1	1	1	1
A_2'	1	1	-1	1	1	-1
E'	2	-1	0	2	-1	0
A_1''	1	1	1	-1	-1	-1
A_2''	1	1	-1	-1	-1	1
E''	2	-1	0	-2	1	0
$A_1' \times E'$	2	-1	0	2	-1	0
$A_2' \times A_2''$	1	1	1	-1	-1	-1
$A_2''^2$	1	1	1	1	1	1
E'^2	4	1	0	4	1	0
$A_1'' \times A_2''$	1	1	-1	-1	-1	1

In general the direct representation is a reducible representation. Thus, it can be reduced and written as a direct sum. Using the standard reduction formula, we can find the following direct sums for the above product representations:

$$A_1' \times E' = E'$$
$$A_2' \times A_2'' = A_1''$$
$$A_1'' \times A_2'' = A_2''$$
$$A_2''^2 = A_1'$$
$$E'^2 = A_1' + A_2' + A_1'' + A_2''$$

6.5 GROUP THEORY AND INTEGRAL EVALUATION

The usefulness of the properties of the direct product becomes apparent when we consider the various integrals which appear in physics and chemistry. An integral whose integrand is the product of two (or more) functions, that is,

$$\int_\tau f_1(\tau) f_2(\tau) f_3(\tau) \cdots d\tau$$

will vanish unless the product function is invariant under all the symmetry operations of the group (for which we constructed $f_1 f_2 f_3$). That is, if the integral can be expressed as a sum, the integral vanishes unless one term is invariant, i.e., forms a basis for the totally symmetric representation of the group (A, A_1, A_{1g}, A_{1g}').

Consider the simpler integral

$$\int_{-\infty}^{\infty} y \, dx$$

This integral vanishes if y is an odd function, that is, $y = x$,

$$f(x) = -f(-x)$$

y is not invariant under reflection across the x axis. However, if $y = x^2$, $f(x) = f(-x)$, and the integral does not vanish.

Thus, the integral of a product of functions will not vanish if the products forms a basis for the totally symmetric representation. We have shown how to determine whether Γ_{AB} contains the totally symmetric species; thus, let us prove a theorem concerning this problem.

Theorem seven: The representation of a direct product Γ_{AB} will contain the totally symmetric species only if $\Gamma_A = \Gamma_B$:

$$m_a = \frac{1}{g} \sum_R \chi^{(R)} \chi_a^{(R)*}$$

Let $\chi^{(R)} \rightarrow \chi_{AB}$. If m_a and $\chi_a^{(R)*}$ refer to A_1, then, $m_a = m_{A_1}$ and

$$\chi^{(R)*} = \chi_{A_1}^{(R)*} = 1$$

So that

$$m_{A_1} = \frac{1}{g} \sum_R \chi_{AB}^{(R)}$$

but

$$\chi_{AB}^{(R)} = \chi_A^{(R)} \chi_B^{(R)}$$

so that

$$m_{A_1} = \frac{1}{g} \sum_R \chi_A^{(R)} \chi_B^{(R)} = \delta_{AB} \tag{6.87}$$

If A_1 occurs, it does so only once.

Integrals of this kind are very important in quantum mechanics. We shall consider the integral

$$\int_\tau \psi_i P \psi_j \, d\tau$$

in later chapters. P is an operator, e.g., angular momentum, or, as will be most important in our later considerations, P may be the hamiltonian operator.

GLOSSARY OF SYMBOLS

$\Gamma^{(R)}$	A representation of group G, sometimes the specific matrix for element R
$\Gamma_\alpha^{(R)}$	The αth irreducible representation of group G
$\Gamma_\alpha^{(\mathcal{C}_i)}$	The class matrix for the ith class of the αth irreducible representation
$[\Gamma_\alpha^{(R)}]_{ij}$	The ijth element of the matrix for R in the αth irreducible representation
U	A unitary matrix, that is, $U^{-1} = U^\dagger$
D	A diagonal matrix
$\mathbb{1}$	The unit, or identity, matrix
A^{-1}	The reciprocal, or inverse, of matrix A
$A^\dagger$	The hermitian conjugate of matrix A, that is, the complex conjugate of the transpose of A
$\tilde{A}$	The transpose of matrix A
A^*	The complex conjugate of matrix A
$\lvert A \rvert$	The determinant of matrix A, that is, the array of numbers (or symbols) of matrix A considered as a determinant
$\text{tr } A$	The trace, or character, of matrix A
$\chi^{(R)}$	The character (sum of the diagonal elements) of the matrix for R in a representation
δ_{ij}	The Kronecker delta $$\delta_{ij} = \begin{cases} 1 & i = j \\ 0 & i \neq j \end{cases}$$
g	The order of group G
n_α	The dimension of the αth irreducible representation
h_l	The number of elements in the lth class
$\mathcal{C}_l$	General symbol for the lth class; may also stand for the class matrix $\Gamma_\alpha^{(\mathcal{C}_l)}$
m_α	The number of times the αth irreducible representation appears in the totally reduced representation
$c_{ij,l}$	The coefficient of the lth class when classes i and j are combined
N_c	The number of classes in group G

PROBLEMS

6.1. Use the criterion established in Schur's lemma to demonstrate whether the following representations are irreducible:

(a) Group C_{2v}

$$\overset{E}{\begin{bmatrix} 1 & 0 \\ 0 & 1 \end{bmatrix}} \overset{C_2}{\begin{bmatrix} 1 & 0 \\ 0 & 1 \end{bmatrix}} \overset{\sigma_v}{\begin{bmatrix} 1 & 0 \\ 0 & -1 \end{bmatrix}} \overset{\sigma_v'}{\begin{bmatrix} 1 & 0 \\ 0 & -1 \end{bmatrix}}$$

(b) Group C_{3v}

$$\overset{E}{\begin{bmatrix} 1 & 0 \\ 0 & 1 \end{bmatrix}} \overset{C_3{}^1}{\begin{bmatrix} -\dfrac{1}{2} & \dfrac{\sqrt{3}}{2} \\ -\dfrac{\sqrt{3}}{2} & -\dfrac{1}{2} \end{bmatrix}} \overset{C_3{}^2}{\begin{bmatrix} -\dfrac{1}{2} & \dfrac{\sqrt{3}}{2} \\ \dfrac{\sqrt{3}}{2} & -\dfrac{1}{2} \end{bmatrix}}$$

$$\overset{\sigma_v}{\begin{bmatrix} 1 & 0 \\ 0 & -1 \end{bmatrix}} \overset{\sigma_v'}{\begin{bmatrix} -\dfrac{1}{2} & -\dfrac{\sqrt{3}}{2} \\ \dfrac{\sqrt{3}}{2} & \dfrac{1}{2} \end{bmatrix}} \overset{\sigma_v''}{\begin{bmatrix} -\dfrac{1}{2} & \dfrac{\sqrt{3}}{2} \\ \dfrac{\sqrt{3}}{2} & \dfrac{1}{2} \end{bmatrix}}$$

(c) Group D_{3h}

E	$C_3{}^1$	$C_3{}^2$	C_2	C_2'	C_2''	σ_h	$S_3{}^1$	$S_3{}^2$	σ_v	σ_v'	σ_v''
[2]	[−1]	[−1]	[0]	[0]	[0]	[−2]	[1]	[1]	[0]	[0]	[0]

6.2. Use Eqs. (6.82) and (6.74) along with the group multiplication tables to determine the character tables for the following groups. (Determine the Mulliken symbol for each irreducible representation and the irreducible representations to which x, y, z, x^2, y^2, z^2, xy, etc., belong.)

    (a) C_{2v}

    (b) D_{2h}

    (c) C_3

6.3. Show that the character systems for group C_{3v} obey the orthogonality relations of Eq. (6.66) [or (6.68)] and Eq. (6.67).

6.4. (a) Construct a matrix representation for point group C_{2v} using three cartesian coordinate systems in the molecule SO_2. Put the origin of each coordinate system on one each of the atoms. Make the z axes all perpendicular to the plane of the molecule; make all the x axes parallel; and make the y axes all parallel. The matrices will be of order 9×9.

    (b) Using the standard reduction formula, Eq. (6.70), reduce the representation in part (a).

6.5. Abelian groups have certain special properties. Use Schur's lemma to prove that all the irreducible representations of an abelian group must be one-dimensional. *Hint:* Use the fact that a diagonal matrix will commute with any matrix with which it is conformable.

6.6. Consider the problem of determining the character table for the group C_3.

(a) Show that the irreducible representations are all one-dimensional.

(b) One of the irreducible representations is totally symmetric. What is its character system?

(c) Find all three character systems simultaneously by diagonalizing a 3×3 matrix representation for the point group C_3, that is, the rotation matrices of Sec. 5.2.

6.7. In the groups specified determine the direct sums for the following product representations:

(a) $E \times E$ in C_{4v}

(b) $E_1 \times E_1$ in D_{4d}

(c) $E_g \times E_g$ in C_{4h}

(d) $T_2 \times T_2$ in T_d

(e) $T_1 \times T_2$ in T_d

6.8. In the equation which represents class multiplication

$$\mathcal{C}_i\mathcal{C}_j = \sum_{l=1}^{N_c} c_{ij,l}\mathcal{C}_l$$

show that

$$c_{ij,l} = c_{ji,l}$$

even when the group is not abelian.   This is a proof that the class matrices are commutative

$$\mathcal{C}_i\mathcal{C}_j = \mathcal{C}_j\mathcal{C}_i$$

6.9. (a) Write out the character table for the group D_{4h} ($4/mmm$) using the fact that D_{4h} can be obtained as the product of the group D_4 and the inversion operation.

(b) By using the transformation properties of the cartesian components x and y in the plane of a square determine a unitary representation for the group D_4.

(c) How can you now proceed to obtain unitary matrices for all the operations in D_{4h}?

6.10. (a) Consider the abstract group $G(E,A,B)$ whose multiplication table is

G	E	A	B
E	E	A	B
A	A	B	E
B	B	E	A

We can define the *regular* representation of G by rearranging the multiplication table so that for row headings we have the inverses of the elements appearing in the same order as the elements appear as column headings

G	E	A	B
$E^{-1} = E$	E	A	B
$A^{-1} = B$	B	E	A
$B^{-1} = A$	A	B	E

The regular representation is of order g and is obtained directly from the rearranged multiplication table; for matrix $\Gamma^{(R)}$ replace element R with 1 and all others with 0.   Write out the matrices for the regular representation of group G.

(b) Show for the regular representation that the character of all the matrices is zero except for $\Gamma^{(E)}$, which is equal to g.

(c) Prove that the regular representation contains (in its totally reduced form) each irreducible representation a number of times equal to the dimensionality of the irreducible representation [use Eq. (6.70)].

(d) Let n_α be the dimension of the αth irreducible representation. Use the results of part (c) to prove

$$\sum_{\alpha=1}^{N_c} n_\alpha{}^2 = g$$

where g is the order of the group.

6.11. Determine the irreducible representation to which each of the following atomic orbitals belongs in each of the following point groups by determining the action of the various symmetry operations on the orbitals:

(a) p_x, p_y, p_z in O_h, D_{4h}, and D_4
(b) p_x, p_y, p_z in T_d, D_{2h}, C_{2h}
(c) The five d orbitals in O_h and D_{4h}
(d) An s orbital and the three p orbitals in D_{3h}

REFERENCES

Birkhoff, G., and S. MacLane: "A Survey of Modern Algebra," 3d ed., The Macmillan Company, New York, 1965.
Eyring, H., J. Walter, and G. E. Kimball: "Quantum Chemistry," chap. 10, John Wiley & Sons, Inc., New York, 1944.
Hammermesh, M.: "Group Theory and Its Applications to Physical Problems," Addison-Wesley Publishing Company, Inc., Reading, Mass., 1962.
Tinkham, M.: "Group Theory and Quantum Mechanics," McGraw-Hill Book Company, New York, 1964.

7

symmetry
aspects
of
molecular
vibrations

In considering the problem of molecular vibrations there are two kinds of information we seek concerning a molecular system: (1) what are the possible modes of vibration of the system, and (2) which vibrational modes will absorb radiation and thus be observed infrared or Raman bands?

In considering the first problem we are concerned with the number of degrees of freedom of the molecule. Each atom in the molecule possesses 3 degrees of freedom, which may be associated with translational motion along three cartesian axes. Thus, a molecule containing N atoms possesses $3N$ degrees of freedom.

How many of the $3N$ degrees of freedom correspond to genuine vibrational degrees of freedom? Since the molecule as a whole may undergo translational motion (as a rigid body), 3 of the $3N$ degrees of freedom correspond to translational degrees of freedom. Further, the molecule may undergo rotations (about its centroid) which correspond to rotational motion about each of the three cartesian axes. There remain $3N - 6$ degrees of freedom which, then, correspond to vibrational degrees of freedom for the (nonlinear) molecule.

The case of the linear molecule must be considered separately. Rotation about the molecular axis consists entirely of rotation of the electrons and the nuclei. The moment of inertia for such motion is so small that the corresponding rotational energy levels are very widely spaced—so widely spaced, in fact, as to preclude excitation. Linear molecules, then, do not have a rotational degree of freedom about their molecular axis. This degree of freedom becomes a vibrational degree, and linear molecules have $3N - 5$ degrees of vibrational freedom.

Let us now consider the mechanics of molecular motion. We can assume that translational motion is exactly separable from rotational and vibrational motion. Further, we can use the approximation that rotation is separable from vibration. In quantum-mechanical language this statement corresponds to writing the total molecular wave function as a product function. (Translational motion will not be considered here.)

$$\psi_{\text{total}} = \psi_{\text{elec}}\psi_{\text{vib}}\psi_{\text{rot}} \tag{7.1}$$

In the following treatment we shall consider the separated vibrational system of the molecule with its $3N - 6$ (or $3N - 5$) degrees of freedom.

7.1 MODES OF MOLECULAR MOTION: THE CLASSICAL MECHANICAL PROBLEM

We can describe the atomic positions in terms of cartesian coordinates:

$$x_1, y_1, z_1; x_2, y_2, z_2; \ldots$$

Let us, however, use coordinates which describe the displacements of the atoms from their equilibrium positions:

$$\Delta x_1, \Delta x_2, \Delta x_3; \Delta x_4, \Delta x_5, \Delta x_6; \ldots$$

The kinetic energy is written as

$$T = \sum_{i=1}^{N} T_i = \sum_{i=1}^{N} \tfrac{1}{2}m\dot{x}_i^2$$

or

$$2T = \sum_{i=1}^{N} m_i(\Delta\dot{x}_i)^2 \tag{7.2}$$

where $m_1 = m_2 = m_3$, $m_4 = m_5 = m_6$, etc.

If we write the Δx_i as vectors and the masses as a matrix M, we can write T as follows:

$$2T = \widetilde{\Delta\dot{\mathbf{x}}}\, M\, \Delta\dot{\mathbf{x}} \tag{7.3}$$

where it can be seen that M is diagonal. T can be shown to be diagonal under a transformation to mass-weighted coordinates. Let

$$q_i = \sqrt{m_i}\, \Delta x_i \qquad (7.4)$$

then

$$\frac{\dot{q}_i{}^2}{m_i} = \Delta \dot{x}_i{}^2$$

so that

$$2T = \sum_{i=1}^{N} \dot{q}_i{}^2$$

The kinetic energy is diagonal, however, only in cartesian-type coordinate systems.

We now consider the potential function for the system, $V = V(q_i)$. In general the functional relationship is not known. So that in order to continue the treatment of molecular vibrations, we must produce an approximation of V. The usual procedure is to expand V in a Taylor's series about the equilibrium position.

$$V = V_0 + \left[\sum_{i=1}^{N} \frac{\partial V}{\partial q_i} \bigg|_{q_i=0} \right] q_i + \frac{1}{2} \left[\sum_{i=1}^{N} \sum_{j=1}^{N} \frac{\partial^2 V}{\partial q_i\, \partial q_j} \bigg|_{\substack{q_i=0 \\ q_j=0}} \right] q_i q_j$$

$$+ \cdots \quad (7.5)$$

The series is cut off after the third term. This approximation is not considered serious for the purposes of our present discussion. Since the zero of potential can be arbitrarily chosen, we can set V_0 equal to zero.

$$V_0 = 0$$

We can also assume that the molecular system does possess a stable equilibrium. At the coordinates corresponding to equilibrium $V(q_i)$ is a minimum and

$$\frac{\partial V}{\partial q_i} \bigg|_{q_i=0} = 0$$

Thus, we are left with only the second-derivative terms:

$$V = \frac{1}{2} \left[\sum_{i=1}^{N} \sum_{j=1}^{N} \frac{\partial^2 V}{\partial q_i\, \partial q_j} \bigg|_{\substack{q_i=0 \\ q_j=0}} \right] q_i q_j \qquad (7.6)$$

Note that the array of second derivatives is symmetric with respect to interchange of i and j. Thus, a matrix constructed for V from the terminated Taylor's series produces a real symmetric (hermitian) matrix.

In order to solve the vibrational problem use is made of the Euler-Lagrange equations:

$$\frac{d}{dt}\frac{\partial L}{\partial \dot{q}_i} - \frac{\partial L}{\partial q_i} = 0 \tag{7.7}$$

The lagrangian L is defined as

$$L = T - V$$

In our case, L is written in terms of the q_i.

$$L = \frac{1}{2}\sum_{i=1}^{N} \dot{q}_i{}^2 - \frac{1}{2}\sum_{i=1}^{N}\sum_{j=1}^{N} f_{ij}q_iq_j \tag{7.8}$$

The f_{ij} are the various second derivatives in the Taylor's series.

$$f_{ij} = \frac{\partial^2 V}{\partial q_i\,\partial q_j}$$

Note that V may be written in a bilinear form.

$$2V = \tilde{q}F\mathbf{q}$$

The solution to the Euler-Lagrange equations is a set of $3N$ linear homogeneous coupled equations

$$\ddot{q}_i + \sum_{j=1}^{N} f_{ij}q_j = 0 \qquad i = 1, 2, 3, 4, \ldots , 3N \tag{7.9}$$

It is a laborious task to solve these equations for each q_i as a function of time. There is, however, a simple method which can be formulated in terms of matrices.

Since F is hermitian, $F = F^\dagger$, it may be diagonalized with a unitary matrix, U.

$$U^{-1}FU = \lambda \tag{7.10}$$

Then

$$F = U\lambda U^{-1}$$

and

$$2V = \tilde{q}F\mathbf{q} = \tilde{q}U\lambda U^{-1}\mathbf{q}$$

Let

$$\mathbf{Q} = U^{-1}\mathbf{q} \qquad \text{and} \qquad \mathbf{q} = U\mathbf{Q} \tag{7.11}$$

where the Q is a new set of coordinates called *normal* coordinates which are related to the mass-weighted coordinates q_i as follows:

$$q_i = \sum_k U_{ik}Q_k \tag{7.12}$$

and

$$Q_k = \sum_i U_{ki}^{-1} q_i = \sum_i \tilde{U}_{ik}^* q_i \qquad \text{for } U^{-1} = \tilde{U}^* \tag{7.13}$$

But λ is diagonal; so that

$$2V = \sum_k \lambda_k Q_k^2 \tag{7.14}$$

i.e., a sum of squares.

Thus, the potential energy is diagonal in the normal coordinates. Each Q_k is associated with a particular frequency. Note that the form of the kinetic energy is also unchanged.

$$2T = \tilde{\dot{q}}\dot{q} = \tilde{\dot{Q}}\tilde{U}U\dot{Q} = \tilde{Q}U^{-1}U\dot{Q} = \tilde{Q}Q \tag{7.15}$$

or

$$2T = \sum_{k=1}^{3N-6} \dot{Q}_k^2$$

If we write the lagrangian in terms of normal coordinates,

$$L = T - V = \frac{1}{2}\sum_k \dot{Q}_k^2 - \frac{1}{2}\sum_k \lambda_k Q_k^2 \tag{7.16}$$

then the equations of motion are given as

$$\frac{d}{dt}\frac{\partial L}{\partial \dot{Q}_i} - \frac{\partial L}{\partial Q_i} = 0 \qquad i = 1, 2, \ldots, 3N - 6$$

which reduces to a second-order differential equation

$$\ddot{Q}_k + \lambda_k Q_k = 0 \qquad k = 1, 2, \ldots, 3N - 6 \tag{7.17}$$

However, this equation is just the equation of motion for a simple harmonic oscillator. The solution may be written in the cosine form

$$Q_k = C_k \cos(\lambda_k^{\frac{1}{2}} t + \epsilon) \tag{7.18}$$

where C_k = amplitude
$\lambda_k^{\frac{1}{2}}$ = frequency
ϵ = phase angle

What is the frequency of the normal mode? The circular frequency ω_k is seen to be the square root of λ_k

$$\omega_k = 2\pi\nu_k = \lambda_k^{\frac{1}{2}}$$

or $\nu_k = (1/2\pi)\sqrt{\lambda_k}$ is the simple harmonic frequency, or

$$\lambda_k = 4\pi^2 \nu_k^2$$

Remember Eq. (7.10):

$$U^{-1}FU = \lambda$$

Thus

$$FU = U\lambda$$

or

$$\sum_j f_{ij}u_{jk} = \sum_j u_{ij}\lambda_{jk}$$

but λ is diagonal; so that

$$\sum_j f_{ij}u_{jk} = u_{ik}\lambda_{kk} = \lambda_k u_{ik} \tag{7.19}$$

and

$$FU = \lambda_k U \tag{7.20}$$

U may be considered as being constructed from vectors $\mathbf{u}_k$. Then

$$F\mathbf{u}_k = \lambda_k \mathbf{u}_k$$

and we obtain the eigenvalue problem. Therefore

$$(F - \lambda_k E) \cdot \mathbf{u}_k = 0 \tag{7.21}$$

The λ_k and $\mathbf{u}_k$ are found in the standard manner. Note that the matrix U, which transforms the mass-weighted (cartesian) coordinates into normal coordinates, is the matrix of the eigenvectors of F where from Eq. (7.6)

$$f_{ij} = \frac{\partial^2 V(q)}{\partial q_i \, \partial q_j}$$

We can show that the normal coordinates form an orthonormal set of functions because F is hermitian.

$$\tilde{Q}_j^* \text{ \S} \qquad FQ_k = \lambda_k Q_k \tag{7.22}$$
$$\tilde{Q}_j^* FQ_k = \tilde{Q}_j^* \lambda_k Q_k = \lambda_k \tilde{Q}_j^* Q_k$$

We also take the complex conjugate of the transpose of Eq. (7.22)

$$\widetilde{FQ_j^*} = \widetilde{\lambda_j Q_j^*}$$
$$\tilde{Q}_j^* \tilde{F}^* = \lambda_j^* \tilde{Q}_j^* \qquad \text{\S } Q_k$$
$$\tilde{Q}_j^* \tilde{F}^* Q_k = \lambda_j^* \tilde{Q}_j^* Q_k \tag{7.23}$$

Obtain the difference of Eqs. (7.22) and (7.23)

$$\tilde{Q}_j^* FQ_k - \tilde{Q}_j^* \tilde{F}^* Q_k = \tilde{Q}_j^* Q_k(\lambda_k - \lambda_j^*)$$

The left-hand side is zero because F is real hermitian, and thus $F = \tilde{F}^*$. Therefore

$$\tilde{Q}_j^* Q_k (\lambda_k - \lambda_j^*) = 0 \qquad (7.24)$$

There are two cases:

Case I   Take $k \neq j$; then $\lambda_k - \lambda_j^* \neq 0$ and $\tilde{Q}_j^* Q_k \equiv 0$. Thus, the normal modes are orthogonal.

Case II   Take $k = j$; then $\lambda_j - \lambda_j^* = 0$ and $\tilde{Q}_j^* Q_j \neq 0$. The normal modes may be normalized, and thus the normal modes form an orthonormal set and the eigenvalues are real, $\lambda_j = \lambda_j^*$.

We can show further that the normal modes form a basis for the completely reduced representation.

$$Q_1 \xrightarrow{R} Q_1' \qquad \text{for } R \in G$$
$$Q_2 \xrightarrow{R} Q_2'$$

Then we want to show that the matrices corresponding to R are in block-diagonal form:

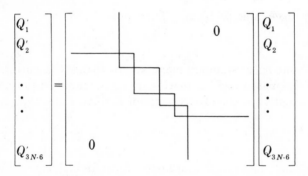

Consider two nondegenerate normal modes, Q_1 and Q_2.

$$Q_1 \xrightarrow{R} Q_1' = aQ_1 + bQ_2$$
$$Q_2 \xrightarrow{R} Q_2' = cQ_1 + dQ_2$$

Let us assume $c \neq 0$ and $b \neq 0$.

However, T and V must be invariant under all $R \in G$.

$$2T = \sum_i \dot{Q}_i{}^2 = \dot{Q}_1{}^2 + \dot{Q}_2{}^2$$

$$2V = \sum_i \lambda_i Q_i{}^2 = \lambda_1 Q_1{}^2 + \lambda_2 Q_2{}^2$$

Now, consider operation R.

$$2T \xrightarrow{R} \dot{Q}_1'^2 + \dot{Q}_1'^2 = a^2\dot{Q}_1^2 + 2ab\dot{Q}_1\dot{Q}_2 + b^2\dot{Q}_2^2$$
$$+ c^2\dot{Q}_1^2 + 2cd\dot{Q}_1\dot{Q}_2 + d^2\dot{Q}_2^2 = \dot{Q}_1^2 + \dot{Q}_2^2$$
$$2V \xrightarrow{R} \lambda_1 Q_1'^2 + \lambda_2 Q_2'^2 = \lambda_1(a^2Q_1^2 + 2abQ_2Q_1 + b^2Q_2^2)$$
$$+ \lambda_2(c^2Q_1^2 + 2cdQ_1Q_2 + d^2Q_2^2)$$
$$= \lambda_1 Q_1^2 + \lambda_2 Q_2^2$$

The coefficients a, b, c, d cannot depend upon the displacements. They depend only on R. Thus, the coefficients of the displacements and velocities must be the same after the application of R.

A term-by-term comparison produces the following equations:

$$a^2 + c^2 = 1 \qquad \lambda_1 a^2 + \lambda_2 c^2 = \lambda_1$$
$$b^2 + d^2 = 1 \qquad \lambda_1 b^2 + \lambda_2 d^2 = \lambda_2$$
$$2(ab + cd) = 0 \qquad \lambda_1 2ab + \lambda_2 2cd = 0$$

However, the eigenfrequencies do not depend on symmetry operations. Thus

$$c^2 = b^2 = 0 \qquad a^2 = d^2 = 1$$

Therefore

$$a = d = \pm 1 \quad \text{and} \quad b = c = 0$$

The matrix for the representation of R is then of the following form:

$$\begin{bmatrix} \pm 1 & 0 \\ 0 & \pm 1 \end{bmatrix}$$

That is, the matrix is totally reduced to one-dimensional irreducible representations in nondegenerate cases. In the cases where degeneracies occur the dimensions of the irreducible representations will be greater than 1. The maximum dimension will be equal to the order of the degeneracy.

7.2 SYMMETRY OF NORMAL MODES

In order to determine the symmetries of the normal modes of vibration, we consider a representation for the molecule in question. Using a basis system for the representation, the character system is determined and put into its totally reduced form by the standard reduction formula.

The most easily handled basis set for this case is a set of N cartesian coordinate systems, one cartesian system for each atom. Each cartesian coordinate system is centered on an atom, so that all the x_i axes are parallel. The dimension of this representation is $3N \times 3N$. Thus, we have taken 6 (5 for linear molecules) too many degrees of freedom corresponding to 3 translational degrees of freedom and 3 (2) rotational degrees of freedom.   However, the situation is easily corrected.   The symmetries of the extra degrees of freedom are indicated in character tables as (x, y, z) and (R_x, R_y, R_z).   Following the reduction process the irreducible representations corresponding to translation and rotation may be removed from the direct sum, allowing the direct sum to correspond to vibrational degrees of freedom alone.

The chemist is interested in relating observed vibrational frequencies determined from the infrared and Raman absorption spectrum to the stretching of bonds and the deformation of bond angles.   In order to make this connection another type of representation must be considered. The basis for this new representation includes vectors along bonds in the molecule and angles of various types including angles between bonds and dihedral angles.   The character system for such a representation is determined and the representation reduced in the standard manner.   When compared to the direct sum obtained from the representation based on the N cartesian coordinate systems, the representations based on the various types of internal coordinate displacements may be matched with those of corresponding symmetry.

Let us consider two specific examples, H_2O and BF_3.   We shall see how the methods of the previous section are put into practice.   We shall thus develop general methods for determining both the symmetry of normal modes and their spectral activity.

7.3 NORMAL MODE ANALYSIS: H_2O, POINT GROUP C_{2v}

It is easy to construct the four 9×9 $(3N \times 3N)$ matrices based on the N sets of cartesian coordinates for H_2O as shown in Fig. 7.1.

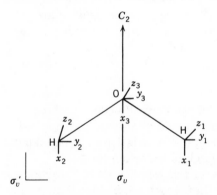

Fig. 7.1 The coordinate system for the water molecule showing the cartesian displacement coordinates for each atom. The three symmetry elements of point group C_{2v} are also shown.

For E

$$
\begin{bmatrix} x_1' \\ y_1' \\ z_1' \\ x_2' \\ y_2' \\ z_2' \\ x_3' \\ y_3' \\ z_3' \end{bmatrix}
=
\begin{bmatrix}
1 & 0 & 0 & 0 & 0 & 0 & 0 & 0 & 0 \\
0 & 1 & 0 & 0 & 0 & 0 & 0 & 0 & 0 \\
0 & 0 & 1 & 0 & 0 & 0 & 0 & 0 & 0 \\
0 & 0 & 0 & 1 & 0 & 0 & 0 & 0 & 0 \\
0 & 0 & 0 & 0 & 1 & 0 & 0 & 0 & 0 \\
0 & 0 & 0 & 0 & 0 & 1 & 0 & 0 & 0 \\
0 & 0 & 0 & 0 & 0 & 0 & 1 & 0 & 0 \\
0 & 0 & 0 & 0 & 0 & 0 & 0 & 1 & 0 \\
0 & 0 & 0 & 0 & 0 & 0 & 0 & 0 & 1
\end{bmatrix}
\begin{bmatrix} x_1 \\ y_1 \\ z_1 \\ x_2 \\ y_2 \\ z_2 \\ x_3 \\ y_3 \\ z_3 \end{bmatrix}
$$

$$\chi^{(E)} = 9$$

For C_2

$$
\begin{bmatrix} x_1' \\ y_1' \\ z_1' \\ x_2' \\ y_2' \\ z_2' \\ x_3' \\ y_3' \\ z_3' \end{bmatrix}
=
\begin{bmatrix}
0 & 0 & 0 & 1 & 0 & 0 & 0 & 0 & 0 \\
0 & 0 & 0 & 0 & -1 & 0 & 0 & 0 & 0 \\
0 & 0 & 0 & 0 & 0 & -1 & 0 & 0 & 0 \\
1 & 0 & 0 & 0 & 0 & 0 & 0 & 0 & 0 \\
0 & -1 & 0 & 0 & 0 & 0 & 0 & 0 & 0 \\
0 & 0 & -1 & 0 & 0 & 0 & 0 & 0 & 0 \\
0 & 0 & 0 & 0 & 0 & 0 & 1 & 0 & 0 \\
0 & 0 & 0 & 0 & 0 & 0 & 0 & -1 & 0 \\
0 & 0 & 0 & 0 & 0 & 0 & 0 & 0 & -1
\end{bmatrix}
\begin{bmatrix} x_1 \\ y_1 \\ z_1 \\ x_2 \\ y_2 \\ z_2 \\ x_3 \\ y_3 \\ z_3 \end{bmatrix}
$$

$$\chi^{(C_2)} = -1$$

For σ_v

$$
\begin{bmatrix} x_1' \\ y_1' \\ z_1' \\ x_2' \\ y_2' \\ z_2' \\ x_3' \\ y_3' \\ z_3' \end{bmatrix}
=
\begin{bmatrix}
0 & 0 & 0 & 1 & 0 & 0 & 0 & 0 & 0 \\
0 & 0 & 0 & 0 & -1 & 0 & 0 & 0 & 0 \\
0 & 0 & 0 & 0 & 0 & 1 & 0 & 0 & 0 \\
1 & 0 & 0 & 0 & 0 & 0 & 0 & 0 & 0 \\
0 & -1 & 0 & 0 & 0 & 0 & 0 & 0 & 0 \\
0 & 0 & 1 & 0 & 0 & 0 & 0 & 0 & 0 \\
0 & 0 & 0 & 0 & 0 & 0 & 1 & 0 & 0 \\
0 & 0 & 0 & 0 & 0 & 0 & 0 & -1 & 0 \\
0 & 0 & 0 & 0 & 0 & 0 & 0 & 0 & 1
\end{bmatrix}
\begin{bmatrix} x_1 \\ y_1 \\ z_1 \\ x_2 \\ y_2 \\ z_2 \\ x_3 \\ y_3 \\ z_3 \end{bmatrix}
$$

$$\chi^{(\sigma_v)} = +1$$

For σ_v'

$$
\begin{bmatrix} x_1' \\ y_1' \\ z_1' \\ x_2' \\ y_2' \\ z_2' \\ x_3' \\ y_3' \\ z_3' \end{bmatrix} =
\begin{bmatrix}
1 & 0 & 0 & 0 & 0 & 0 & 0 & 0 & 0 \\
0 & 1 & 0 & 0 & 0 & 0 & 0 & 0 & 0 \\
0 & 0 & -1 & 0 & 0 & 0 & 0 & 0 & 0 \\
0 & 0 & 0 & 1 & 0 & 0 & 0 & 0 & 0 \\
0 & 0 & 0 & 0 & 1 & 0 & 0 & 0 & 0 \\
0 & 0 & 0 & 0 & 0 & -1 & 0 & 0 & 0 \\
0 & 0 & 0 & 0 & 0 & 0 & 1 & 0 & 0 \\
0 & 0 & 0 & 0 & 0 & 0 & 0 & 1 & 0 \\
0 & 0 & 0 & 0 & 0 & 0 & 0 & 0 & -1
\end{bmatrix}
\begin{bmatrix} x_1 \\ y_1 \\ z_1 \\ x_2 \\ y_2 \\ z_2 \\ x_3 \\ y_3 \\ z_3 \end{bmatrix}
$$

$\chi^{(\sigma_v')} = +3$

The character table for C_{2v} and for Γ_{cart} is given in Table 7.1. The direct sum for Γ_{cart} is obtained by using the standard reduction formula, Eq. (6.70), rewritten as

$$
m_\alpha = \frac{1}{g} \sum_{n=1}^{N_c} \chi^{(\mathfrak{e}_n)} h_n \chi_\alpha^{(\mathfrak{e}_n)}
$$

where g = order of group

N_c = number of classes in group

h_n = number of elements in nth class

$\chi^{(\mathfrak{e}_n)}$ = character of the nth class in reducible representation

$\chi_\alpha^{(\mathfrak{e}_n)}$ = character of the nth class in the αth irreducible representation

$m_{A_1} = \frac{1}{4}[9 \cdot 1 \cdot 1 + (-1) \cdot 1 \cdot 1 + 1 \cdot 1 \cdot 1 + 3 \cdot 1 \cdot 1] = 3$

$m_{A_2} = \frac{1}{4}[9 \cdot 1 \cdot 1 + (-1) \cdot 1 \cdot 1 + 1 \cdot 1 \cdot (-1) + 3 \cdot 1 \cdot (-1)] = 1$

$m_{B_1} = \frac{1}{4}[9 \cdot 1 \cdot 1 + (-1) \cdot 1 \cdot (-1) + 1 \cdot 1 \cdot 1 + 3 \cdot 1 \cdot (-1)] = 2$

$m_{B_2} = \frac{1}{4}[9 \cdot 1 \cdot 1 + (-1) \cdot 1 \cdot (-1)$
$\qquad\qquad\qquad + 1 \cdot 1 \cdot (-1) + 3 \cdot 1 \cdot 1] = 3$

Table 7.1 Character table for C_{2v}

C_{2v}	E	C_2	σ_v	σ_v'	
A_1	1	1	1	1	z
A_2	1	1	-1	-1	R_z
B_1	1	-1	1	-1	x, R_y
B_2	1	-1	-1	1	y, R_x
Γ_{cart}	9	-1	1	3	

So that

$$\Gamma_{\text{cart}} = 3A_1 + A_2 + 2B_1 + 3B_2$$

From the character table we can determine the symmetries of the "extra" translational and rotational degrees of freedom.

Translation		*Rotation*	
x	B_1	R_x	B_2
y	B_2	R_y	B_1
z	A_1	R_z	A_2

so that

$$\Gamma_{\text{rot, trans}} = A_1 + A_2 + 2B_1 + 2B_2$$

Therefore the direct sum for vibrational degrees of freedom is

$$\Gamma_{\text{vib}} = \Gamma_{\text{cart}} - \Gamma_{\text{rot, trans}} = 3A_1 + A_2 + 2B_1 + 3B_2$$
$$- (A_1 + A_2 + 2B_1 + 2B_2)$$
$$= 2A_1 + B_2$$

In order to identify the symmetries of the normal modes (as determined above) with the internal displacement coordinates, consider the various bond stretches and angle bends for H_2O as follows: (1) take as two internal coordinates the vectors from the oxygen atom along the O—H bonds and call them r_1 and r_2; (2) take the remaining vibrational degree of freedom as the H—O—H angle. These internal coordinates are shown in Fig. 7.2.

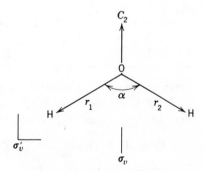

Fig. 7.2 Internal coordinates for the water molecule showing the two bond-stretch vectors r_i and H—O—H angle deformation coordinate α.

$$\Gamma^{(E)}: \quad \begin{bmatrix} r_1' \\ r_2' \\ \alpha' \end{bmatrix} = \begin{bmatrix} 1 & 0 & 0 \\ 0 & 1 & 0 \\ \hline 0 & 0 & 1 \end{bmatrix} \begin{bmatrix} r_1 \\ r_2 \\ \alpha \end{bmatrix}$$

$$\Gamma^{(C_2)}: \quad \begin{bmatrix} r_1' \\ r_2' \\ \alpha' \end{bmatrix} = \begin{bmatrix} 0 & 1 & 0 \\ 1 & 0 & 0 \\ \hline 0 & 0 & 1 \end{bmatrix} \begin{bmatrix} r_1 \\ r_2 \\ \alpha \end{bmatrix}$$

$$\Gamma^{(\sigma_v)}: \quad \begin{bmatrix} r_1' \\ r_2' \\ \alpha' \end{bmatrix} = \begin{bmatrix} 0 & 1 & 0 \\ 1 & 0 & 0 \\ \hline 0 & 0 & 1 \end{bmatrix} \begin{bmatrix} r_1 \\ r_2 \\ \alpha \end{bmatrix}$$

$$\Gamma^{(\sigma_v')}: \quad \begin{bmatrix} r_1' \\ r_2' \\ \alpha' \end{bmatrix} = \begin{bmatrix} 1 & 0 & 0 \\ 0 & 1 & 0 \\ \hline 0 & 0 & 1 \end{bmatrix} \begin{bmatrix} r_1 \\ r_2 \\ \alpha \end{bmatrix}$$

The character system for this representation is

C_{2v}	E	C_2	σ_v	σ_v'
Γ_{int}	3	1	1	3

However, we note that no symmetry operation in the group interchanges the $\mathbf{r}$ vectors with the angle α. Thus, the two vectors $\mathbf{r}_1$ and $\mathbf{r}_2$ form an independent basis for a 2×2 representation, and the angle α forms a basis for a 1×1 representation. The character systems for these two independent representations can be determined from the above matrices by observing the partitioning of the matrices (indicated by dashed lines):

C_{2v}	E	C_2	σ_v	σ_v'
Γ_r	2	0	0	2
Γ_α	1	1	1	1

Either by use of the standard reduction formula or by direct comparison with the character table for C_{2v} the direct sum for these representations may be determined as follows:

$$\Gamma_r = A_1 + B_2 \quad \text{and} \quad \Gamma_\alpha = A_1$$

The normal modes of vibration for H_2O, Cl_2O, and SO_2 have been worked out in detail by Herzberg. Diagrams of the modes are shown in Fig. 7.3. It can be seen that ν_3 corresponds to the only "pure" mode, i.e., a vibrational mode in which only bonds are stretched (in an anti-symmetric manner). It can also be observed that ν_1 and ν_2 are mixed modes, containing both bond-stretching and angle-deformation internal coordinates. However, in H_2O (as contrasted to SO_2, which also pos-

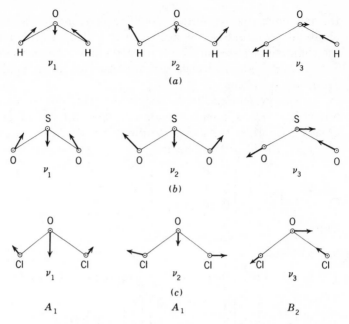

Fig. 7.3 Diagrams of the normal modes of vibration in (a) H_2O, (b) SO_2, and (c) Cl_2O. (*Taken by permission from G. Herzberg, "Infrared and Raman Spectra," p. 171, D. Van Nostrand Company, Inc., Princeton, N.J., 1959.*)

sesses C_{2v} symmetry) the ν_1 mode is mainly O—H bond stretching because of the relative masses of oxygen and hydrogen. In SO_2 the ν_1 mode is clearly of mixed character.

In Cl_2O, on the other hand, ν_1 and ν_2 are mainly of the angle-deformation type, and ν_3 is purely of the bond-stretch type because of symmetry. Thus, interpretation of spectral frequencies must be made with care. Each molecular species must be considered individually.

Thus, the three pure vibrational modes for H_2O consist of one mode, B_2, which is purely a stretching of the O—H bonds and two other modes of A_1 symmetry which are a combination of O—H bond stretch and H—O—H angle deformation.

7.4 GENERAL PROCEDURE IN NORMAL MODE ANALYSIS: BF_3, POINT GROUP D_{3h}

Figure 7.4 shows the coordinate system for the displacement coordinates BF_3. Before we construct the character system for Γ_{cart} for BF_3 let us consider the corresponding matrices for H_2O. We note that not all atom coordinates yield a nonzero contribution to the character. In fact, when considering the dashed lines in the H_2O matrices, it is observed that the only nonzero contributions to $\chi^{(R)}$ correspond to coordinates centered on atoms unshifted by the operation R. Thus, in the determination of the character system for N sets of cartesian coordinate systems, we need only consider atoms which remain unshifted upon application of the symmetry operation.

Let us systematically determine the contribution *per unshifted atom* for each of the symmetry operations encountered in molecular point groups. Consider the x, y, z coordinates centered on an unshifted atom:

1. E, the identity operation

$$\mathbf{v}' = \begin{bmatrix} x' \\ y' \\ z' \end{bmatrix} = \begin{bmatrix} 1 & 0 & 0 \\ 0 & 1 & 0 \\ 0 & 0 & 1 \end{bmatrix} \begin{bmatrix} x \\ y \\ z \end{bmatrix} = \Gamma^{(E)}\mathbf{v}$$

Thus,

$$\chi^{(E)} = 3$$

2. σ, the reflection across a mirror plane. (a) σ_{zz} (see Fig. 7.5a).

$$\mathbf{v}' = \begin{bmatrix} x' \\ y' \\ z' \end{bmatrix} = \begin{bmatrix} 1 & 0 & 0 \\ 0 & -1 & 0 \\ 0 & 0 & 1 \end{bmatrix} \begin{bmatrix} x \\ y \\ z \end{bmatrix} = \Gamma^{(\sigma_{zz})}\mathbf{v}$$

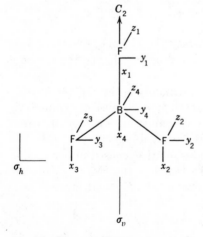

Fig. 7.4 The coordinate system used to describe the cartesian displacement coordinates in boron trifluoride. Some of the symmetry elements of the point group D_{3h} are shown. The threefold proper and improper axes are perpendicular to the plane of the paper through the boron atom.

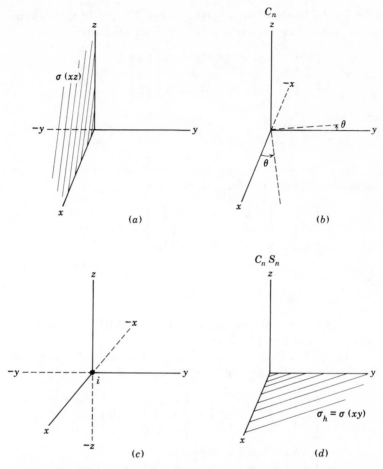

Fig. 7.5 Coordinate systems used to describe the orientation of various symmetry elements. (*a*) A mirror plane in the *xz* plane; (*b*) an *n*-fold rotation axis along the *z* direction; (*c*) a center of inversion at the origin; (*d*) an improper rotation axis along the *z* direction.

(*b*) σ_{xy} (see Fig. 7.5*d*).

$$\mathbf{v}' = \begin{bmatrix} x' \\ y' \\ z' \end{bmatrix} = \begin{bmatrix} 1 & 0 & 0 \\ 0 & 1 & 0 \\ 0 & 0 & -1 \end{bmatrix} \begin{bmatrix} x \\ y \\ z \end{bmatrix} = \Gamma^{(\sigma_{xy})}\mathbf{v}$$

In both cases

$$\chi^{(\sigma)} = +1$$

3. $C_n{}^k$, the rotation of $k2\pi/n$ about an *n*-fold axis.

Let C_n lie along the z axis, (see Fig. 7.5b). In this case use is made of the three-dimensional rotation matrix introduced earlier.

$$\mathbf{v}' = \begin{bmatrix} x' \\ y' \\ z' \end{bmatrix} = \begin{bmatrix} \cos\theta & -\sin\theta & 0 \\ \sin\theta & \cos\theta & 0 \\ 0 & 0 & 1 \end{bmatrix} \begin{bmatrix} x \\ y \\ z \end{bmatrix} = \Gamma^{(C_n{}^k)}\mathbf{v}$$

So that

$$\chi(C_n{}^k) = 1 + 2\cos\theta$$

4. i, the inversion-through-a-center operation; the atom must be located on the center of inversion (see Fig. 7.5c).

$$\mathbf{v}' = \begin{bmatrix} x' \\ y' \\ z' \end{bmatrix} = \begin{bmatrix} -1 & 0 & 0 \\ 0 & -1 & 0 \\ 0 & 0 & -1 \end{bmatrix} \begin{bmatrix} x \\ y \\ z \end{bmatrix} = \Gamma^{(i)}\mathbf{v}$$

Thus,

$$\chi(i) = -3$$

5. $S_n{}^k$, the improper rotation: rotation of $k2\pi/n$ about C_n followed by reflection in σ_h (see Fig. 7.5d).

Let C_n lie along z; σ_h is, then, σ_{xy}. The matrix for this operation can be obtained as the product of $\Gamma^{(\sigma_{xy})}$ and $\Gamma^{(C_n{}^k)}$.

$$\mathbf{v}' = \begin{bmatrix} x' \\ y' \\ z' \end{bmatrix} = \Gamma^{(\sigma_{xy})}\Gamma^{(C_n{}^k)}\mathbf{v} = \begin{bmatrix} 1 & 0 & 0 \\ 0 & 1 & 0 \\ 0 & 0 & -1 \end{bmatrix} \begin{bmatrix} \cos\theta & -\sin\theta & 0 \\ \sin\theta & \cos & 0 \\ 0 & 0 & 1 \end{bmatrix} \mathbf{v}$$

$$= \begin{bmatrix} \cos\theta & -\sin\theta & 0 \\ \sin\theta & \cos\theta & 0 \\ 0 & 0 & -1 \end{bmatrix} \begin{bmatrix} x \\ y \\ z \end{bmatrix} = \Gamma^{(S_n{}^k)}\mathbf{v}$$

Thus,

$$\chi(S_n{}^k) = -1 + 2\cos\theta$$

By making use of these formulas and making reference to Table 7.2, Table 7.3 can be constructed for the N ($= 4$) cartesian coordinate systems in BF$_3$. This representation is reduced with the standard reduction formula. The direct sum is found to be

$$\Gamma_{\text{cart}} = A_1' + A_2' + 3E' + 2A_2'' + E''$$

From the character table given in Table 7.4 the symmetries of the translations and rotations can be obtained.

Table 7.2 Contribution to the character system for N sets of cartesian systems

R	$\chi^{(R)}$ (per unshifted atom)
E	$+3$
σ	$+1$
C_n^k	$1 + 2\cos\dfrac{2\pi k}{n}$
i	-3
S_n^k	$-1 + 2\cos\dfrac{2\pi k}{n}$

Table 7.3 Character system for BF$_3$

R	Number of unshifted atoms	$\chi^{(R)}$
E	4	12
$2C_3$	1	0
$3C_2$	2	-2
σ_h	4	4
$2S_3$	1	-2
$3\sigma_v$	2	2

Table 7.4 Character table for D_{3h}

D_{3h}	E	$2C_3$	$3C_2$	σ_h	$2S_3$	$3\sigma_v$		
A_1'	1	1	1	1	1	1		$x^2+y^2,\ z^2$
A_2'	1	1	-1	1	1	-1	R_z	
E'	2	-1	0	2	-1	0	(x,y)	$x^2-y^2,\ xy$
A_1''	1	1	1	-1	-1	-1		
A_2''	1	1	-1	-1	-1	1	z	
E''	2	-1	0	-2	1	0	(R_x, R_y)	(xz, yz)

$$Translation \qquad\qquad Rotation$$

$$\left.\begin{array}{c} x \\ y \end{array}\right\} E' \qquad\qquad \left.\begin{array}{c} R_x \\ R_y \end{array}\right\} E''$$

$$z \quad A_2'' \qquad\qquad\quad R_z \quad A_2'$$

Thus

$$\Gamma_{\text{rot, trans}} = E' + A_2'' + E'' + A_2'$$

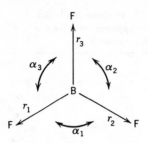

Fig. 7.6 Internal coordinates for B—F bond stretching and F—B—F in-the-plane bond-angle deformations.

Thus,

$$\Gamma_{\text{vib}} = \Gamma_{\text{cart}} - \Gamma_{\text{rot, trans}}$$
$$= (A_1' + A_2' + 3E' + 2A_2'' + E'') - (E' + A_2'' + E'' + A_2')$$
$$= A_1' + 2E' + A_2''$$

The total of the degrees of freedom is 6, which is equal to $3N - 6$: $3 \cdot 4 - 6 = 6$.

The normal modes of vibration for BF_3 and for CO_3^{--} (both of D_{3h} symmetry) are shown in Fig. 7.7.

In order to relate such internal coordinates as bond-stretch vectors and bond angles to the symmetries of the normal modes (as determined for D_{3h} above) we must construct the character system for the appropriate basis vectors and angles. Since it is clear that no symmetry operation in the point group (or in any point group) can interchange bond-stretch vectors and bond angles, any set of bond-stretch vectors may be used as an independent basis set. Let us first consider such a set of bond-stretch vectors for BF_3, as shown in Fig. 7.6. The character system is easily determined for this basis set (compare hybrid orbitals for sigma bonds for BF_3). Only vectors which are unshifted by a symmetry operation make a contribution to the character of the matrix which represents that operation. The contribution of an unshifted vector is $+1$. Thus, the character system for Γ_r is

D_{3h}	E	$2C_3$	$3C_2$	σ_h	$2S_3$	$3\sigma_v$
Γ_r	3	0	1	3	0	1

This representation is easily reduced to the direct sum

$$\Gamma_r = A_1' + E'$$

Thus, bond stretches contribute to both the A_1' and E' normal modes.

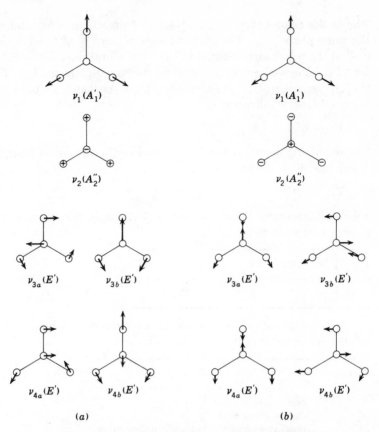

Fig. 7.7 Diagrams depicting the normal modes of vibration in (a) the CO_3^{--} ion and (b) BF_3. (*Taken by permission from G. Herzberg, "Infrared and Raman Spectra," p. 179, D. Van Nostrand Company, Inc., Princeton, N.J., 1959.*)

Next let us consider the three F—B—F bond angles, α_1, α_2, α_3. Again the character system for this representation is easily obtained.

D_{3h}	E	$2C_3$	$3C_2$	σ_h	$2S_3$	$3\sigma_v$
Γ_α	3	0	1	3	0	1

It is seen to be identical to the system for Γ_r. Thus, the direct sum for Γ_α is

$$\Gamma_\alpha = A_1' + E'$$

However, for two reasons we must consider this result carefully: (1) an A_1' mode is not physically possible for the three angles α_1, α_2, α_3.

The angles cannot increase in a totally symmetric manner and remain in the same plane. (2) The total number of degrees of freedom contained in $\Gamma_r + \Gamma_\alpha$ is 6, which is equal to the total vibrational degrees of freedom for BF_3. Yet we have not considered the out-of-plane mode. Therefore, the A_1' representation contained in Γ_α is considered spurious and is removed from its direct sum

$$\Gamma_\alpha = E'$$

The remaining degree of freedom must describe the out-of-plane mode ν_2, which has A_2'' symmetry.

$$\Gamma_{oop} = A_2''$$

By consideration of the symmetry of ν_2 it can be seen that its character system corresponds to A_2''

D_{3h}	E	$2C_3$	$3C_2$	σ_h	$2S_3$	$3\sigma_v$
Γ_{oop}	1	1	-1	-1	-1	1

The relationship between the normal modes and the internal bond-related coordinates is shown to be as follows:

Symmetry	Internal coordinate type
A_1	Bond stretch alone
A_2''	Out-of-plane mode
$2E'$	Bond stretch plus bond-angle deformation

7.5 NORMAL MODES AS CARTESIAN COMPONENTS

In the previous section we presented a method for determining the symmetries of the normal modes, and we discussed the relation of these normal modes to various internal coordinates. Let us now consider the mathematical form of normal modes. The definition of a *normal mode* states that the normal mode is a linear combination of the displacements of all the atoms such that as the molecule executes the normal vibration, the relative magnitudes and directions of the displacements remain fixed but their absolute magnitudes vary periodically with time.

As a specific example consider the normal modes of the BF_3 molecule as determined previously. First, let us consider ν_1, which is totally symmetric, having A_1 symmetry. We can immediately write down ν_1 in terms of the internal coordinates r_1, r_2, and r_3.

$$Q_1' = r_1 + r_2 + r_3$$

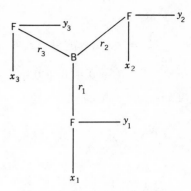

Fig. 7.8 The coordinate system for BF_3 used for the resolution of the bond-stretch vectors $\mathbf{r}_i$ into the cartesian displacement vectors.

To obtain this mode in terms of cartesian coordinates we need only refer to Fig. 7.8 and resolve each $\mathbf{r}_i$ into its cartesian components.

$$r_1 = x_1$$

$$r_2 = -\frac{\sqrt{3}}{2} x_2 + \tfrac{1}{2} y_2$$

$$r_3 = -\tfrac{1}{2} x_3 - \frac{\sqrt{3}}{2} y_3$$

Thus

$$Q_1' = -\frac{\sqrt{3}}{2} (x_2 + y_3) + \tfrac{1}{2}(y_2 - x_3) + x_1$$

In a similar manner we can write Q_2 as a function of cartesian displacement coordinates, being careful to weight the displacements so that no net translation of the molecule occurs during the vibration. The boron atom must move three times as far as each fluorine atom and be weighted according to the relative atomic weights:

$$Q_2' = 11(z_1 + z_2 + z_3) - (3 \cdot 19)z_4$$

By inspection it is seen that this normal mode is a basis for the A_2'' representation in D_{3h}.

Just as we consider the set of cartesian axes to be an orthonormal set of basis vectors, we can make the normal coordinates orthonormal as follows:

$$Q_j Q_k = \delta_{jk} \qquad Q_j = N Q_j'$$
$$Q_1 Q_1 = 1 = N^2 (r_1 + r_2 + r_3)(r_1 + r_2 + r_3)$$

so that

$$\frac{1}{N^2} = r_1r_1 + r_1r_2 + r_1r_3 + r_2r_1 + r_2r_2 + r_2r_3 + r_3r_1 + r_3r_2 + r_3r_3$$

$$= 1 + 0 + 0 + 0 + 1 + 0 + 0 + 0 + 1 \qquad \mathbf{r}_j \cdot \mathbf{r}_k = 0$$

Thus,

$$N = \frac{1}{\sqrt{3}}$$

and

$$Q_1 = \frac{1}{\sqrt{3}} (r_1 + r_2 + r_3)$$

and similarly for

$$Q_2 = N(z_1 + z_2 + z_3 - \tfrac{5\,7}{1\,1}z_4)$$

$$\frac{1}{N^2} = z_1z_1 + 2z_1z_2 + 2z_1z_3 - 2(\tfrac{5\,7}{1\,1})z_1z_4 \cdots$$

$$\frac{1}{N^2} = 1 + 1 + 1 + (\tfrac{5\,7}{1\,1})^2 = (\tfrac{9\,0}{1\,1})^2$$

or

$$Q_2 = \tfrac{1\,1}{9\,0}[(z_1 + z_2 + z_3) - \tfrac{5\,7}{1\,1}z_4]$$

7.6 SELECTION RULES FOR MOLECULAR VIBRATIONAL SPECTRA: THE QUANTUM-MECHANICAL PROBLEM

Thus far we have implicitly treated the molecule as a collection of masses and springs, i.e., in the classical mechanical sense. In order to determine selection rules we must learn something of the wave functions for the vibrational modes. Since the potential function involved in molecular vibrations is not known, we must use an approximation. Thus, we consider each bond to be represented by a spring which obeys Hooke's law. We shall find that through this approximation we are able to account for the gross features of molecular vibrations.

Since we have chosen the potential of a harmonic oscillator,

$$V(x) = -\tfrac{1}{2}kx^2$$

we may write the Schrödinger equation as follows (treating the harmonic oscillator as a one-dimensional problem):

$$\left(\frac{-\hbar^2}{2m}\frac{d^2}{dx_i{}^2} + \frac{1}{2}kx_i{}^2\right)\psi_i(n) = E_i(n)\psi_i(n) \tag{7.25}$$

In this equation x_i refers to the ith normal mode and n to the nth eigenfrequency. The solution may be written

$$\psi_i(n) = N_i \exp\left(-\frac{\alpha_i}{2}Q_i^2\right) H_n\left(\sqrt{\alpha_i}\, Q_i\right) \tag{7.26}$$

where N_i = normalization constant
$\alpha_i = (2\pi\nu/h)i$
ν_i = frequency of ith normal mode
n = quantum number (zero for the ground state)
$H_n(x)$ = Hermite polynomials
Some of the Hermite polynomials are

$$H_0(x) = 1$$
$$H_1(x) = 2x$$
$$H_2(x) = 4x^2 - 2$$
$$H_3(x) = 8x^3 - 12x$$

We have shown earlier that normal coordinates form bases for the irreducible representations of point groups. Also, we have shown that wave functions form bases for irreducible representations. Let us now determine the irreducible representation for which the ground-state vibrational wave function forms a basis. We can write the ground-state function as

$$\psi_i(0) = N_i \exp\left(-\frac{\alpha_i}{2}Q_i^2\right)$$

For a nondegenerate mode all operations in the group change Q_i into $\pm Q_i$ and thus Q_i^2 is unchanged. For degenerate cases the symmetry operations change Q_i into $\pm Q_i$ or into linear combinations

$$RQ_a = Q_a' = r_a Q_a + r_b Q_b$$

However, if Q_a is normalized, r_a and r_b must be such that Q_a' is also normalized

$$Q_a^2 = 1 \quad \text{and} \quad Q_a'^2 = 1$$

Thus, $\psi_i(0)$ is invariant under all symmetry operations and forms a basis for the totally symmetric irreducible representation of the point group to which the molecule belongs.

The excited-state wave functions are seen to be a product of the same exponential as the ground-state function (which is totally symmetric) and the nth Hermite polynomial. Therefore, $\psi_i(n)$ has the symmetry of the nth Hermite polynomial. By examining the list of Hermite polynomials it can be seen that $\psi_i(1)$ has the symmetry of Q_i; $\psi_i(2)$ has the symmetry of Q_i^2, which means it is totally symmetric, and so on.

We must now consider the quantum-mechanical expression for the calculation of the transition probability; i.e., since the spectral intensity I is proportional to the coefficient of absorption $B_{nn'}$, selection rules can be obtained from a consideration of possible nonzero values of $B_{nn'}$. The coefficient of absorption is given as

$$B_{nn'} = \frac{8\pi^3}{3h^2} [|(\mu_x)_{nn'}|^2 + |(\mu_y)_{nn'}|^2 + |(\mu_z)_{nn'}|^2] \tag{7.27}$$

In this equation n and n' refer to the quantum numbers of the ground state and the excited state to which the transition is made; (μ_x) is the expectation value of the x component of the electric dipole moment, as given by

$$(\mu_x)_{nn'} = \int \psi_n^* \mu_x \psi_n \, d\tau \tag{7.28}$$

In order to consider this quantity we must find expressions for the total wave function ψ_n and for μ_x, the x component of the dipole moment. We write the total wave function as a product function as in Eq. (7.1).

$$\psi_n = \psi_{\text{elec}} \psi_{\text{vib}} \psi_{\text{rot}} \psi_{\text{trans}}$$

Further, we shall assume for the present case that there is no interaction between the vibrational states and both the electronic and translational wave functions. We assume a similar separability of rotational and vibrational wave functions even though such an approximation must be considered as only a first approximation. Therefore

$$(\mu_x)_{nn'} = \int \psi_{\text{elec}}^*(n) \psi_{\text{vib}}^*(n) \psi_{\text{rot}}^*(n) \psi_{\text{trans}}^*(n) \mu_x \psi_{\text{elec}}(n')$$
$$\psi_{\text{vib}}(n') \psi_{\text{rot}}(n') \psi_{\text{trans}}(n') \, d\tau \tag{7.29}$$

(We can reduce this equation to simpler form because we are assuming no coupling of electronic and rotational motion to vibrational motions.) In addition the other functions form orthonormal sets. *The only restriction arising here is that during a vibrational transition no other transition may occur;* that is, $n = n'$ for electronic, rotational, and translational states. Then

$$(\mu_x)_{nn'} = \int \psi_{\text{vib}}^*(n) \mu_x \psi_{\text{vib}}(n') \, d\tau \tag{7.30}$$

We must now write $\psi_{\text{vib}}(n)$ as a product function taking all the modes into account:

$$\psi_{\text{vib}}(n) = \psi_1(n_1) \psi_2(n_2) \psi_3(n_3) \cdots \psi_k(n_k) \qquad k = 3N - 6 \tag{7.31}$$

When all $n_i = 0$, $\psi_{\text{vib}}(0)$ is in its ground state.

Now we must determine the expression for μ_x. The usual definition of the dipole moment is

$$\mu_x = \sum_j e_j x_j \tag{7.32}$$

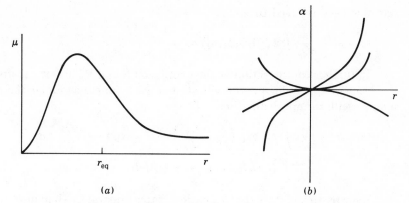

(a)   (b)

Fig. 7.9 (a) The qualitative functional dependence of a component of the electric dipole moment on a linear displacement of the atom(s) in a molecule. (b) Curves representing several types of functional dependence of the polarizability on atomic displacement. (*Taken by permission from G. Herzberg, "Infrared and Raman Spectra," pp. 241 and 242, D. Van Nostrand Company, Inc., Princeton, N.J., 1959.*)

where e_j is the charge on the jth election or nucleus, x_j is the x component of its position, and the sum is over all charged particles in the molecular system. However, the electric dipole moment varies during the execution of a normal vibration. Thus, we must assume a functional dependence of μ_x on x, as shown in Fig. 7.9a. We can expand μ_x in terms of the various normal coordinates Q_k as follows:

$$\mu_x = \mu_x{}^0 + \sum_k \frac{\partial \mu_x}{\partial Q_k} Q_k + \cdots + \text{higher terms} \qquad (7.33)$$

We can now write the expression $(\mu_x)_{nn'}$ as a sum of two integrals.

$$(\mu_x)_{nn'} = \mu_x{}^0 \int \psi_1^*(0)\psi_1(n_1') \, d\tau \int \psi_2^*(0)\psi_2(n_2') \, d\tau \cdots$$
$$\int \psi_k^*(0)\psi_k(n_k') \, d\tau \cdots$$
$$+ \sum_k \frac{\partial \mu_x}{\partial Q_k} \int \psi_1^*(0)\psi_1(n_1') \, d\tau \int \psi_2^*(0)\psi_2(n_2') \, d\tau \cdots$$
$$\int \psi_k^*(0)Q_k\psi_k(n_k') \, d\tau \cdots$$

Because of the orthogonality of the vibrational wave functions, the first term is zero unless all $n_i = 0$. Since we are discussing a transition to an excited state for which at least one $n_i' = 0$, the first term vanishes.

In considering the second term we see that all n_i' must be zero except n_k', so that the second term does not vanish. *This result means that only one vibrational transition may occur at a time.* The expression for $(\mu_x)_{nn'}$

has now been reduced to

$$(\mu_x)_{nn'} = \frac{\partial \mu_x}{\partial Q_k} \int \psi_k^*(0) Q_k \psi_k(n_k') \, d\tau \tag{7.34}$$

In further consideration of the expression for $(\mu_x)_{nn'}$ let us substitute the proper expressions for the vibrational wave functions under the harmonic-oscillator approximation. Then,

$$\begin{aligned}(\mu_x)_{nn'} &= \frac{\partial \mu_x}{\partial Q_k} \int H_n \exp\left(-\frac{\alpha_k Q_k^2}{2}\right) Q_k H_{n'} \exp\left(-\frac{\alpha_k Q_k^2}{2}\right) d\tau \\ &= \frac{\partial \mu_x}{\partial Q_k} \int H_n Q_k N_{n'} \exp\left(-\alpha_k Q_k^2\right) d\tau \end{aligned} \tag{7.35}$$

In order to facilitate the evaluation of this integral we shall now introduce the Hermite polynomial recursion relation:

$$H_{n+1} - 2\alpha_k Q_k H_n + 2n H_{n-1} = 0 \tag{7.36}$$

or

$$Q_k H_n = \frac{1}{2\alpha_k^{\frac{1}{2}}} H_{n+1} + \frac{n}{\alpha_k^{\frac{1}{2}}} H_{n-1}$$

Substituting into the above integral, we find

$$\begin{aligned}(\mu_x)_{nn'} &= \frac{1}{2\alpha_k^{\frac{1}{2}}} \int H_n H_{n'+1} \exp\left(-\alpha_k Q_k^2\right) d\tau \\ &\quad + \frac{n'}{\alpha_k^{\frac{1}{2}}} \int H_n H_{n'-1} \exp\left(-\alpha_k Q_k^2\right) d\tau \end{aligned} \tag{7.37}$$

Because of the orthogonality condition on the Hermite polynomials

$$\int H_n(x) H_{n'}(x) \exp\left(-x^2\right) dx = \delta_{nn'} \tag{7.38}$$

the expression for $(\mu_x)_{nn'}$ vanishes unless

$$n' = n + 1 \qquad \text{or} \qquad n = n' + 1$$

Thus, in transitions involving absorption of infrared radiation only one quantum transition is allowed under the harmonic-oscillator approximation. This selection rule is usually expressed as

$$\Delta n = \pm 1 \tag{7.39}$$

In this form the so-called *rigorous selection rule* is obvious. The dipole moment must change during the normal vibration so that $(\mu_x)_{nn'}$ is nonzero. That is, $\partial \mu_x / \partial Q_k \neq 0$. Thus, it can be determined whether infrared radiation will be absorbed when a normal mode is excited simply by determining whether a component of the dipole moment changes during the vibration. Note that the molecule need not possess a permanent dipole moment for absorption of infrared radiation to occur; only a change in the dipole moment is necessary.

When one begins to look at the normal modes of complex molecules, one soon realizes that it is not a simple matter to determine whether the dipole moment does in fact change. However, we can bring symmetry arguments to bear on the problem at this point to determine whether the dipole moment changes during a normal vibration. We may write the above expression as follows based on Eq.(7.30).

$$(\mu_x)_{nn'} = \frac{\partial \mu_x}{\partial Q_k} \int \psi_k^*(0) Q_k \psi_k(n_k') \, d\tau \approx e \int \psi_k^*(0) x \psi_k(n_k') \, d\tau$$

We have previously shown that the quantum number may change by only one unit during a transition. Thus, $n_k' = 1$. Further, we have shown earlier that the symmetry of the vibrational wave function in the first excited state is the same as the symmetry of the normal mode Q_k, and the symmetry of the ground-state vibrational wave function is that of the totally symmetric representation A_1. Thus, we can represent the integral for $(\mu_x)_{nn'}$ as

$$(\mu_x)_{nn'} = e \int \psi_k^*(0) x \psi_k(1) \, d\tau = e \int \Gamma_{A_1} \Gamma_x \Gamma_{Q_k} \tag{7.40}$$

Since the product representation for the integrand must contain the totally symmetric species A_1 so as not to vanish, and since the product $x\Gamma_{Q_k}$ can belong to the representation A_1 only if Γ_{Q_k} belongs to the same representation as x, the normal coordinate Q_k must belong to an irreducible representation Γ_{Q_k} which has the symmetry of a translation, i.e., has the same transformation properties as a translation along x, y, or z.

Thus, we have obtained a simple rule for determining whether a normal vibration can appear in the infrared spectrum. The excited normal coordinate must have the same symmetry as one of the cartesian coordinates.

The rules for Raman spectra are determined in much the same way. It is found that Raman spectral absorption is dependent not on the dipole-moment operator but on the polarizability operator P, which contains binary and quadratic cartesian terms: x^2, y^2, z^2, xy, xz, yz, $x^2 - y^2$. Thus, in order for a Raman transition probability to be nonzero, the normal coordinate must belong to the same irreducible representation as one of the quadratic or binary cartesian terms.

Under the approximations we have made in our treatment of molecular vibrations, the following list of selection rules has been obtained:

1. Transitions between vibrational states are not accompanied by transitions between other states accessible to the molecule.
2. Only one normal mode may be excited at a time.
3. The change in the vibrational quantum number cannot be other than ± 1.
4. There must be a change (in at least one component) of the dipole

moment during the normal vibration in order for infrared radiation to be absorbed.

5. Rule 4 is equivalent to the statement that in order for a normal mode to absorb infrared radiation it must belong to the same irreducible representation as one of the cartesian coordinates x, y, z.

6. In order for a molecule to give rise to a Raman transition the polarizability must change during the normal vibration.

7. Rule 6 is equivalent to the statement that a Raman transition is possible for a normal vibration only if the normal vibration belongs to the same irreducible representation as one of the quadratic or binary cartesian coordinates, x^2, y^2, $x^2 - y^2$, z^2, xy, xz, yz.

A consequence of rules 5 and 7 is that in centrosymmetric molecules no infrared-active vibration can also be Raman active and vice versa. That this is true can be determined from the following consideration. Point groups containing the inversion operation i have two sets of irreducible representations, those with the subscript g and those with the subscript u. Consider the use of the cartesian coordinates as a basis set: once a cartesian coordinate is inverted by the center of symmetry, it becomes its negative. Thus, the x, y, z coordinates can form bases only for the u irreducible representations and not for the g representations. On the other hand, the quadratic terms such as xz and $x^2 + y^2$ must go into themselves when acted upon by a center because each coordinate goes into its negative and the product of two negatives is positive. Thus, the quadratic terms may be used as bases for the g set of irreducible representations and not for the u set.

Therefore, in a centrosymmetric point group it is not possible to have both x and $x^2 + y^2$ form a basis for the same irreducible representation. Thus, a normal coordinate cannot transform both as x and $x^2 + y^2$ and thus cannot be both infrared and Raman active.

Some further comments on the above selection rules are in order. As a result of the various approximations used in the derivation of these rules, most of them are not rigorously held.

Because we considered the various energy states of a molecule as being completely separable we have artificially prohibited interaction between the vibrational states and other states such as electronic and rotational. It is observed that rotational transitions do occur simultaneously with vibrational transitions. It is the envelope of rotational spectral lines which gives vibrational bands their various characteristic shapes.

A consequence of writing the vibrational wave function as a product function is the so-called *fundamental rule*, rule 2. However, combination bands do occur; i.e., two normal vibrations may be excited simultaneously and give rise to a single band whose frequency is the sum of the frequencies

Table 7.5 Infrared frequencies for HCl

n	$\nu,\ cm^{-1}$	$\Delta\nu,\ cm^{-1}$
1	2885.9	2885.9
2	5668.1	2782.2
3	8347.0	2678.9
4	10,923.1	2576.1
5	13,396.6	2473.5

of the two excited vibrations. Rules for such bands often involve subtleties, and the novice should consult a detailed treatment of molecular vibrations.

Rule 3 results from the use of the simple-harmonic-oscillator approximation. Although the transitions for which $\Delta n = \pm 1$ are usually the strongest, overtones ($\Delta n = \pm 2,\ \pm 3,\ .\ .\ .$) of the fundamental may be observed. Consider the data for HCl given in Table 7.5. The intensity of the lines decreases rapidly with increasing n. The fact that the differences in frequencies also decrease is evidence confirming the anharmonicity of the bonding force.

7.7 OVERTONE AND COMBINATION BANDS

Separate attention to the selection rules for overtone and combination bands is merited at this point. We have shown that the restriction of bonding forces to those of the simple harmonic type has introduced certain artificial selection rules. Our chemical intuition, along with a large body of experimental facts, indicates that there are significant anharmonic contributions to bonding forces. Thus, certain of the restrictions artificially placed on transitions earlier in the text must now be relaxed if we are to be able to deal with real physical systems.

In order to discover the selection rules which may be applicable once we admit the possibility of the simultaneous excitation of two (or more) normal modes, let us reconsider Eq. (7.40) relating the wave functions to the Einstein coefficient $B_{nn'}$

$$I_{nn'} \sim B_{nn'} \sim (\mu_x)_{nn'} \sim \int \psi_k(0)(\mathrm{ex})\psi_{k'}(1)\ d\tau$$

By allowing more than one transition simultaneously we must then write the wave function for the excited state as a product of the functions for the excited modes. Hence, the equation for two modes excited by one quantum jump is

$$(\mu_x)_{nn'} \sim \int \psi_k(0)(\mathrm{ex})\psi_{k'}(1)\psi_{k''}(1)\ d\tau$$

(Because we have also relaxed the fundamental rule that $\Delta n = \pm 1$, the quantum numbers for the excited states need not necessarily be 1.) When wave functions are written as products, the corresponding energies may be written as a sum (to the first approximation)

$$\Delta E_{nn'} = \Delta E(0 \to k') + \Delta E(0 \to k'') \tag{7.41}$$

But

$$\Delta E = hc\bar{\nu}$$

thus

$$\bar{\nu}_{nn'} = \bar{\nu}_{k'} + \bar{\nu}_{k''} \tag{7.42}$$

The symmetry selection rule for combination bands is now apparent: the product representation $\Gamma_{Q_{k'}}\Gamma_{Q_{k''}}$ must transform as x, y, or z. Sometimes the product representation is reducible and hence must itself be expressed as a direct sum. This is the case when degenerate representations are involved. In the case of degeneracies the combination band will appear in the infrared spectrum if at least *one* of the irreducible representations appearing in the direct sum transforms like a cartesian component. The analogous rule holds for Raman selection rules in relation to polarizability components.

Consider some combination bands which appear in ethylene, C_2H_4. The mode corresponding to a torsion about the carbon-carbon double bond, ν_4 (A_u), is not active as a fundamental in either the infrared or Raman (see Fig. 7.15). However, the combination (or summation) band $\nu_4 + \nu_7$ transforms as B_{1g}: $A_u \times B_{1u} = B_{1g}$. Thus, by consulting the character table for point group D_{2h} it is determined that the combination band $\nu_4 + \nu_7$ is Raman allowed. Because of this effect it is possible to observe the frequency of a mode whose fundamental is forbidden to appear in either the infrared or Raman spectrum.

Combination bands are not restricted to the simple combination used in the preceding example. Some of the possible combinations observed in the ethylene spectrum are $\nu_6 + \nu_8$, $\nu_6 + \nu_8 + \nu_7$, $\nu_5 + 2\nu_6$, $\nu_2 + \nu_7 + \nu_8$, and $\nu_3 + \nu_5 + \nu_6$.

In principle, transitions from states other than the "vibrationless" ground state are possible. The intensity of spectral bands involving excited states as initial states in the transition usually will be weak when the spectrum is taken at room temperature because of the low population of such states (as expressed by the Boltzmann distribution). It is possible, then, to observe a difference band, i.e., the combination of an absorption and an emission. For example, in ethylene the following difference bands are observed: $\nu_4 - \nu_7$ and $\nu_3 - \nu_9$.

To obtain the proper perspective on the importance of combination bands in understanding the vibrational spectrum of a given molecule the reader should consult texts that specialize in molecular vibrations.

Since we have removed the artificial prohibition of transitions in which the vibrational quantum number changes by more than one unit, $\Delta n = \pm 1, \pm 2, \ldots$, let us examine the symmetry selection rules for the observation of the overtones of a fundamental. The approach to this problem is identical with that for combination bands.

We have shown that the excited-state wave functions possess a symmetry related to the normal coordinates, Eq. (7.27).

$$\psi_k(0) \to \text{const} \to \Gamma_{A_1}$$
$$\psi_k(1) \to f(Q_k) \to \Gamma_{Q_k}$$
$$\psi_k(2) \to f(Q_k^2) \to \Gamma_{Q_k} \cdot \Gamma_{Q_k}$$
$$\psi_k(3) \to f(Q_k^3) \to \Gamma_{Q_k} \cdot \Gamma_{Q_k} \cdot \Gamma_{Q_k}$$

These relations are valid only to the extend to which the harmonic approximation holds. However, it is possible to determine the transformation properties of the product representations for the overtone vibrational states and thus determine their spectral activity. Further, even when the harmonic approximation is a poor one, the theory can be improved by the introduction of anharmonic terms into the potential function. As this modification is made in the expression for the force field of the molecule, the vibrational wave functions are changed: their dependence on the normal coordinates is altered. However, often the symmetry of the altered wave functions can be determined along with their spectral activity. Since the problem becomes rapidly more complex at this point, the reader is urged to consult the more advanced and specialized treatises on molecular vibrations.

7.8 POLARIZATION OF RAMAN SPECTRA

Valuable information concerning the assignment of Raman bands to normal modes can be obtained from a study of the state of polarization of the scattered radiation. Hence, we shall now consider the Raman effect in somewhat more detail.

For our purposes here a combination of a quantum-mechanical and a classical treatment will be sufficient. In the Raman effect the molecular system is bombarded with monochromatic radiation. Induced dipoles are produced in the molecules as a result of the oscillation of the electric vector of the radiation and its interaction with the electrons of the molecules. The oscillating (induced) dipole radiates with frequency ν according to the classical equation for Raleigh scattering:

$$I = \frac{16\pi^4 \nu^4}{3c^3} \mu_0{}^2$$

In this expression μ_0 is the amplitude of the oscillating dipole as shown by

$$\mu = \mu_0 \cos 2\pi\nu t$$

Simultaneously transitions between vibrational states may occur with the observed radiation then possessing frequency $\nu \pm \nu_{\text{vib}}$.

If we make the x direction the direction of observation, the total radiation emitted per unit of solid angle is given as

$$I = \frac{2\pi^3\nu^4}{c^3} \left(\mu_{0y}{}^2 + \mu_{0z}{}^2\right)$$

The induced dipole $\mathbf{\mu}$ is proportional to the electric field vector $\mathcal{E}$.

$$\mathbf{\mu} = \alpha\mathcal{E}$$

If the molecule is isotropic, α is a scalar; if the molecule is anisotropic, however, the equation must be written in matrix form.

$$\mathbf{\mu} = \begin{bmatrix} \mu_x \\ \mu_y \\ \mu_z \end{bmatrix} = \begin{bmatrix} \alpha_{x^2} & \alpha_{xy} & \alpha_{xz} \\ \alpha_{xy} & \alpha_{y^2} & \alpha_{yz} \\ \alpha_{xz} & \alpha_{yz} & \alpha_{z^2} \end{bmatrix} \begin{bmatrix} \mathcal{E}_x \\ \mathcal{E}_y \\ \mathcal{E}_z \end{bmatrix} = \alpha\mathcal{E}$$

The α_{ij} are usually referred to as the *components of the polarizability tensor* because of their transformation properties.

We can now write the intensity of the scattered (Raman) radiation in terms of the polarizability-tensor components. Figure 7.10 shows the conventional coordinate system we shall adopt here. The radiation is incident along the y direction, and the scattered radiation may be observed

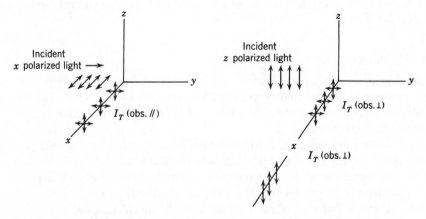

Fig. 7.10 Coordinate systems showing the relative orientations of the directions of incident polarized light to the polarized light observed at right angles to the directions of incidence. (*Taken by permission from E. B. Wilson, J. C. Decius, and P. C. Cross, "Molecular Vibrations." Copyright 1955. McGraw-Hill Book Company.*)

along the x direction. Consider two cases of polarization. In the first case, the light is polarized such that the electric vector lies parallel to the x direction, and the intensity of the scattered radiation will be designated $I_T(\text{obs } \|)$; when the polarization is in the z direction, the observed intensity will be designated $I_T(\text{obs } \perp)$.

We can therefore write expressions for these two intensities based on the definition of the polarizability α.

$$I_T(\text{obs } \|) = \frac{2\pi^3\nu^4}{c^3} (\alpha_{yx}^2 + \alpha_{zx}^2)\mathcal{E}_0^2$$

$$I_T(\text{obs } \perp) = \frac{2\pi^3\nu^4}{c^3} (\alpha_{yz}^2 + \alpha_{zz}^2)\mathcal{E}_0^2$$

Further, in the second case that part of the light which is polarized parallel to the electric vector ε is

$$I_\|(\text{obs } \perp) = \frac{2\pi^3\nu^4}{c^3} \alpha_{zz}^2\mathcal{E}_0^2$$

A more convenient form of these equations is obtained by converting from the magnitude of the electric vector to the intensity, using the classical expression

$$I_0 = \frac{c}{8\pi} \mathcal{E}_0^2$$

The new equations are

$$I_T(\text{obs } \|) = \frac{16\pi^4\nu^4}{c^4} I_0(\alpha_{yx}^2 + \alpha_{zx}^2)$$

$$I_T(\text{obs } \perp) = \frac{16\pi^4\nu^4}{c^4} I_0(\alpha_{yz}^2 + \alpha_{zz}^2)$$

$$I_\|(\text{obs } \perp) = \frac{16\pi^4\nu^4}{c^4} I_0\alpha_{zz}^2$$

Since in a gas or liquid all orientations of the molecule (and, hence, all orientations of the polarizability tensor) are present in the Raman sample, an average over all possible orientations must be performed. We shall omit the details of the averaging and give only the resulting equations.

$$I_T(\text{obs } \|) = \frac{16\pi^4\nu^4}{c^4} NI_0 \frac{2\beta^2}{15}$$

$$I_T(\text{obs } \perp) = \frac{16\pi^4\nu^4}{c^4} NI_0 \frac{45\alpha^2 + 7\beta^2}{45}$$

$$I_\|(\text{obs } \perp) = \frac{16\pi^4\nu^4}{c^4} NI_0 \frac{45\alpha^2 + 4\beta^2}{45}$$

The quantity α is called the *spherical* or *isotropic part* of the polarizability, and β is called the *anisotropy*.

$$\alpha = \tfrac{1}{3}(\alpha_{x^2} + \alpha_{y^2} + \alpha_{z^2})$$
$$\beta = \tfrac{1}{2}[(\alpha_{x^2} - \alpha_{y^2})^2 + (\alpha_{y^2} - \alpha_{z^2})^2 + (\alpha_{z^2} - \alpha_{x^2})^2]$$

The quantities usually measured experimentally are the following ratios. For plane-polarized incident radiation (linear) the ratio ρ_l is given as

$$\rho_l = \frac{I_T(\text{obs } \perp) - I_{\parallel}(\text{obs } \perp)}{I_{\parallel}(\text{obs } \perp)} = \frac{3\beta^2}{45\alpha^2 + 4\beta^2}$$

In the case of unpolarized (natural) radiation we can consider the scattered radiation as a sum of observations made both parallel and perpendicular to the electric vector of the incident beam. In that case, the part of the light from the parallel observation (being unpolarized) contributes one-half of its intensity, respectively, to the parallel and perpendicular components. Thus,

$$\rho_n = \frac{I_T(\text{obs } \perp) - I_{\parallel}(\text{obs } \perp) + \tfrac{1}{2}I_T(\text{obs } \parallel)}{I_{\parallel}(\text{obs } \perp) + \tfrac{1}{2}I_T(\text{obs } \parallel)}$$
$$= \frac{6\beta^2}{45\alpha^2 + 7\beta^2}$$

In order to determine the effect on measured intensities we must compute the quantum-mechanical expression of the dipole-moment operator as done for infrared radiation since it is proportional to the Raman intensity.

$$I_{nn'} \approx \mu_{nn'} = \int \psi_n^* \mu \psi_{n'} \, d\tau$$

In the evaluation of these integrals we encounter the expectation values for the components of the polarizability in analogy to those for the dipole-moment components.

$$(\alpha_{ii'})_{nn'} = \int \psi_n^* \alpha_{ii'} \psi_{n'} \, d\tau$$

In this evaluation we face two further considerations: (1) we must take into account the population of the various vibrational states involved (the Boltzmann distribution is used for this purpose); (2) the relation of the spatial orientations of the molecule to the magnetic properties of the electron distributions (as expressed by the magnetic quantum numbers M) must be considered. We shall not deal with these problems explicitly since they are not fundamental to an understanding of symmetry selection rules. These considerations are not unimportant, however, for they bear on the relative intensities of certain Raman lines.

We can now write the intensities and polarization ratios in terms of

the quantum-mechanical expectation values of the isotropic and anisotropic polarizability components.

$$I_T(\text{obs } \|) = NI_0 \tfrac{2}{15}\langle \beta^2 \rangle$$
$$I_T(\text{obs } \perp) = NI_0(\langle \alpha^2 \rangle + \tfrac{7}{45}\langle \beta^2 \rangle)$$
$$I_\|(\text{obs } \perp) = NI_0(\langle \alpha^2 \rangle + \tfrac{4}{45}\langle \beta^2 \rangle)$$

in which

$$\langle \alpha^2 \rangle = \tfrac{1}{3}(\langle \alpha_{x^2} \rangle + \langle \alpha_{y^2} \rangle + \langle \alpha_{z^2} \rangle)$$

and

$$\langle \beta^2 \rangle = \frac{1}{2} \sum_{\substack{i \quad j \\ i<j}} \sum ((\langle \alpha_i \rangle - \langle \alpha_j \rangle)^2$$

and

$$N = \frac{64\pi^4 \nu^4}{c^4}$$

$$\rho_l = \frac{3\langle \beta^2 \rangle}{45\langle \alpha^2 \rangle + 4\langle \beta^2 \rangle}$$

$$\rho_n = \frac{6\langle \beta^2 \rangle}{45\langle \alpha^2 \rangle + 7\langle \beta^2 \rangle}$$

So that the polarizability expectation values do not vanish, the first
excited-state wave function (which has the transformation property of
the normal mode) must belong to the irreducible representation to which
the polarizability component belongs.   This is the basis of the selection
rules introduced earlier for Raman spectra.

There is one further consequence.   Since the spherical part of the
polarizability transforms as $x^2 + y^2 + z^2$, it belongs to the totally symmetric irreducible representation of each point group.   Hence $\langle \alpha^2 \rangle$ is zero
unless the excited normal mode is totally symmetric.   Under this condi-
tion the polarization ratios become

$$\rho_l{}^{\max} = \tfrac{3}{4} \quad \text{and} \quad \rho_n{}^{\max} = \tfrac{6}{7}$$

regardless of the value of $\langle \beta^2 \rangle$.   Hence, if a Raman line has these polarization ratios, the corresponding excited normal mode must *not* belong to the
totally symmetry irreducible representation of the molecular point group.

Those Raman lines for which $0 < \rho_n < \tfrac{6}{7}$ are called *polarized lines*
and correspond to vibrations of the molecule which *are* totally symmetric.
Those Raman lines for which $\rho_n = \tfrac{6}{7}$ are called *depolarized lines* and correspond to vibrations which are *not* totally symmetric.

7.9 EXAMPLES OF NORMAL–MODE ANALYSIS

Example 1 XY_3 pyramidal molecules (NH_3, PH_3, ND_3), point group
C_{3v} ($3N - 6 = 6$).

Table 7.6   Character table for point group C_{3v}

C_{3v}	E	$2C_3$	$3\sigma_v$
A_1	1	1	1
A_2	1	1	-1
E	2	-1	0
Γ_{cart}	12	0	2

$$\Gamma_{\text{cart}} = 3A_1 + A_2 + 4E$$

The irreducible representations for translations and rotations are as follows:

Translation		*Rotation*	
$\left.\begin{array}{c}x\\y\end{array}\right\}$	E	$\left.\begin{array}{c}R_x\\R_y\end{array}\right\}$	E
z	A_1	R_z	A_2

Therefore

$$\begin{aligned}\Gamma_{\text{vib}} &= \Gamma_{\text{cart}} - (A_1 + A_2 + 2E)\\ &= 2A_1 + 2E\end{aligned}$$

The most obvious internal coordinates for use in describing the normal vibrations of XY_3 are three X—Y bond-stretch vectors **r** and three bond angles α_i. Each set of three forms an independent basis set.

C_{3v}	E	$2C_3$	$3\sigma_v$
Γ_r	3	0	1
Γ_α	3	0	1

The totally reduced representations for Γ_r and Γ_α are

$$\Gamma_r = A_1 + E$$
$$\Gamma_\alpha = A_1 + E$$

From the character table it can be determined that A_1 and E are both infrared and Raman active. However, the bands which may be observed are neither purely X—Y bond stretching or Y—X—Y angle deformation. From Fig. 7.11, which shows ND_3, it can be seen that the A_1 species is nearly a pure N—D stretching mode.

$\left.\begin{array}{c}A_1\\E\end{array}\right\}$ infrared and Raman active;
combination of bond stretch and bending modes

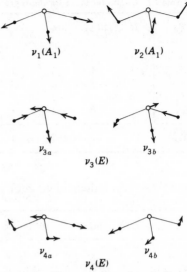

Fig. 7.11 The normal modes of vibration of ND_3. (*Taken by permission from G. Herzberg, "Infrared and Raman Spectra," p. 110, D. Van Nostrand Company, Inc., Princeton, N.J., 1959.*)

Example 2 XY_4 tetrahedral molecules (BH_4^-, CH_4, NH_4^+, MnO_4^-, SiH_4), point group T_d ($3N - 6 = 9$).

The direct sum obtained in the standard manner for the cartesian representation is

$$\Gamma_{cart} = A_1 + E + T_1 + 3T_2$$

The species belonging to translations and rotations are as follows:

Translation   *Rotation*

$$\left.\begin{array}{c} x \\ y \\ z \end{array}\right\} T_2 \qquad \left.\begin{array}{c} R_x \\ R_y \\ R_z \end{array}\right\} T_1$$

Thus, the direct sum for genuine vibrational degrees of freedom is

$$\Gamma_{vib} = \Gamma_{cart} - (T_1 + T_2)$$
$$= A_1 + E + 2T_2$$

In order to determine the contribution of the various internal coordinates to the normal modes, consider the set of four X—Y bond-stretch vectors $\mathbf{r}_i$ and the six Y—X—Y bond angles α_i. The character systems

Table 7.7   Character table for point group T_d

T_d	E	$8C_3$	$3C_2$	$6S_4$	$6\sigma_d$
A_1	1	1	1	1	1
A_2	1	1	1	-1	-1
E	2	-1	2	0	0
T_1	3	0	-1	1	-1
T_2	3	0	-1	-1	1
Γ_{cart}	15	0	-1	-1	3

for these two independent representations are

T_d	E	$8C_3$	$3C_2$	$6S_4$	$6\sigma_d$
Γ_{X-Y}	4	1	0	0	2
Γ_{Y-X-Y}	6	0	2	0	2

The totally reduced forms are found to be

$$\Gamma_{X-Y} = A_1 + T_2$$

and

$$\Gamma_{Y-X-Y} = A_1 + E + T_2$$

It is obvious that an extra A_1 species has appeared. However, it is clear that the six Y—X—Y angles cannot all increase as in an A_1 mode, and thus the A_1 species for Γ_{Y-X-Y} must be deleted. We are left with the nine allowed normal modes. By consulting the character table the following table concerning spectral activity may be found:

A_1	Only Raman active; pure X—Y bond-stretch mode
E	Only Raman active; pure bending mode
$2T_2$	Infrared and Raman active; angle-deformation and bond-stretching mode

Figure 7.12 shows the set of diagrams for the normal vibrations of the XY_4 tetrahedral molecule.

The normal modes for a Y_4 tetrahedral molecule with no central atom, e.g., the boron tetrahedron in B_4Cl_4, the carbon skeleton in the proposed tetrahedrane, C_4R_4, or elemental phosphorus, P_4, can be derived from the preceding considerations. For such a molecule the following representations are found.

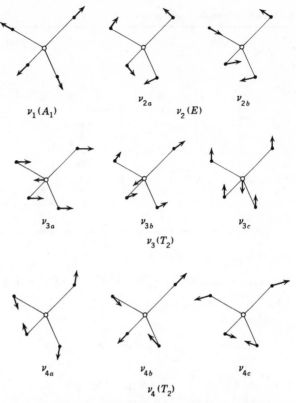

Fig. 7.12 The normal modes of vibration of methane. *(Taken by permission from G. Herzberg, "Infrared and Raman Spectra," p. 100, D. Van Nostrand Company, Inc., Princeton, N.J., 1959.)*

T_d	E	$8C_3$	$3C_2$	$6S_4$	$6\sigma_d$
Γ_{cart}	12	0	0	0	2

$$\Gamma_{\text{cart}} = A_1 + E + T_1 + 2T_2$$
$$\Gamma_{\text{vib}} = \Gamma_{\text{cart}} - (T_1 + T_2)$$
$$= A_1 + E + T_2$$

The normal mode which is lost is the triply degenerate mode ν_4, which involves motion of the central atom in the XY_4 tetrahedral molecule.

Example 3 XY_6 octahedral molecules (FeF_6^{3-}, $PtCl_6^{--}$, $Co\text{-}(H_2O)_6^{++}$, CoF_6^{3-}), point group O_h ($3N - 6 = 15$).

The direct sum for the totally reduced cartesian representation is

Table 7.8 Character table for point O_h

O_h	E	$8C_3$	$6C_2$	$6C_4$	$3C_2$	i	$6S_4$	$8S_6$	$3\sigma_h$	$6\sigma_d$
A_{1g}	1	1	1	1	1	1	1	1	1	1
A_{2g}	1	1	-1	-1	1	1	-1	1	1	-1
E_g	2	-1	0	0	2	2	0	-1	2	0
T_{1g}	3	0	-1	1	-1	3	1	0	-1	-1
T_{2g}	3	0	1	-1	-1	3	-1	0	-1	1
A_{1u}	1	1	1	1	1	-1	-1	-1	-1	-1
A_{2u}	1	1	-1	-1	1	-1	1	-1	-1	1
E_u	2	-1	0	0	2	-2	0	1	-2	0
T_{1u}	3	0	-1	1	-1	-3	-1	0	1	1
T_{2u}	3	0	1	-1	-1	-3	1	0	1	-1
Γ_{cart}	21	0	-1	3	-3	-3	-1	0	5	3

easily obtained as follows:

$$\Gamma_{\text{cart}} = A_{1g} + E_g + T_{1g} + T_{2g} + 3T_{1u} + T_{2u}$$

The irreducible representations which transform as the translations and rotations are

Translation		*Rotation*	
$\left.\begin{array}{l} x \\ y \\ z \end{array}\right\}$	T_{1u}	$\left.\begin{array}{l} R_x \\ R_y \\ R_z \end{array}\right\}$	T_{1g}

The direct sum for geniune vibrations is given as

$$\begin{aligned} \Gamma_{\text{vib}} &= \Gamma_{\text{cart}} - (T_{1u} + T_{1g}) \\ &= A_{1g} + E_g + T_{2g} + T_{2u} + 2T_{1u} \end{aligned}$$

The character systems based on the 6 X—Y bond-stretch vectors and the 12 possible Y—X—Y bond angles are given below.

O_h	E	$8C_3$	$6C_2$	$6C_4$	$3C_2$	i	$6S_4$	$8S_6$	$3\sigma_h$	$6\sigma_d$
$\Gamma_{\text{X—Y}}$	6	0	0	2	2	0	0	0	4	2
$\Gamma_{\text{Y—X—Y}}$	12	0	2	0	0	0	0	0	4	2

In reduced form these appear as

$$\begin{aligned} \Gamma_{\text{X—Y}} &= A_{1g} + E_g + T_{1u} \\ \Gamma_{\text{Y—X—Y}} &= A_{1g} + E_g + T_{2g} + T_{1u} + T_{2u} \end{aligned}$$

Since the total internal degrees of freedom used above, that is, 18, exceeds $3N - 6$ by 3, there are 3 spurious degrees of freedom contained in

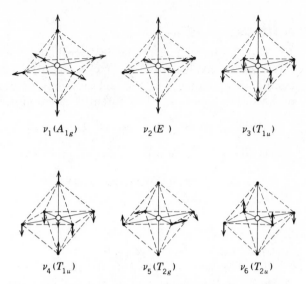

$$\nu_1(A_{1g}) \qquad \nu_2(E) \qquad \nu_3(T_{1u})$$

$$\nu_4(T_{1u}) \qquad \nu_5(T_{2g}) \qquad \nu_6(T_{2u})$$

Fig. 7.13 The normal modes of vibration of a molecule or ion with octahedral geometry corresponding to point group O_h. Only one of a group of degenerate vibrations is shown. (*Taken by permission from G. Herzberg, "Infrared and Raman Spectra," p. 122, D. Van Nostrand Company, Inc., Princeton, N.J., 1959.*)

$\Gamma_{X-Y} + \Gamma_{Y-X-Y}$. By previous experience we suspect that the extra degrees are contained in the angle representation. By comparison of Γ_{vib} with $\Gamma_{X-Y} + \Gamma_{Y-X-Y}$ we see that there are extra A_{1g} and E_g species in Γ_{Y-X-Y}. Thus, these are deleted

$$\Gamma_{X-Y} = A_{1g} + E_g + T_{1u}$$
$$\Gamma_{Y-X-Y} = T_{2g} + T_{1u} + T_{2u}$$

The character table shows that only T_{1u} is infrared active but E_g, A_{1g}, and T_{2g} are Raman active while T_{2u} is inactive. The following table is a summary of the normal-mode analysis by group theory for XY_6 octahedral molecules (see Fig. 7.13).

A_{1g}	Raman active; bond stretch only
E_g	Raman active; bond stretch only
T_{2g}	Raman active; angle deformation only
T_{1u}	Infrared active; bond stretch and angle bending
T_{2u}	Inactive; pure bending mode

Notice that the exclusion rule is operative in this problem because the molecule is centrosymmetric.

PROBLEMS

7.1. Use the formalism of classical mechanics developed in Sec. 7.1 to solve the eigenvalue problem of CO_2 for motion constrained along the bond axis. Assume that the molecule may be described as a collection of masses and springs. The potential function is, then, given as

$$V(x_1, x_2, x_3) = \tfrac{1}{2}k(x_2 - x_1)^2 + \tfrac{1}{2}k(x_3 - x_2)^2$$

$$m = m_1 \qquad M = m_2 \qquad m = m_3$$

$$\mathrm{O}\text{-}\!\wedge\!\wedge\!\wedge\!\wedge\!\wedge\!\wedge\text{-}\mathrm{C}\text{-}\!\wedge\!\wedge\!\wedge\!\wedge\!\wedge\!\wedge\!\wedge\text{-}\mathrm{O}$$

$$x_1 \qquad\qquad x_2 \qquad\qquad\quad x_3$$

At equilibrium $x_1 = x_2 = x_3 = 0$.

(a) The matrix to be solved has the form $\{\Lambda - \omega_i{}^2 E\} \cdot \mathbf{r}_i = 0$, in which $\Lambda_{ij} = V_{ij}/\sqrt{m_i m_j}$ and $\omega_i{}^2 = k\lambda_i$. Find the eigenvalues.

(b) Find the normalized eigenvectors. What is the symmetry of each eigenvector?

7.2. Trichlorophosphine oxide, Cl_3P—O, has the same symmetry as NH_3.

(a) Determine the number and symmetry of the vibrational modes of freedom.

(b) Discuss the role of the P—O stretch in the normal modes (see Fig. 7.14).

7.3. Discuss the differences in the infrared and Raman spectra of methane and monodeuteromethane by determining the number of active bands and their symmetries.

7.4. Show that on the basis of infrared and Raman measurements it is possible to distinguish between two forms of octachlorocyclooctane in which the hydrogen atoms are either all cis or all trans.

7.5. Consider the molecule ethylene (see Fig. 7.15).

(a) What is its point group?

(b) Determine the number and symmetry of the vibrational modes of motion.

(c) Determine the spectral activity of each mode.

(d) Discuss the contribution of each of the following types of internal coordinate to the normal modes:

> C—H stretch
> C=C stretch
> H—C—H angle deformation
> Out-of-plane bending
> Totally in-plane motions

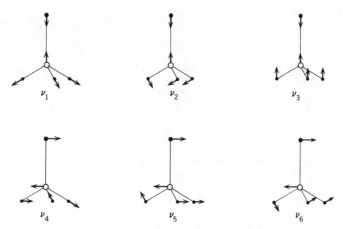

Fig. 7.14 The normal modes of vibration of an XYZ_3 molecule of C_{3v} symmetry. *(Reproduced from Russell Drago, "Physical Methods in Inorganic Chemistry," by permission of Reinhold Book Corp., a subsidiary of Chapman-Reinhold, Inc., New York, 1965.)*

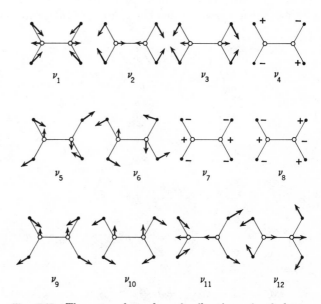

Fig. 7.15 The normal modes of vibration of ethylene. *(Reproduced from Russell Drago, "Physical Methods in Inorganic Chemistry," by permission of Reinhold Book Corp., a subsidiary of Chapman-Reinhold, Inc., New York, 1965.)*

Out-of-phase twist of one CH_2 group relative to the other CH_2 group (torsional motion about the $C{=}C$ bond)

7.6. Consider the linear triatomic molecule HCN of $C_{\infty v}$ symmetry. The following information concerns the bond distances and observed spectrum for HCN and DCN:

$$r(C{-}H) = 1.060 \text{ Å}$$
$$r(C{\equiv}N) = 1.159 \text{ Å}$$

Mode designation	Frequency	
	HCN, cm⁻¹	DCN, cm⁻¹
ν_1	3312	2629
ν_2	2089	1906
ν_3, ν_4	712	569

(a) Determine the symmetries of the normal modes. How many vibrational degrees of freedom are allowed? What is the spectral activity of each mode?

(b) Verify that the normal coordinates for HCN may be written in terms of the cartesian displacement coordinates as follows:

$$Q_1 = c_{11}\left(-\frac{M}{m_2 + m_3}\right)z_1 + c_{21}\frac{M}{m_1}z_2 + c_{31}\frac{M}{m_1}z_3$$

$$Q_2 = c_{12}\left(-\frac{M}{m_3}\right)z_1 + c_{22}\left(-\frac{M}{m_3}\right)z_2 + c_{32}\frac{M}{m_1 + m_2}z_3$$

$$Q_{3x} = c_{13}{}^x\left(-\frac{Nr_1{}^{\frac{1}{2}}}{m_2 m_3 r_2{}^{\frac{1}{2}}}\right)x_1$$
$$\qquad\qquad + c_{23}{}^x\frac{Nr_1{}^{\frac{1}{2}}r_2{}^{\frac{1}{2}}}{m_1 m_3 (r_1 + r_2)}x_2 + c_{33}{}^x\left(-\frac{Nr_2{}^{\frac{1}{2}}}{m_1 m_2 r_1{}^{\frac{1}{2}}}\right)x_3$$

$$Q_{3y} = c_{13}{}^y\left(-\frac{Nr_1{}^{\frac{1}{2}}}{m_2 m_3 r_2{}^{\frac{1}{2}}}\right)y_1$$
$$\qquad\qquad + c_{23}{}^y\frac{Nr_1{}^{\frac{1}{2}}r_2{}^{\frac{1}{2}}}{m_1 m_3 (r_1 + r_2)}y_2 + c_{33}{}^y\left(-\frac{Nr_2{}^{\frac{1}{2}}}{m_1 m_2 r_1{}^{\frac{1}{2}}}\right)y_3$$

where

$$M = m_1 + m_2 + m_3$$
$$N = \frac{m_1 m_2 r_1{}^2 + m_1 m_3 (r_1 + r_2)^2 + m_2 m_3 r_2{}^2}{r_1 r_2}$$

The following diagram illustrates the coordinate systems used.

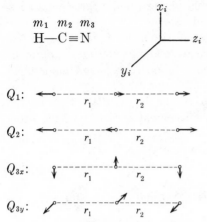

Q_1:

Q_2:

Q_{3x}:

Q_{3y}:

(c) The eigenvalue problem can now be set up. Verify that the following equations represent the set of matrix equations as follows:

$$\{F - \lambda_k E\} \cdot C_k = 0$$
$$(f_{11} - \lambda_k \mu_{11})C_{1k} + (f_{12} - \lambda_k \mu_{12})C_{2k} + 0 = 0$$
$$(f_{12} - \lambda_k \mu_{12})C_{1k} + (f_{22} - \lambda_k \mu_{22})C_{2k} + 0 = 0$$
$$0 + 0 + (f_{33} - \lambda_k \mu_{33})C_{3k} = 0$$

where

$$\mu_{11} = \frac{m_1(m_2 + m_3)}{M}$$

$$\mu_{12} = \mu_{21} = \frac{m_1 m_3}{M}$$

$$\mu_{22} = \frac{m_3(m_1 + m_2)}{M}$$

$$\mu_{33} = \frac{m_1 m_2 m_3}{N}$$

$$\mu_{13} = \mu_{31} = \mu_{23} = \mu_{32} = 0$$

Since by symmetry Q_{3x} and Q_{3y} must be even functions of the displacements,

$$f_{13} = f_{31} = f_{23} = f_{32} = 0$$

(d) In the equations developed in part (c) f_{12} represents the interaction of the stretching of the C—H bond with the stretching of the C≡N bond. Since our chemical intuition suggests that this interaction is smaller than the stretch constants, $f_{12} < f_{11}$, and $f_{12} < f_{22}$, let $f_{12} = 0$. This approximation is called the *simple valence-force-field approximation*. Under this simplifying approximation solve the eigenvalue problem for the eigenfrequencies λ_k. Substitute the values for the atomic masses and the bond distances and obtain numerical values for the force constants, f_{11}, f_{22}, and f_{33}.   Compare the magnitudes.

(e) Use the values for the observed frequencies together with the computed force constants to find the relative amplitudes c_{ik}.   Comment on the makeup of the modes in terms of bond-stretch and angle-bend internal coordinates.

(f) Show why it should be no surprise that the *so-called* C≡N stretch frequency (2089 cm^{-1}) is affected by replacement of the hydrogen atom with deuterium.

7.7. Consider the vibrational spectrum of acetylene ($D_{\infty h}$).

(a) Determine the number and symmetry of the normal modes. How many are nonlinear modes?

(b) Draw schematic versions of the normal modes and associate the following frequencies with them:

Symmetric C—H stretch	$\nu_1 = 3374$ cm^{-1}
C≡C stretch	$\nu_2 = 1974$ cm^{-1}
Antisymmetric C—H stretch	$\nu_3 = 3287$ cm^{-1}
Doubly degenerate (trans)	
H—C—C angle bend	$\nu_4 = 612$ cm^{-1}
Doubly degenerate (cis)	
H—C—C angle bend	$\nu_5 = 729$ cm^{-1}

7.8. Verify the results for the vibrational analysis for Examples 1 to 3 given in Sec. 7.9.

7.9. The diagrams of the normal modes of vibration of a square planar molecule are given in Fig. 7.16a and for a trigonal bipyramidal molecule in Fig. 7.16b.

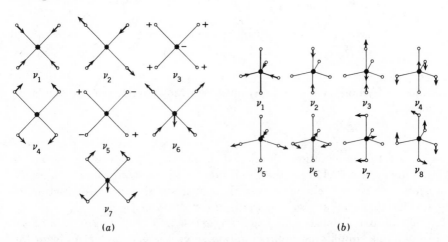

(a)   (b)

Fig. 7.16   The normal modes of vibration for (a) a square planar molecule and (b) a trigonal bipyramidal molecule.   (*Taken by permission from G. Herzberg, "Infrared and Raman Spectra," p. 107, D. Van Nostrand Company, Inc., Princeton, N.J., 1959.*)

(a) Determine the number and symmetry of the vibrational modes for both cases.

(b) Identify the various allowed symmetries calculated in part (a) with the diagrams in Fig. 7.16. Make a list of the frequencies ν_i and their symmetries.

(c) Determine the spectral activity for each mode for both molecular species.

7.10. Consider the two possible isomers of N_2F_2, cis and trans.

(a) Determine the number and symmetry of the normal modes of each isomer.

(b) Can these two forms be distinguished by infrared and Raman measurements?

7.11. Benzene is an important molecule in organic chemistry.

(a) Determine the number and symmetry of the vibrational modes of C_6H_6.

(b) Show that the vibrational modes are divided between in-the-plane and out-of-the-plane modes as follows: eight nondegenerate and seven doubly degenerate in-the-plane modes, three nondegenerate and three doubly degenerate out-of-the plane modes.

(c) Discuss the contribution of C—H stretch and C—C stretch to the various modes.

(d) Determine the spectral activity of each mode.

7.12. Consider the molecules of the XYZ_3 type (C_{3v}) such as the methyl halides.

(a) Determine the number and symmetry of the normal modes.

(b) Prepare a table showing all the possible combination bands by determining all the product representations of the normal modes found in part (a).

(c) Determine the spectral activity of the combination bands.

7.13. For the point groups and their irreducible representations on page 185 prepare a table of the product representations and their spectral activity under the headings as shown on page 185.

7.14. Consider the ν_3 (Σ^+) fundamental of an XY_2 linear $(D_{\infty h})$ molecule. Show that there is an alternation of infrared and Raman activity of the ν_3 fundamental and its overtones.

7.15. Perform a vibrational analysis for both *cis*- and *trans*-butadiene.

(a) Determine the number and symmetry of the normal modes.

(b) Determine the spectral activity of each mode.

(c) Determine the contribution of the following internal coordinates to each mode:

C=C stretch
C—C stretch
C—H stretch
Out-of-plane modes

Point group	Excited species	Resultant state(s)	Spectral activity
C_{2v}	$A_2 \times B_1$		
	$A_2 \times B_2$		
	$B_1 \times B_2$		
C_{2h}	$A_u \times B_g$		
	$A_u \times B_u$		
	$B_g \times B_u$		
D_{3h}	$A_1'' \times A_2'$		
	$A_2' \times E'$		
	$A_2'' \times E'$		
	$A_1'' \times A_2''$		
	$E' \times E'$		
	$E' \times E''$		
	$E'' \times E''$		
D_{3d}	$A_{2g} \times B_{1g}$		
	$A_{1g} \times E_g$		
	$A_{1g} \times E_u$		
	$A_{2g} \times E_g$		
	$E_g \times E_g$		
	$E_g \times E_u$		
	$E_u \times E_u$		
$C_{\infty v}$	$\Sigma^+ \times \Pi$		
	$\Sigma^+ \times \Delta$		
	$\Sigma^- \times \Pi$		
	$\Sigma^- \times \Delta$		
	$\Pi \times \Pi$		
	$\Pi \times \Delta$		
$D_{\infty h}$	$\Sigma_g^+ \times \Pi_g$		
	$\Sigma_g^+ \times \Delta_g$		
	$\Sigma_g^+ \times \Pi_u$		
	$\Sigma_g^+ \times \Delta_u$		
	$\Pi_g \times \Pi_g$		
	$\Pi_g \times \Pi_u$		
	$\Pi_g \times \Delta_u$		
	$\Pi_g \times \Delta_g$		

REFERENCES

Dixon, R. H.: "Spectroscopy and Structure," John Wiley & Sons, Inc., New York, 1965.

Herzberg, G.: "Infrared and Raman Spectra," D. Van Nostrand Company, Inc., Princeton, N.J., 1959.

Wilson, E. B., J. C. Decius, and P. C. Cross: "Molecular Vibrations," McGraw-Hill Book Company, New York, 1955.

8
hybridized equivalent orbitals

The use of the one-electron hydrogen-like atomic orbitals (AOs) is common in the construction of wave functions as well as in the description of the geometry of polyatomic molecules and ions. Terms such as sp^3 hybrid orbitals are very familiar to chemists in general. When we adopt the one-electron orbital picture of atomic electronic structure, however, a problem arises as we attempt to understand the chemical equivalence of the several chemically identical bonds to a given atom, i.e. the four C—H bonds in methane or the three N—O bonds in the nitrate ion. In addition, a mathematical form of the hybrid-orbital set is necessary for quantitative calculations. We shall discuss in this section the selection of AOs and the construction of the sets of equivalent hybrid orbitals as linear combinations of AOs. We may write the wave function for atomic carbon as a product of doubly occupied one-electron orbitals in the following product form:

$$\psi_C = \phi_{1s}^2 \phi_{2s}^2 \phi_{2p}^2 \qquad \text{neglecting spin} \qquad (8.1)$$

We say, then, that the electrons which play the most significant role in bonding occupy the outermost orbitals, $2s$ and $2p$, in this case. Yet it may be difficult to see that there can be a chemical equivalence of four bonds to carbon since we say that two of the bonding electrons possess the spherical symmetry of the $2s$ orbital and are lower in energy than the $2p$ electrons, whose orbitals are nonspherical. How is it possible for four equivalent tetrahedral bonds to arise from this combination of orbitals?

We shall see that the four tetrahedral bonds in CH_4 may serve as a basis set of functions for a representation of the point group of CH_4, T_d $(\overline{4}3m)$, and this representation is *reducible*. Further, the hydrogen-like AOs have been shown to be bases for the *irreducible* representations of the various point groups. Thus, a comparison of the totally reduced representation based on the equivalent bonds with the irreducible representations to which AOs belong reveals which combinations of AOs will yield equivalent orbitals of a specified symmetry for a given point group.

However, an ambiguity becomes apparent. In point group D_{3h}, for example, it will be found that the following combinations all yield trigonal hybrids: sp^2, sd^2, dp^2, d^3. This difficulty serves to point up the kind of information which group theory can provide; i.e., it is primarily qualitative in nature. To determine the relative importance of the various combinations one must consider the details of the quantum mechanics of the specific problem. For example, the atom in question may not possess accessible d orbitals (BF_3), or d electrons may be energetically favored (as in some transition metals).

The question of the mathematical form of hybrid AOs can be resolved into two separate problems: (1) the determination of the appropriate AOs which may be combined to give hybrid orbitals of the desired symmetry and (2) the actual determination of the linear combinations of the appropriate orbitals including the calculation of the values of the coefficients in the linear combinations. We shall consider these two problems separately and in the order given. Further, separate consideration will be given to sigma and pi bonding since, in general, these two problems are usually separated conceptually. Sigma systems will be discussed first since (on an energetic basis) usually electrons and orbitals are assigned to pi (or multiple) bonding only after the sigma system has been defined.

8.1 TRANSFORMATION PROPERTIES OF ATOMIC ORBITALS

Let us first determine the irreducible representations to which the various AOs belong. This entails the use of the orbital functions as basis functions and a determination of their transformation properties. Table 8.1 lists some of the commonly used hydrogen wave functions (atomic orbit-

Table 8.1 Unnormalized hydrogen AOs in spherical coordinates

Quantum numbers			Designation	Functional form (unnormalized)‡
n	l	m		
1	0	0	$1s$	e^{-r}
2	0	0	$2s$	$(r - 2)e^{-r/2}$
2	1	+1	$2p$	$re^{-r/2} \sin\theta\, e^{i\phi}$
2	1	0	$2p$	$re^{-r/2} \cos\theta$
2	1	-1	$2p$	$re^{-r/2} \sin\theta\, e^{-i\phi}$
3	0	0	$3s$	$(2r^2 - 18r + 27)e^{-r/3}$
3	1	+1	$3p$	$(r - 6)re^{-r/3} \sin\theta\, e^{i\phi}$
3	1	0	$3p$	$(r - 6)re^{-r/3} \cos\theta$
3	1	-1	$3p$	$(r - 6)re^{-r/3} \sin\theta\, e^{-i\phi}$
3	2	+2	$3d$	$r^2e^{-r/3} \sin^2\theta\, e^{i2\phi}$
3	2	+1	$3d$	$r^2e^{-r/3} \cos\theta \sin\theta\, e^{i\phi}$
3	2	0	$3d$	$r^2e^{-r/3}\,(3\cos^2\theta - 1)$
3	2	-1	$3d$	$r^2e^{-r/3} \cos\theta \sin\theta\, e^{-i\phi}$
3	2	-2	$3d$	$r^2e^{-r/3} \sin^2\theta\, e^{-i2\phi}$

‡ For a complete listing of hydrogen wave functions including the normalization constants see L. Pauling and E. B. Wilson, "Introduction to Quantum Mechanics," pp. 132–139, McGraw-Hill Book Company, New York, 1935, or H. Eyring, J. Walter, and G. E. Kimball, "Quantum Chemistry," pp. 89–90, John Wiley & Sons, Inc., New York, 1960.

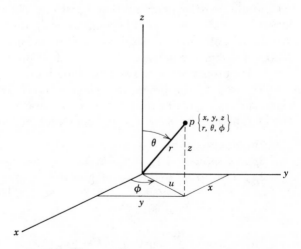

Fig. 8.1 The coordinate systems used to represent atomic wave functions. The cartesian coordinates (x, y, z) of point p are shown along with the spherical polar coordinates (r, θ, ϕ).

als) in an unnormalized form. Figure 8.1 shows a diagram of both the cartesian and spherical coordinate systems which may be used to describe the one-electron atomic system. It should be noted that the r used here is actually a reduced coordinate, r'/a_0, in which a_0 is the Bohr radius.

The following relations are useful in converting from cartesian to spherical coordinates:

$$
\begin{aligned}
x &= u \cos \phi \qquad u = r \sin \theta \\
y &= u \sin \phi \\
z &= r \cos \theta
\end{aligned}
\tag{8.2}
$$

or

$$
\begin{aligned}
x &= r \sin \theta \cos \phi \\
y &= r \sin \theta \sin \phi \\
z &= r \cos \theta
\end{aligned}
\tag{8.3}
$$

In order to consider these orbital functions as bases for a representation, let us convert them into a more convenient form. First, let us observe that each orbital function may be written as a product of a function of r, $R_{n,l}(r)$, and a function of θ and ϕ, $Y_{l,m}(\theta, \phi)$.

$$
\psi_{nlm}(r, \theta, \phi) = R_{n,l}(r) Y_{l,m}(\theta, \phi)
\tag{8.4}
$$

The integers n, l, m are the quantum numbers. Since r is the magnitude of the polar "vector" in spherical coordinates, i.e., a vector with one terminus at the origin of the coordinate system, no symmetry operation in any point group can alter r since symmetry operations do not affect the magnitude r—only its orientation θ and ϕ. Thus, the magnitude of r is invariant to any point-group symmetry operation. However, the angles θ and ϕ are, of course, generally altered by symmetry operations. Thus, $R_{nl}(r)$ is symmetry-invariant, and we shall direct our attention to the symmetry properties of the angular functions.

To simplify the procedure, let us convert the angular functions to cartesian space utilizing the relations given above. Consider, for instance, the $2p$ functions for $m = \pm 1$ and construct two linear combinations:

$$
2p_+ = 2p(m = +1) + 2p(m = -1)
\tag{8.5}
$$
$$
2p_- = 2p(m = +1) - 2p(m = -1)
\tag{8.6}
$$
$$
\begin{aligned}
2p_+ &= re^{-r/2} \sin \theta \, e^{i\phi} + re^{-r/2} \sin \theta \, e^{-i\phi} \\
&= re^{-r/2} \sin \theta \, (e^{i\phi} + e^{-i\phi}) \\
&= (r \sin \theta \cos \phi) 2e^{-r/2}
\end{aligned}
$$

or

$$
2p_+ = 2xe^{-r/2} = \text{const} \cdot xe^{-r/2} = 2p_x
\tag{8.7}
$$

Likewise

$$
2p_- = 2ye^{-r/2} = \text{const} \cdot ye^{-r/2} = 2p_y
\tag{8.8}
$$

Finally

$$2p_0 = 2p(m = 0) = re^{-r/2} \cos \theta = e^{-r/2}(r \cos \theta)$$

and

$$2p_0 = ze^{-r/2} = 2p_z \qquad (8.9)$$

Table 8.2 lists the functions in Table 8.1 with the angular part converted to cartesian form. This form of hydrogen AOs is useful not only in determining their symmetry properties but also in visualizing their spatial orientation.

Table 8.2 Unnormalized hydrogen AOs with angular part converted to cartesian coordinates

Designation	Functional form (unnormalized)
$1s$	e^{-r}
$2s$	$(r - 2)e^{-r}$
$2p_x$	$xe^{-r/2}$
$2p_y$	$ye^{-r/2}$
$2p_z$	$ze^{-r/2}$
$3s$	$(2r^2 - 18r + 27)e^{-r/3}$
$3p_x$	$xre^{-r/3}$
$3p_y$	$yre^{-r/3}$
$3p_z$	$zre^{-r/3}$
$3d_{z^2}$	$(3z^2 - r^2)e^{-r/3}$
$3d_{x^2-y^2}$	$(x^2 - y^2)e^{-r/3}$
$3d_{xy}$	$xye^{-r/3}$
$3d_{xz}$	$xze^{-r/3}$
$3d_{yz}$	$yze^{-r/3}$

The transformation properties of a function are often described in terms of the transformation of various cartesian components. These transformation properties are usually listed on the right-hand side of character tables. By observing the partially converted form of the hydrogen AOs in Table 8.2, we can easily deduce their transformation properties. Each orbital is written as a constant (r is a constant relative to symmetry operations) times a function of x, y, and z.

$$\phi = \text{const} \cdot f(x, y, z) \qquad (8.10)$$

Thus, each orbital transforms as the function $f(x, y, z)$ does. In addition each orbital is identified by a subscript which is identical with, or similar to, $f(x, y, z)$. We can then make a very simple statement concerning the transformation properties of AOs: an orbital transforms just as its subscripts. Hence, in any point group a p_x orbital transforms as the cartesian coordinate x does, and a $d_{x^2-y^2}$ orbital has the same transformation properties as the function $x^2 - y^2$. Since the s orbitals possess no angular dependence, they are invariant to all symmetry operations and hence form a basis for the totally symmetric irreducible representation of each point group.

For example, in the tetrahedral molecule CH_4 the s orbital belongs to the A_1 irreducible representation, and the $2p$ orbitals form a basis for the triply degenerate irreducible representation T_2. For the nitrate ion (D_{3h}), however, s orbitals belong to A_1', but $2p_x$ and $2p_y$ belong to E', whereas $2p_z$ belongs to A_2''.

8.2 THE APPROXIMATION FOR MANY-ELECTRON ATOMS

The discussion up to this point has dealt exclusively with hydrogen-atom wave functions which can be obtained in analytical form as exact solutions to the Schrödinger equation for one-electron atoms. However, the Schrödinger equation for polyelectronic atoms and molecules can be solved only approximately. The usual approximation for atoms is the so-called *one-electron product-function* approximation, Eq. (8.1). In this approximation each electron is said to occupy (be described by) a one-electron hydrogen-like function, and the total wave function may be written as a product of the one-electron orbitals $\phi(i)$.

$$\phi(i) = N_i R'(r_i) Y(\theta_i, \phi_i) \tag{8.11}$$

and

$$\psi(1, 2, \ldots, i, \ldots, n) = N'\phi(1)\phi(2) \cdots \phi(i) \cdots \phi(n) \tag{8.12}$$

Each $\phi(i)$ is a hydrogen-like function in which only the radial function $R'(r_i)$ is different from the hydrogen orbitals. The $R'(r_i)$ may be a complicated analytical function—or a tabulated set of numbers—determined by semiempirical rules (Slater orbitals) or by a sophisticated procedure such as the Hartree-Fock method.

Because of the form of this approximation each orbital has exactly the same transformation properties as the corresponding hydrogen function. Hence, we may proceed to describe the symmetry properties of the polyelectronic atom in the same fashion as we did the hydrogen orbitals because the two systems share identical angular functions.

8.3 EQUIVALENT HYBRID ORBITALS FOR SIGMA BONDING SYSTEMS

In order to determine the appropriate orbitals which may be combined to produce a new set of orbitals all of which are equivalent and possess the

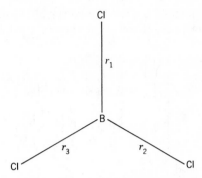

Fig. 8.2 The molecular geometry of boron trichloride depicting the three vectors r_1, r_2, and r_3, which represent the boron-chloride sigma bonds.

desired symmetry, we consider the set of equivalent orbitals as a set of basis functions for a matrix representation Γ_{hyb}. We shall find that the representation is reducible. [We reduce it using the standard reduction formula of Eq. (6.70).] The totally reduced form is written as the direct sum $\Gamma_{\text{hyb}} = \sum_{\alpha} m_\alpha \Gamma_\alpha$, a sum of irreducible representations. The correct orbitals are, then, those atomic orbitals which belong to the irreducible representations Γ_α in the totally reduced representation Γ_{hyb}.

In order to present the details of this method let us consider two specific examples, BCl_3 and CH_4.

BCl: (D_{3h}) TRIGONAL PLANAR

The first step is to consider the trigonal planar sigma bonding system as a basis for a representation. In order to visualize the process let us consider the sigma bonds to be vectors, as shown in Fig. 8.2. We can now construct matrices to represent the operations of the various classes of point group D_{3h} (Table 8.3) by writing the equations relating vectors as trans-

Table 8.3 Character table for point group D_{3h} ($\bar{6}m2$)

D_{3h}	E	$2C_3$	$3C_2$	σ_h	$2S_3$	$3\sigma_v$		
A_1'	1	1	1	1	1	1		$x^2 + y^2;\ z^2$
A_2'	1	1	-1	1	1	-1	R_z	
E'	2	-1	0	2	-1	0	(x, y)	$(x^2 - y^2,\ xy)$
A_1''	1	1	1	-1	-1	-1		
A_2''	1	1	-1	-1	-1	1	z	
E''	2	-1	0	-2	1	0	(R_x, R_y)	(xz, yz)
Γ_σ	3	0	1	3	0	1		

formed by the symmetry operations of D_{3h} as is shown here for the identity E, the class of threefold rotations $2C_3$, and the vertical mirrors $3\sigma_v$.

$$\begin{bmatrix} r_1' \\ r_2' \\ r_3' \end{bmatrix} = \begin{matrix} 1 \cdot r_1 + 0 \cdot r_2 + 0 \cdot r_3 \\ 0 \cdot r_1 + 1 \cdot r_2 + 0 \cdot r_3 \\ 0 \cdot r_1 + 0 \cdot r_2 + 1 \cdot r_3 \end{matrix}$$

$$\begin{bmatrix} r_1' \\ r_2' \\ r_3' \end{bmatrix} = \begin{bmatrix} 1 & 0 & 0 \\ 0 & 1 & 0 \\ 0 & 0 & 1 \end{bmatrix} \begin{bmatrix} r_1 \\ r_2 \\ r_3 \end{bmatrix} = \Gamma^{(E)} \begin{bmatrix} r_1 \\ r_2 \\ r_3 \end{bmatrix}$$

and

$$\begin{bmatrix} r_1' \\ r_2' \\ r_3' \end{bmatrix} = \begin{matrix} 0 \cdot r_1 + 1 \cdot r_2 + 0 \cdot r_3 \\ 0 \cdot r_1 + 0 \cdot r_2 + 1 \cdot r_3 \\ 1 \cdot r_1 + 0 \cdot r_2 + 0 \cdot r_3 \end{matrix}$$

$$\begin{bmatrix} r_1' \\ r_2' \\ r_3' \end{bmatrix} = \begin{bmatrix} 0 & 1 & 0 \\ 0 & 0 & 1 \\ 1 & 0 & 0 \end{bmatrix} \begin{bmatrix} r_1 \\ r_2 \\ r_3 \end{bmatrix} = \Gamma^{(C_3)} \begin{bmatrix} r_1 \\ r_2 \\ r_3 \end{bmatrix}$$

and

$$\begin{bmatrix} r_1' \\ r_2' \\ r_3' \end{bmatrix} = \begin{matrix} 1 \cdot r_1 + 0 \cdot r_2 + 0 \cdot r_3 \\ 0 \cdot r_1 + 0 \cdot r_2 + 1 \cdot r_3 \\ 0 \cdot r_1 + 1 \cdot r_2 + 0 \cdot r_3 \end{matrix}$$

$$\begin{bmatrix} r_1' \\ r_2' \\ r_3' \end{bmatrix} = \begin{bmatrix} 1 & 0 & 0 \\ 0 & 0 & 1 \\ 0 & 1 & 0 \end{bmatrix} \begin{bmatrix} r_1 \\ r_2 \\ r_3 \end{bmatrix} = \Gamma^{(\sigma_v)} \begin{bmatrix} r_1 \\ r_2 \\ r_3 \end{bmatrix}$$

However, since we need only the characters of these matrices in order to use the standard reduction formula, Eq. (6.70),

$$m_\alpha = \frac{1}{g} \sum_l \chi^{(e_l)} h_l \chi_l^{(e_l)*} = \frac{1}{g} \sum_R \chi^{(R)} \chi_\alpha^{(R)*}$$

we need to devise a scheme for obtaining only the characters of the matrices. In the three matrices above we observe that the only nonzero contributions to $\chi^{(R)}$ arise from those vectors which are unshifted by a given symmetry operation and that then the contribution is $+1$. Thus, we can state the following general rule: *the character of the sigma-system matrices is equal to the number of unshifted vectors for each symmetry operation.* In this manner we obtain the character system shown as Γ_σ in Table 8.3. Using the standard reduction formula, the following direct sum is obtained for the totally reduced representation:

$$\Gamma_\sigma = A_1' + E'$$

Table 8.4 lists the appropriate AOs and their symmetry representations as determined from their transformation properties listed in the character

Table 8.4 AOs and their irreducible representations in D_{3h}

A_1'	E'
s	$p_x,\ p_y$
d_{z^2}	$d_{x^2-y^2},\ d_{xy}$

table. There appears to be an ambiguity here, for there are four possible combinations of orbitals all yielding three equivalent hybrid orbitals of D_{3h} symmetry:

Tr^1: $(s,\ p_x,\ p_y)$ or sp^2
Tr^2: $(s,\ d_{x^2-y^2},\ d_{xy})$ or sd^2
Tr^3: $(d_{z^2},\ p_x,\ p_y)$ or dp^2
Tr^4: $(d_{z^2},\ d_{x^2-y^2},\ d_{xy})$ or d^3

Thus, the most general solution to this problem would be a linear combination of all four possibilities:

$$\psi = a(sp^2) + b(sd^2) + c(dp^2) + d(d^3) \tag{8.13}$$

The coefficients might be determined by a quantum-mechanical technique such as the variational method.

However, our chemical intuition can assist us in determining the relative importance of the four types of hybrid orbitals. In boron the d orbitals are not available, and contribution of d-orbital hybrids will certainly be negligible relative to the sp^2 type. Thus, we are safe in using the sp^2 type hybrid orbitals within the framework of the one-electron orbital approximation introduced at the outset of this section.

CH₄ (T_d) TETRAHEDRAL

The four tetrahedrally oriented orbitals of CH_4 with T_d $(\bar{4}3m)$ symmetry are shown in Fig. 8.3. Using the rule developed in the previous section, we can obtain the character system for the representation based on these four vectors. The character system is shown in Table 8.5, along with the character table for T_d. Using the standard reduction formula, we get the direct sum

$$\Gamma_\sigma = A_1 + T_2$$

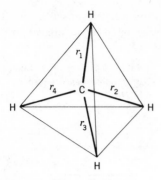

Fig. 8.3   The molecular geometry of methane showing four vectors r_1 to r_4 which represent the carbon-hydrogen sigma bonds.

Table 8.5   Character table for $T_d(\overline{4}3m)$

T_d	E	$8C_3$	$3C_2$	$6S_4$	$6\sigma_d$		
A_1	1	1	1	1	1		$x^2 + y^2 + z^2$
A_2	1	1	1	-1	-1		
E	2	-1	2	0	0		$(2z^2 - x^2 - y^2; x^2 - y^2)$
T_1	3	0	-1	1	-1	(R_x, R_y, R_z)	
T_2	3	0	-1	-1	1	(x, y, z)	(xy, xz, yz)
Γ_σ	4	1	0	0	2		

Table 8.6 shows the possible combinations of orbitals with A_1 and T_2 symmetry.   Thus, there are two possible types of hybrid orbitals with

Table 8.6   AOs and their irreducible representations in T_d

A_1	T_2
s	p_x, p_y, p_z
	d_{xy}, d_{xz}, d_{yz}

tetrahedral symmetry, sp^3 and sd^3.   Once again we select the sp^3 set as being the more important for CH_4.   Several examples are presented as problems at the end of this chapter.

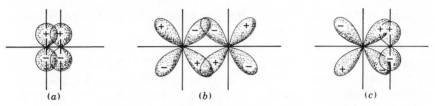

Fig. 8.4 The arrangements of various typical AOs which are favorable for multiple bonding. (a) p-p pi bonding; (b) d-d pi bonding; (c) d-p pi bonding.

8.4 MULTIPLE-BONDING CONSIDERATIONS: PI SYSTEMS

The terms double and triple bond are so familiar even to the college fresh-man in chemistry that a detailed review of their basic principles appears to be unnecessary.   Therefore, let us just observe that the principal differ-ence between sigma and pi orbitals—as far as symmetry is concerned—is that pi bonds possess nodal planes (a plane of zero probability) at least one of which contains the bond axis, in contrast to sigma orbitals, in which no nodal plane contains the bond axis.   The pi bond possesses maximum stability when the two (or more) combining orbitals are lined up in such a way that their combined nodal properties produce the nodal plane con-taining the bond axis.   Such requirements place certain restrictions on the relative alignment of the pi orbitals.   In the case of p orbitals they must be parallel.   Typical arrangements for pi bonding are shown in Fig. 8.4.

Let us now consider planar molecules of the type XY_3 as a means of demonstrating the method.   As in the case of sigma bonding, we shall use vectors to represent the orbitals so that the character system of the pi bonding system can be determined.   A maximum of two pi AOs is permitted on each Y atom.   The proper orientation of the six vectors is shown in Fig. 8.5.   It is now very easy to determine the character system of these six vectors.   The rule developed above for the sigma systems applies here with one change.   Since in this case a vector may go into its

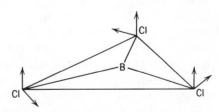

Fig. 8.5 The relative orientations of the chlorine AOs which are available for pi bonding are represented here by two orthogonal vectors, one pair centered on each chlorine atom.

negative as the result of a symmetry operation, the possible contributions to the character are $+1$, 0, -1.

Further, we may observe that no symmetry operation interchanges an out-of-plane vector with an in-the-plane vector. Hence, the two sets of three vectors each form independent basis sets and may be considered separately. We shall see that this is a wise procedure. The character systems are determined as follows:

D_{3h}	E	$2C_3$	$3C_2$	σ_h	$3S_3$	$3\sigma_v$
Γ_π	6	0	-2	0	0	0
Γ_{oop}	3	0	-1	-3	0	1
Γ_{itp}	3	0	-1	3	0	-1

The direct sums for these representations are obtained in the standard manner.

$$\Gamma_\pi = A_2' + A_2'' + E' + E''$$
$$\Gamma_{\text{oop}} = A_2'' + E''$$
$$\Gamma_{\text{itp}} = A_2' + E'$$

The possible AOs are listed in Table 8.7.

Table 8.7   Possible AOs for pi bonding in D_{3h}

Out of plane		In the plane	
A_2''	E''	A_2'	E'
p_z	d_{xz}, d_{yz}	None	$(p_x, p_y)(d_{x^2-y^2}, d_{xy})$

Thus, in order to form three equivalent pi bonds with the chlorine atoms the boron atom must supply orbitals with A_2'' and E'' transformation properties. If the p_z, d_{xz}, and d_{yz} orbitals are not used in sigma bonding in XY_3, they may be used to form a set of three equivalent orbitals for pi bonding to orbitals of the appropriate symmetry located on the three Y atoms. However, such is not the case with the in-plane pi bonding. Only the $d_{x^2-y^2}$ and d_{xy} orbitals remain available after sigma-bonding requirements are fulfilled (s, p_x, p_y, or sp^2). Because no orbital of A_2' symmetry exists, only two pi-type AOs are available and must be shared equivalently between three atoms. This kind of situation is not unusual and is found in other systems, such as those of tetrahedral and octahedral symmetry. The various possibilities may be worked out readily by the reader for the point groups O_h, D_{4h}, and T_d. The results are summarized below for comparison.

1. T_d

T_d	E	$8C_3$	$3C_2$	$6S_4$	$6\sigma_d$
Γ_π	8	-1	0	0	0

$$\Gamma_\pi = E + T_1 + T_2$$

E	T_1	T_2
$d_{x^2-y^2}, d_{z^2}$	None	p_x, p_y, p_z d_{xy}, d_{xz}, d_{yz}

(Carefully consider the sigma-system requirements here!)

2. O_h

O_h	E	$8C_3$	$6C_2$	$6C_4$	$3C_2$	i	$6S_4$	$8S_6$	$3\sigma_h$	$6\sigma_d$
Γ_π	12	0	0	0	-4	0	0	0	0	0

$$\Gamma_\pi = T_{1g} + T_{2g} + T_{1u} + T_{2u}$$

T_{1g}	T_{2g}	T_{1u}	T_{2u}
None	d_{xy}, d_{xz}, d_{yz}	p_x, p_y, p_z	None

3. D_{4h} (square planar)

D_{4h}	E	$2C_4$	C_2	$2C_2'$	$2C_2''$	i	$2S_4$	σ_h	$2\sigma_v$	$2\sigma_d$
Γ_π	8	0	0	-4	0	0	0	0	0	0
Γ_{oop}	4	0	0	-2	0	0	0	-4	2	0
Γ_{itp}	4	0	0	-2	0	0	0	4	-2	0

$$\Gamma_\pi = \Gamma_{\text{oop}} + \Gamma_{\text{itp}}$$
$$\Gamma_{\text{oop}} = A_{2u} + B_{2u} + E_g$$
$$\Gamma_{\text{itp}} = A_{2g} + B_{2g} + E_u$$

Out of plane		In the plane	
A_{2u}	p_z	A_{2g}	none
B_{2u}	none	B_{2g}	d_{xy}
E_g	d_{xz}, d_{yz}	E_u	p_x, p_y

8.5 MATHEMATICAL FORM OF THE EQUIVALENT HYBRID ORBITALS

We have already shown how to determine which AOs may be combined to produce a set of equivalent hybrid orbitals. However, we have not yet shown how to determine the exact mathematical form of the combinations. The reader may wonder at this point why the mathematical form is required whenever one desires to perform quantitative calculations. In the section concerning molecular-orbital theory we shall show how to use hybrid orbitals to good advantage. Further, when one deals with coordination compounds, it is often necessary to use equivalent hybrid orbitals for computing overlap integrals which may be related to bond strengths or may be necessary for energy-level calculations.

Let us now proceed to define hybrid orbitals as a linear combination of AOs and discuss the principles which govern the determination of the linear coefficients. We shall define the ith equivalent hybrid orbital ψ_i in terms of AOs ϕ_j

$$\psi_i = \sum_{j=1}^{N} c_{ij}\phi_j \tag{8.14}$$

There are two fundamental principles which will help us at this point.

1. The set of equivalent orbitals forms an orthonormal set.

(a) Each hybrid orbital may be normalized as expressed in the following equations:

$$\int \psi_i\psi_i^* \, d\tau = 1 = \int |\psi_i|^2 \, d\tau$$

or

$$\int \left(\sum_j c_{ij}\phi_j\right)\left(\sum_k c_{ik}^*\phi_k^*\right) d\tau = 1$$

and since we shall use only real coefficients here,

$$\sum_j \sum_k c_{ij}c_{ik}\int \phi_j\phi_k^* \, d\tau = 1$$

However, since the AOs form an orthonormal set,

$$\int \phi_j\phi_k^* \, d\tau = \delta_{jk}$$

Thus, when we sum over k, we obtain the following useful equation:

$$\sum_j c_{ij}^2 = 1 \tag{8.15}$$

(b) Each hybrid orbital must be orthogonal to all the other hybrid orbitals.

$$\int \psi_m\psi_n^* \, d\tau = 0 \qquad m \neq n$$

Following the procedure outlined above, we obtain a similar equation

$$\sum_j \sum_k c_{mj} c_{nk} = 0 \quad \begin{matrix} m \neq n \\ j \neq k \end{matrix} \quad (8.16)$$

2. Each hybrid is equivalent to the other hybrid orbitals in the set under the symmetry operations of the group. The coefficients must be so chosen that when a symmetry operation is performed on one member of the set, its symmetry equivalent member is produced.

$$R\psi_i = \psi_j$$

or

$$R\left(\sum_m c_{im}\phi_m\right) = \sum_n c_{jn}\phi_n \quad (8.17)$$

The coefficients c_{ij} of each *atomic* orbital must be equal on the two sides of this equation. Hence, relations among the coefficients are readily obtained. In order to demonstrate these principles let us consider the following examples: sp^3 in CH_4 and dsp^3 in PF_5.

TETRAHEDRAL sp^3 EQUIVALENT HYBRID ORBITALS IN CH_4

We shall consider methane first and orient the molecule within a cartesian coordinate system, as shown in Fig. 8.6, using the following symbols for

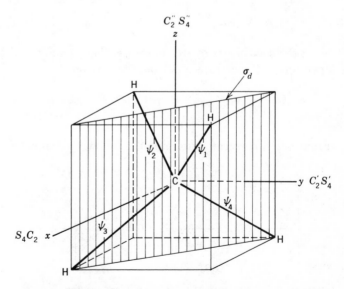

Fig. 8.6   The coordinate system used to describe the hybridized orbitals of the carbon atom in methane. The relative orientation of several of the symmetry elements is indicated.

the AOs involved:

$$s \equiv 2s$$
$$p_x \equiv 2p_x$$
$$p_y \equiv 2p_y$$
$$p_z \equiv 2p_z$$

We can write the four hybrid sp^3 orbitals as follows:

$$\psi_1 = c_{11}s + c_{12}p_x + c_{13}p_y + c_{14}p_z \qquad (8.18)$$
$$\psi_2 = c_{21}s + c_{22}p_x + c_{23}p_y + c_{24}p_z \qquad (8.19)$$
$$\psi_3 = c_{31}s + c_{32}p_x + c_{33}p_y + c_{34}p_z \qquad (8.20)$$
$$\psi_4 = c_{41}s + c_{42}p_x + c_{43}p_y + c_{44}p_z \qquad (8.21)$$

The form of the coefficients and their arrangement in these equations suggest that the array of the coefficients may be thought of as a matrix which represents a transformation. Such a notion is proper, for the equivalent hybridized orbitals are simply transformed AOs.

We first use the symmetry relations among the equivalent orbitals (principle 2) in order to establish some relationships among the coefficients. The twofold axis along z, C_2'', relates ψ_1 to ψ_2 and ψ_3 to ψ_4. Let us consider ψ_1 first.

$$C_2'' \psi_1 = \psi_2 \qquad (8.22)$$
$$C_2''(c_{11}s + c_{12}p_x + c_{13}p_y + c_{14}p_z) = c_{21}s + c_{22}p_x + c_{23}p_y + c_{24}p_z$$

Since the coefficients c_{ij} are constants, they commute with the symmetry operators. Hence Eq. (8.22) may be written

$$c_{11}(C_2''s) + c_{12}(C_2''p_x) + c_{13}(C_2''p_y) + c_{14}(C_2''p_z)$$
$$= c_{21}s + c_{22}p_x + c_{23}p_y + c_{24}p_z$$

From Fig. 8.7 we can determine the following symmetry relations among

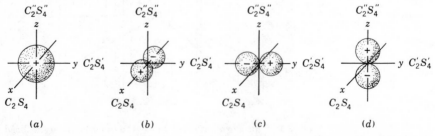

Fig. 8.7   The orientation of the carbon AOs with respect to the symmetry axes used to describe the point-group symmetry of methane. (a) $2s$; (b) $2p_x$; (c) $2p_y$; (d) $2p_z$.

the AOs

$$C_2'' s = s \qquad C_2'' p_x = -p_x$$
$$C_2'' p_y = -p_y \qquad C_2'' p_z = p_z$$

Thus

$$c_{11}s - c_{12}p_x - c_{13}p_y + c_{14}p_z = c_{21}s + c_{22}p_x + c_{23}p_y + c_{24}p_z \qquad (8.23)$$

In order that ψ_1 and ψ_2 be equivalent under the symmetry operations of the group T_d, the coefficients of each AO must be equal on both sides of Eq. (8.23). Thus

$$c_{11} = c_{21}$$
$$-c_{12} = c_{22}$$
$$-c_{13} = c_{23}$$
$$c_{14} = c_{24}$$

At this point we can make the generalization that all the coefficients of the s AOs, c_{i1}, must be equal in sp^3 hybrids. The reader can easily determine this by carrying out the above procedure for all hybrid orbitals. Our chemical intuition also suggests that the contribution of the s AO must be equal if the hybrid orbitals are to be equivalent. Therefore,

$$c_{11} = c_{21} = c_{31} = c_{41}$$

Without performing the analogous operations (C_2'') on ψ_3 and ψ_4 we can see that the following relations must hold by analogy to Eq. (8.23):

$$c_{31} = c_{41}$$
$$-c_{32} = c_{42}$$
$$-c_{33} = c_{43}$$
$$c_{34} = c_{44}$$

and we can now write the hybrid orbitals as follows:

$$\psi_1 = c_{11}s + c_{12}p_x + c_{13}p_y + c_{14}p_z$$
$$\psi_2 = c_{11}s - c_{12}p_x - c_{13}p_y + c_{14}p_z$$
$$\psi_3 = c_{11}s + c_{32}p_x + c_{33}p_y + c_{34}p_z \qquad (8.24)$$
$$\psi_4 = c_{11}s - c_{32}p_x - c_{33}p_y + c_{34}p_z$$

We have eliminated 9 of the original 16 unknown coefficients.

We can now proceed to make use of the information developed in the relationship between ψ_1 and ψ_3 under the improper rotation axis S_4''.

$$S_4'' \psi_1 = \psi_3$$
$$S_4''(c_{11}s + c_{12}p_x + c_{13}p_y + c_{14}p_z) = c_{11}s + c_{32}p_x + c_{33}p_y + c_{34}p_z \qquad (8.25)$$

But from Fig. 8.7

$$S_4'' s = s \qquad S_4'' p_x = -p_y$$
$$S_4'' p_y = p_x \qquad S_4'' p_z = -p_z$$

Thus

$$c_{11}s - c_{12}p_y + c_{13}p_x - c_{14}p_z = c_{11}s + c_{32}p_x + c_{33}p_y + c_{34}p_z$$

and by setting coefficients of identical AOs equal

$$c_{11} = c_{11}$$
$$-c_{12} = c_{33}$$
$$c_{13} = c_{32}$$
$$-c_{14} = c_{34}$$

We can write the hybrid orbitals now with only four unknown coefficients

$$\psi_1 = c_{11}s + c_{12}p_x + c_{13}p_y + c_{14}p_z$$
$$\psi_2 = c_{11}s - c_{12}p_x - c_{13}p_y + c_{14}p_z$$
$$\psi_3 = c_{11}s + c_{13}p_x - c_{12}p_y - c_{14}p_z \qquad (8.26)$$
$$\psi_4 = c_{11}s - c_{13}p_x + c_{12}p_y - c_{14}p_z$$

We now make use of just one more symmetry relation, as seen in Fig. 8.6, the dihedral mirror plane σ_d.

$$\sigma_d \psi_1 = \psi_2 \qquad (8.27)$$
$$\sigma_d(c_{11}s + c_{12}p_x + c_{13}p_y + c_{14}p_z) = c_{11}s - c_{12}p_x - c_{13}p_y + c_{14}p_z$$

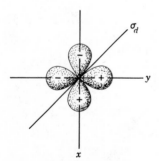

Fig. 8.8 The orientation of the carbon atomic $2p_x$ and $2p_y$ orbitals relative to one of the dihedral mirror planes σ_d of the point group of methane.

We can write the following equations based on Fig. 8.8:

$$\sigma_d s = s \qquad \sigma_d p_x = -p_y$$
$$\sigma_d p_y = -p_x \qquad \sigma_d p_z = p_z$$

Hence

$$c_{11}s - c_{12}p_y - c_{13}p_x + c_{14}p_z = c_{11}s - c_{12}p_x - c_{13}p_y + c_{14}p_z$$

and

$$c_{12} = c_{13}$$

With only three unknown coefficients remaining we can write the hybrid orbitals as follows:

$$
\begin{aligned}
\psi_1 &= c_{11}s + c_{12}p_x + c_{12}p_y + c_{14}p_z \\
\psi_2 &= c_{11}s - c_{12}p_x - c_{12}p_y + c_{14}p_z \\
\psi_3 &= c_{11}s + c_{12}p_x - c_{12}p_y - c_{14}p_z \\
\psi_4 &= c_{11}s - c_{12}p_x + c_{12}p_y - c_{14}p_z
\end{aligned}
\tag{8.28}
$$

If we were to continue to use symmetry relations among the hybrid orbitals, we would find that no further information is available. Equations developed in this manner would be equivalent to the ones already developed. However, to obtain the values of the remaining three unknown coefficients we shall make use of the orthonormal properties (principle 1) of the equivalent hybrid orbitals, as shown in the following three (independent) equations

$$\int \psi_1 \cdot \psi_1 \, d\tau = 1 \qquad c_{11}{}^2 + c_{12}{}^2 + c_{12}{}^2 + c_{14}{}^2 = 1 \tag{8.29}$$
$$\int \psi_1 \cdot \psi_2 \, d\tau = 0 \qquad c_{11}{}^2 - c_{12}{}^2 - c_{12}{}^2 + c_{14}{}^2 = 0 \tag{8.30}$$
$$\int \psi_1 \cdot \psi_3 \, d\tau = 0 \qquad c_{11}{}^2 + c_{12}{}^2 - c_{12}{}^2 - c_{14}{}^2 = 0 \tag{8.31}$$

Solving Eq. (8.31), we obtain a relation between c_{11} and c_{14}

$$c_{11}{}^2 = c_{14}{}^2 \qquad \text{or} \qquad c_{11} = \pm c_{14} \tag{8.32}$$

Subtracting Eq. (8.30) from Eq. (8.29), we obtain

$$2c_{12}{}^2 + 2c_{12}{}^2 = 1 \tag{8.33}$$

or

$$c_{12} = \pm \tfrac{1}{2} \tag{8.34}$$

Substituting Eqs. (8.32) and (8.33) into Eq. (8.29), we obtain

$$c_{11}{}^2 + \tfrac{1}{4} + \tfrac{1}{4} + c_{11}{}^2 = 1$$

or

$$c_{11} = \pm \tfrac{1}{2} \tag{8.35}$$

Since a change of sign for all the hybrid orbitals merely produces an inverted but equivalent set of hybrids, we shall choose the plus-sign results of Eqs. (8.32), (8.34), and (8.35).

$$c_{11} = c_{14} = c_{12} = +\tfrac{1}{2}$$

Now we can write the complete set of equivalent hybrid sp^3 orbitals, which we have obtained in an orthogonal and normalized set as follows:

$$\psi_1 = \tfrac{1}{2}(s + p_x + p_y + p_z)$$
$$\psi_2 = \tfrac{1}{2}(s - p_x - p_y + p_z)$$
$$\psi_3 = \tfrac{1}{2}(s + p_x - p_y - p_z) \qquad (8.36)$$
$$\psi_4 = \tfrac{1}{2}(s - p_x + p_y - p_z)$$

We saw in Sec. 8.3 that a set of equivalent tetrahedral orbitals could also be built up from the $3s$, $3d_{xy}$, $3d_{xz}$, and $3d_{yz}$ orbitals. This sd^3 set can easily be obtained from the sp^3 set [Eq. (8.36)] by the following transformations:

$$p_x \to d_{xz}$$
$$p_y \to d_{yz}$$
$$p_z \to d_{xy}$$

so that

$$\psi_1(sd^3) = \tfrac{1}{2}(s + d_{xz} + d_{yz} + d_{xy})$$

The reader may verify this as an exercise in Prob. 8.7. In the most general case, then, a tetrahedral hybrid orbital might be represented as a linear combination of an sp^3 and an sd^3 hybrid. For example ψ_1 (tetra) may be written as follows

$$\psi_1 \text{ (tetra)} = a\psi_1(sp^3) + b\psi_1(sd^3) \qquad (8.37)$$

TRIGONAL BIPYRAMIDAL dsp^3 HYBRID ORBITALS IN PF$_5$

It can be shown by the techniques of Sec. 8.3 that one of the possible combinations of AOs which possess trigonal bipyramidal symmetry is composed of the following orbitals with their respective symmetries:

A_1'	A_2''	E''
s	p_z	p_x, p_y
d_{z^2}		

Here a problem arises due to the nonequivalence of axial and equatorial bonds. That is, since no symmetry operation in the group D_{3h} interchanges an axial with an equatorial bond, there can be no requirement that any AO contribute equally to all five hybrid orbitals. By observing Fig. 8.9, we can see that there is no problem with the p orbitals; p_x and p_y can contribute only to equatorial hybrids and p_z only to axial hybrids. However, since the s and d_{z^2} orbitals possess the same symmetry in group D_{3h} (have the same transformation properties; belong to the same irreducible representation), it is not possible to assign either of them exclusively to axial or equatorial hybrid orbitals. The extent to which each one contributes to a given set must be determined by the particular problem at hand (by a quantum-mechanical calculation). Thus, the proper approach to the solution of this problem is to use a linear combination of the s and d_{z^2} orbitals, as in

$$\mathcal{S}' = a's + b'd_{z^2} \tag{8.38}$$

(The significance of the primes is to allow for a possible difference in the axial and equatorial hybrids.)

In order to solve the problem using $\mathcal{S}$ in place of s or d_{z^2}, the procedure is simplified if $\mathcal{S}$ is normalized. This may be accomplished as follows:

$$\int \mathcal{S} \cdot \mathcal{S} \, d\tau = 1 = \int (as + bd_{z^2})(as + bd_{z^2}) \, d\tau$$

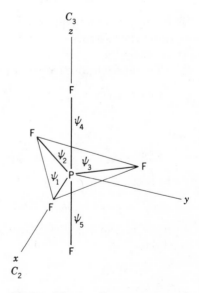

Fig. 8.9 The coordinate system used to describe the hybridized AOs of phosphorus in phosphorus pentafluoride showing the relative orientation of two of the rotation axes.

Since s and d_z are orthogonal and normalized,

$$\int s d_{z^2}\, d\tau = 0 \qquad \text{and} \qquad \int s \cdot s\, d\tau = \int d_{z^2} \cdot d_{z^2}\, d\tau = 1$$

Thus

$$\int \mathcal{S} \cdot \mathcal{S}\, d\tau = a^2 + b^2 = 1$$

So long as a and b (and a', b') are chosen such that the sum of their squares is unity, $\mathcal{S}$ (and $\mathcal{S}'$) are normalized. A common choice for the form of a and b is

$$a = \frac{1}{\sqrt{1 + \lambda^2}} \qquad b = \frac{\lambda}{\sqrt{1 + \lambda^2}}$$

The problem can now be solved using the spherical (totally symmetric) "hybrid" orbital $\mathcal{S}$ (or $\mathcal{S}'$). Let us write the five hybrid orbitals, then, as follows:

$$\psi_1 \text{ (eq)} = c_{11}\mathcal{S} + c_{12}p_x + c_{13}p_y$$
$$\psi_2 \text{ (eq)} = c_{21}\mathcal{S} + c_{22}p_x + c_{23}p_y$$
$$\psi_3 \text{ (eq)} = c_{31}\mathcal{S} + c_{32}p_x + c_{33}p_y$$
$$\psi_4 \text{ (ax)} = c_{41}\mathcal{S}' + c_{42}p_z$$
$$\psi_5 \text{ (ax)} = c_{51}\mathcal{S}' + c_{52}p_z$$

Since the axial and equatorial bonds are symmetry independent, we may consider the two sets separately and independently. We shall take up the axial set first.

The horizontal mirror (xy plane) of D_{3h} interchanges ψ_4 and ψ_5.

$$\sigma_h \psi_4 = \psi_5$$
$$\sigma_h(c_{41}\mathcal{S}' + c_{42}p_z) = c_{51}\mathcal{S}' + c_{52}p_z \tag{8.39}$$

and

$$c_{41}\mathcal{S} - c_{42}p_z = c_{51}\mathcal{S}' + c_{52}p_z$$

Note that

$$\sigma_h\mathcal{S}' = \sigma_h(as + bd_{z^2}) = a(\sigma_h s) + b(\sigma_h d_{z^2}) = as + bd_{z^2} = \mathcal{S}'$$

Because of the equality of coefficients of identical AOs we obtain the relations

$$c_{41} = c_{51}$$
$$-c_{42} = c_{52}$$

Thus, we can write the axial orbitals with only two coefficients

$$\psi_4 \text{ (ax)} = c_{41}\mathcal{S}' + c_{51}p_z$$
$$\psi_5 \text{ (ax)} = c_{41}\mathcal{S}' - c_{51}p_z \tag{8.40}$$

Using the orthonormal relations of these two orbitals, we can determine the two unknown coefficients from the equations

$$\int \psi_4 \cdot \psi_4 \, d\tau = 1 \qquad c_{41}{}^2 + c_{51}{}^2 = 1 \qquad (8.41)$$
$$\int \psi_4 \cdot \psi_5 \, d\tau = 0 \qquad c_{41}{}^2 - c_{51}{}^2 = 0 \qquad (8.42)$$

and

$$c_{41}{}^2 = c_{51}{}^2 \qquad \text{or} \qquad c_{41} = \pm c_{51} \qquad (8.43)$$

Then

$$c_{41}{}^2 + c_{51}{}^2 = c_{41}{}^2 + c_{41}{}^2 = 1$$

and

$$c_{41} = \pm \frac{1}{\sqrt{2}} \qquad (8.44)$$

Taking both positive roots in Eqs. (8.43) and (8.44), we obtain the following linear combinations for the axial orbitals:

$$\psi_4 \, (\text{ax}) = \frac{1}{\sqrt{2}} \, (\mathscr{S}' + p_z) \qquad \psi_5 \, (\text{ax}) = \frac{1}{\sqrt{2}} \, (\mathscr{S}' - p_z) \qquad (8.45)$$

Note that these two hybrid orbitals have the form of a symmetric and antisymmetric combination.

We can now consider the equatorial set. Because of the orientation we have chosen for the PF_5 molecule in the cartesian coordinate system (Fig. 8.9), it can be seen that the p_y orbital makes a zero contribution to ψ_1 which has its positive extent directed along the x axis. Since the p orbital has equal positive and negative lobes, any contribution of the positive lobe along the x direction (in a linear combination) is exactly canceled by the contribution of the negative lobe. The molecule was so oriented as to introduce this simplicity. This example emphasizes the care one should take in setting up coordinate systems. In addition, our previous experience has shown us that the $\mathscr{S}$ orbital must contribute equally to the equatorial hybrids (as it does in the axial hybrids and as the s orbital does in sp^3 hybrids). Thus, we can now write the equatorial set as

$$\psi_1 = c_{11}\mathscr{S} + c_{12}p_x + 0 \cdot p_y$$
$$\psi_2 = c_{11}\mathscr{S} + c_{22}p_x + c_{23}p_y \qquad (8.46)$$
$$\psi_3 = c_{11}\mathscr{S} + c_{32}p_x + c_{33}p_y$$

We can use the C_2 axis (Fig. 8.10) to produce a relationship between ψ_2 and ψ_3.

$$C_2{}^1\psi_2 = \psi_3$$
$$C_2{}^1(c_{11}\mathscr{S} + c_{22}p_x + c_{23}p_y) = c_{11}\mathscr{S} + C_{32}p_x + c_{33}p_y$$

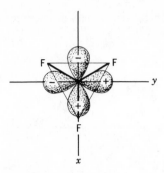

Fig. 8.10 The orientation of the equatorial phosphorus-fluorine bonds relative to the phosphorus $3p_x$ and $3p_y$ AOs.

and

$$c_{11}\mathscr{S} + c_{22}p_x - c_{23}p_y = c_{11}\mathscr{S} + c_{32}p_x + c_{33}p_y$$

Since

$$c_{22} = c_{32} \quad \text{and} \quad -c_{23} = c_{33}$$

we have

$$\psi_3 = c_{11}\mathscr{S} + c_{22}p_x - c_{23}p_y \tag{8.47}$$

Let us now consider the C_3 axis, which relates the coefficients of all three hybrid orbitals.

$$
\begin{aligned}
C_3{}^1\psi_1 &= \psi_2 \\
C_3{}^1\psi_2 &= \psi_3 \\
C_3{}^1\psi_3 &= \psi_1
\end{aligned}
\tag{8.48}
$$

We shall have to consider only the first of these relations

$$C_3{}^1(c_{11}\mathscr{S} + c_{12}p_x) = c_{11}\mathscr{S} + c_{22}p_x + c_{23}p_y$$

By making use of Fig. 8.10 and the rotation matrix developed earlier we obtain

$$C_3{}^1p_x = \cos 120°\, p_x - \sin 120°\, p_y = -\tfrac{1}{2}p_x - \frac{\sqrt{3}}{2}\, p_y$$

$$C_3{}^1p_y = \sin 120°\, p_x + \cos 120°\, p_y = \frac{\sqrt{3}}{2}\, p_x - \tfrac{1}{2}p_y$$

Thus

$$c_{11}\mathcal{S} + c_{12}\left(-\tfrac{1}{2}p_x - \frac{\sqrt{3}}{2}\,p_y\right) = c_{11}\mathcal{S} + c_{22}p_x + c_{23}p_y$$

Upon collecting like coefficients we find

$$-\tfrac{1}{2}c_{12} = c_{22} \quad \text{and} \quad -\frac{\sqrt{3}}{2}\,c_{12} = c_{23}$$

or

$$c_{12} = -2c_{22} = -\frac{2}{\sqrt{3}}\,c_{23}$$

Thus, we can now write the three equatorial hybrids with two unknown coefficients remaining.

$$\psi_1 = c_{11}\mathcal{S} + c_{12}p_x$$

$$\psi_2 = c_{11}\mathcal{S} - \tfrac{1}{2}c_{12}p_x - \frac{\sqrt{3}}{2}\,c_{12}p_y \qquad (8.49)$$

$$\psi_3 = c_{11}\mathcal{S} - \tfrac{1}{2}c_{12}p_x + \frac{\sqrt{3}}{2}\,c_{12}p_y$$

From the orthonormal properties of these hybrid orbitals we obtain

$$\int\psi_1 \cdot \psi_1\,d\tau = 1 \qquad c_{11}^2 + c_{12}^2 = 1 \qquad (8.50)$$
$$\int\psi_1 \cdot \psi_2\,d\tau = 0 \qquad c_{11}^2 - \tfrac{1}{2}c_{12}^2 = 0 \qquad (8.51)$$

Combining these equations, we get

$$c_{12}^2 = \tfrac{2}{3} \qquad c_{11}^2 = \tfrac{1}{2}c_{12}^2 = \tfrac{1}{3}$$

Thus, taking all positive square roots,

$$c_{12} = +\frac{\sqrt{2}}{3} \qquad c_{11} = +\frac{1}{\sqrt{3}}$$

we can write the hybrid equatorial orbitals with no unknown coefficients

$$\psi_1\,(\text{eq}) = \frac{1}{\sqrt{3}}\,\mathcal{S} + \frac{2}{\sqrt{6}}\,p_x$$

$$\psi_2\,(\text{eq}) = \frac{1}{\sqrt{3}}\,\mathcal{S} - \frac{1}{\sqrt{6}}\,p_x - \frac{1}{\sqrt{2}}\,p_y \qquad (8.52)$$

$$\psi_3\,(\text{eq}) = \frac{1}{\sqrt{3}}\,\mathcal{S} - \frac{1}{\sqrt{6}}\,p_x + \frac{1}{\sqrt{2}}\,p_y$$

GROUP THEORY AND SYMMETRY IN CHEMISTRY

Table 8.8   Stable bond arrangements and multiple-bond possibilities

Coordination number	Sigma designation	Geometry	Pi designation Strong	Pi designation Weak
2	sp	Linear	p^2d^2	
	dp	Linear	p^2d^2	
	p^2	Angular	$d(pd)$	$d(sd)$
	ds	Angular	$d(pd)$	$p(pd)$
	d^2	Angular	$d(pd)$	$p(spd)$
3	sp^2	Trigonal plane	pd^2	d^2
	dp^2	Trigonal plane	pd^2	d^2
	ds^2	Trigonal plane	pd^2	p^2
	d^3	Trigonal plane	pd^2	p^2
	dsp	Unsymmetrical plane	pd^2	$(pd)d$
	p^3	Trigonal pyramid		$(sd)d^4$
	d^2p	Trigonal pyramid		$(sd)p^2d^2$
4	sp^3	Tetrahedral	d^2	d^3
	d^3s	Tetrahedral	d^2	p^3
	dsp^2	Tetragonal plane	d^3p	
	d^2p^2	Tetragonal plane	d^3p	
	d^2sp	Irregular tetrahedron		d
	dp^3	Irregular tetrahedron		s
	d^3p	Irregular tetrahedron		s
	d^4	Tetragonal pyramid		$(sp)p$
5	dsp^3	Bipyramid	d^2	d^2
	d^3sp	Bipyramid	d^2	p^2
	d^2sp^2	Tetragonal pyramid	d	pd^2
	d^4s	Tetragonal pyramid	d	p^3
	d^2p^3	Tetragonal pyramid	d	sd^2
	d^4p	Tetragonal pyramid	d	sp^2
	d^3p^2	Pentagonal plane	pd^2	
	d^5	Pentagonal pyramid		$(sp)p^2$
6	d^2sp^3	Octahedron	d^3	
	d^4sp	Trigonal prism	p^2d	
	d^5p	Trigonal prism	p^2s	
	d^3p^3	Trigonal antiprism	sd	
	d^3sp^2	Mixed		
	d^5s	Mixed		
	d^4p^2	Mixed		
7	d^3sp^3	$ZrF_7{}^{3-}$		d^2
	d^5sp	$ArF_7{}^{3-}$		p^2
	d^4sp^2	$TaF_7{}^{--}$		dp
	d^4p^3	$TaF_7{}^{--}$		ds
	d^5p^2	$TaF_7{}^{--}$		ps
8	d^4sp^3	Dodecahedron	d	
	d^5p^3	Antiprism		s
	d^5sp^2	Face-centered prism	p	

Source: Taken by permission from H. Eyring, J. Walter, and G. E. Kimball, "Quantum Chemistry," John Wiley & Sons, Inc., New York, 1960.

and the axial hybrid orbitals can now be included

$$\psi_4 \, (\text{ax}) = \frac{1}{\sqrt{2}} \, (\mathcal{S}' + p_z)$$

$$\psi_5 \, (\text{ax}) = \frac{1}{\sqrt{2}} \, (\mathcal{S}' - p_z)$$

(8.53)

In order to write the full set of five hybridized (not necessarily equivalent) orbitals without unknown coefficients for a specific case, we have yet to determine the mixing parameters in $\mathcal{S}$ and $\mathcal{S}'$.

$$\mathcal{S} = as + bd_{z^2} \qquad \mathcal{S}' = a's + b'd_{z^2}$$

A specific set of values for a, b, a', and b' can be determined only by a solution (perhaps approximate) of the Schrödinger equation for the specific problem. A suggestion for reducing the problem to one variable is offered in Prob. 8.9.

In the development of the hybrid orbitals for the dsp^3 case two additional benefits have accrued. We have obtained expressions for the linear combinations for both the linear case (either sp or dp) and for the trigonal planar (sp^2 or dp^2) case. Because the axial and equatorial hybrid bonds are symmetry-independent, they may be used separately in the treatment of hybrids of the appropriate geometry. Therefore, we can write the following sets of equations for the linear and trigonal planar cases.

Linear

sp

$$\psi_1 = \frac{1}{\sqrt{2}} \, (s + p_z)$$

$$\psi_2 = \frac{1}{\sqrt{2}} \, (s - p_z)$$

dp

$$\psi_1 = \frac{1}{\sqrt{2}} \, (d_{z^2} + p_z)$$

$$\psi_2 = \frac{1}{\sqrt{2}} \, (d_{z^2} - p_z)$$

Trigonal planar

sp^2

$$\psi_1 = \frac{1}{\sqrt{3}} s + \frac{2}{\sqrt{6}} p_x$$

$$\psi_2 = \frac{1}{\sqrt{3}} s - \frac{1}{\sqrt{6}} p_x + \frac{1}{\sqrt{2}} p_y$$

$$\psi_3 = \frac{1}{\sqrt{3}} s - \frac{1}{\sqrt{6}} p_x - \frac{1}{\sqrt{2}} p_y$$

dp^2

$$\psi_1 = \frac{1}{\sqrt{3}} d_{z^2} + \frac{2}{\sqrt{6}} p_x$$

$$\psi_2 = \frac{1}{\sqrt{3}} d_{z^2} - \frac{1}{\sqrt{6}} p_x + \frac{1}{\sqrt{2}} p_y$$

$$\psi_3 = \frac{1}{\sqrt{3}} d_{z^2} - \frac{1}{\sqrt{6}} p_x - \frac{1}{\sqrt{2}} p_y$$

Further examples are given in Probs. 8.10 and 8.11.

PROBLEMS

8.1. The following are the unnormalized functions for $4f$ orbitals:

n	l	m	Function
4	3	+3	$r^3 e^{-r/4} \sin^2 \theta \, e^{i3\phi}$
4	3	+2	$r^3 e^{-r/4} \sin^2 \theta \cos \theta \, e^{i2\phi}$
4	3	+1	$r^3 e^{-r/4} \sin \theta \, (5 \cos^2 \theta - 1)e^{i\phi}$
4	3	0	$r^3 e^{-r/4} \left(\frac{5}{3} \cos^3 \theta - \cos \theta\right)$
4	3	−1	$r^3 e^{-r/4} \sin \theta \, (5 \cos^2 \theta - 1)e^{-i\phi}$
4	3	−2	$r^3 e^{-r/4} \sin^2 \theta \cos \theta \, e^{-i2\phi}$
4	3	−3	$r^3 e^{-r/4} \sin^2 \theta \, e^{-i3\phi}$

Determine the transformation properties of these orbitals by converting the angular parts to cartesian coordinates and determine the irreducible representations to which they belong in point groups T_d, O_h, and D_{4h}.

8.2. Show that the following combinations yield trigonal bipyramidal orbitals, as in PCl_5.

D_{3h}	E	$2C_3$	$3C_2$	σ_h	$2S_3$	$3\sigma_v$
Γ_σ	5	2	1	3	0	3

$$\Gamma_\sigma = 2A_1' + A_2'' + E'$$

Possible combinations:

(a) $s, p_z, p_x, p_y, d_{z^2}$

(b) $s, p_z, d_{xy}, d_{x^2-y^2}, d_{z^2}$

(c) $nd_{z^2}, p_z, p_x, p_y, (n+1)d_{z^2}$

(d) $nd_{z^2}, p_z, d_{xy}, d_{x^2-y^2}, (n+1)d_{z^2}$

(e) $ns, p_z, p_x, p_y, (n+1)s$

(f) $ns, p_z, d_{x^2-y^2}, d_{xy}, (n+1)s$

8.3. Show that the only possible combination for hybrid orbitals with octahedral (O_h) symmetry is d^2sp^3 $(s, p_x, p_y, p_z, d_{z^2}, d_{x^2-y^2})$.

8.4. Determine the two possible sets of orbitals possessing D_{4h} symmetry as in $Ni(CO)_4$ or XeF_4.

8.5. Determine the AOs which possess appropriate symmetry for pi bonding in the following types of compounds:

(a) Tetrahedral molecules or ions

(b) Octahedral molecules or ions

(c) Square planar molecules or ions

8.6. Find the appropriate linear combination of $2s$ and $2p$ atomic orbitals for a set of four tetrahedral hybrid orbitals for the following orientation of the tetrahedral orbitals.   (Note that this orientation is different from that of Fig. 8.6.)   A simple transformation of the atomic orbitals is sufficient.

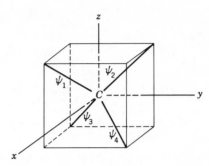

8.7. Verify that the set of tetrahedral hybrid sd^3 orbitals has the following form:

$$\psi_1 = \tfrac{1}{2}(s + d_{xz} + d_{yz} + d_{xy})$$
$$\psi_2 = \tfrac{1}{2}(s - d_{xz} - d_{yz} + d_{xy})$$
$$\psi_3 = \tfrac{1}{2}(s + d_{xz} - d_{yz} - d_{xy})$$
$$\psi_4 = \tfrac{1}{2}(s - d_{xz} + d_{yz} - d_{xy})$$

8.8. Sketch the d pi orbitals centered on X in an octahedral complex XY_6 and show their relation to p pi orbitals centered on the Y atoms. This sketch can also be used to discuss the bonding in square planar (D_{4h}) molecules or ions.

8.9. Consider the form of the following set of hybrid orbitals in trigonal bipyramidal geometry using the dsp^3 set as suggested by F. A. Cotton:[1]

$$\psi_1 \,(\text{eq}) = \frac{1}{\sqrt{3}} (s \sin \alpha - d_{z^2} \cos \alpha) + \frac{2}{\sqrt{6}} p_x$$

$$\psi_2 \,(\text{eq}) = \frac{1}{\sqrt{3}} (s \sin \alpha - d_{z^2} \cos \alpha) - \frac{1}{\sqrt{6}} p_x + \frac{1}{\sqrt{2}} p_y$$

$$\psi_3 \,(\text{eq}) = \frac{1}{\sqrt{3}} (s \sin \alpha - d_{z^2} \cos \alpha) - \frac{1}{\sqrt{6}} p_x - \frac{1}{\sqrt{2}} p_y$$

$$\psi_4 \,(\text{ax}) = \frac{1}{\sqrt{2}} (s \sin \alpha + d_{z^2} \cos \alpha) + \frac{1}{\sqrt{2}} p_z$$

$$\psi_5 \,(\text{ax}) = \frac{1}{\sqrt{2}} (s \sin \alpha + d_{z^2} \cos \alpha) - \frac{1}{\sqrt{2}} p_z$$

The parameter α may be determined empirically or theoretically.   Show that this set of orbitals is normalized and orthogonal.

[1] F. A. Cotton, "Chemical Applications of Group Theory," p. 116, John Wiley & Sons, Inc., New York, 1964.

8.10. Show that the following set of equations represents linear combinations for square planar (D_{4h}) hybrid orbitals, using s, p_x, p_y, and $d_{x^2-y^2}$ AOs

$$\psi_1(+x) = \tfrac{1}{2}s + \frac{1}{\sqrt{2}}\,p_x + \tfrac{1}{2}d_{x^2-y^2}$$

$$\psi_2(+y) = \tfrac{1}{2}s + \frac{1}{\sqrt{2}}\,p_y - \tfrac{1}{2}d_{x^2-y^2}$$

$$\psi_3(-x) = \tfrac{1}{2}s - \frac{1}{\sqrt{2}}\,p_x + \tfrac{1}{2}d_{x^2-y^2}$$

$$\psi_4(-y) = \tfrac{1}{2}s - \frac{1}{\sqrt{2}}\,p_y - \tfrac{1}{2}d_{x^2-y^2}$$

$\psi_1(+x)$ is a hybrid orbital with its positive extent along the $+x$ direction.
8.11. Derive the following set of equivalent hybrid AOs for an octahedral symmetry in which the hybrids are directed along the (positive and negative) cartesian axes.

$$\psi_1 = \frac{1}{\sqrt{6}}\,s + \frac{1}{\sqrt{2}}\,p_z + \frac{1}{\sqrt{3}}\,d_{z^2}$$

$$\psi_2 = \frac{1}{\sqrt{6}}\,s - \frac{1}{\sqrt{2}}\,p_z + \frac{1}{\sqrt{3}}\,d_{z^2}$$

$$\psi_3 = \frac{1}{\sqrt{6}}\,s + \frac{1}{\sqrt{2}}\,p_x - \frac{1}{\sqrt{12}}\,d_{z^2} + \tfrac{1}{2}d_{x^2-y^2}$$

$$\psi_4 = \frac{1}{\sqrt{6}}\,s - \frac{1}{\sqrt{2}}\,p_x - \frac{1}{\sqrt{12}}\,d_{z^2} + \tfrac{1}{2}d_{x^2-y^2}$$

$$\psi_5 = \frac{1}{\sqrt{6}}\,s + \frac{1}{\sqrt{2}}\,p_y - \frac{1}{\sqrt{12}}\,d_{z^2} - \tfrac{1}{2}d_{x^2-y^2}$$

$$\psi_6 = \frac{1}{\sqrt{6}}\,s - \frac{1}{\sqrt{2}}\,p_y - \frac{1}{\sqrt{12}}\,d_{z^2} - \tfrac{1}{2}d_{x^2-y^2}$$

Caution must be exercised in determining the symmetry relations among the AOs.   The reader may wish to consult a textbook which presents a full development of AO wave functions.
8.12. Verify that $\mathscr{S}$ is normalized when a and b are defined as follows:

$$\mathscr{S} = as + bd_{z^2}$$

$$a = \frac{1}{\sqrt{1 + \lambda^2}} \qquad b = \frac{\lambda}{\sqrt{1 + \lambda^2}}$$

8.13. In order to determine the hybrid orbitals for a molecule of C_{3v} symmetry such as NH_3, all the p orbitals must be used in addition to the s orbital.   The four orbitals in the resulting set are not all equivalent: three equivalent orbitals for the N—H bonds and one for the lone pair of electrons. These four orbitals may be obtained by a consideration of the form of the orbitals of D_{3h} symmetry of the sp^2 type. If the z axis is taken as the principal axis, the lone-pair hybrid orbital is composed of a linear combination of the s and p_z orbitals.

(a) Show that the three equivalent hybrid orbitals can be obtained from the trigonal planar sp^2 orbitals by simply replacing the contribution of the s orbital with an orbital which itself is a *normalized* linear combination of the s and p_z orbitals. The usual symbol for the mixing parameter is λ. *Hint:* Write a linear combination of s and p_z using λ as the coefficient of p_z. Normalize this combination in terms of λ.

(b) The "extra" coefficient or mixing parameter can be related to the angle between the N—H bonds. Show that the relation is

$$\theta = \frac{1}{3\lambda^2 + 2}$$

Hint: The hybrid orbital may be thought of as a vector, and the dot (scalar) product between any two of the three equivalent bond orbitals is a function of the angle θ between them.

9

molecular orbital theory

Since the Schrödinger equation cannot be solved exactly for molecular systems containing more than one electron, many approximation techniques have been developed. They all involve the construction of approximate wave functions under a set of rules. These methods fall into two general classifications: molecular-orbital (MO) theory and valence-bond theory. Valence-bond theory emphasizes the two-electron two-center bond concept, holding to the localized nature of electrons in bonds. By contrast MO theory emphasizes the idea that bonding electrons are somehow the property of the whole molecule. Because a specific MO may be heavily concentrated in the area of one bond, some have said that MO theory encompasses valence-bond theory.

Because MO theory treats the wave functions as involving the whole molecule, the notions of group theory can be applied to the solution of the problem. The calculation of the energies associated with the various MOs involves the evaluation of integrals of the type

$$\int \phi_i^* \mathcal{3C} \phi_j \, d\tau$$

The labor of solving the problem is greatly reduced if some of these integrals can be shown to be zero simply by symmetry arguments.

9.1 THE LCAO METHOD AND THE SECULAR EQUATIONS

The usual method for constructing MOs is the linear combination of AOs (LCAO). Each atom in the molecular system is considered to contribute at least one atomic orbital to the MO system. Thus, each MO is written as

$$\psi_i = \sum_j c_{ij} \phi_j$$

Using this definition of the wave function, the corresponding energy can be calculated from the usual energy expression:

$$E_i = \frac{\int \psi_i^* \mathfrak{K} \psi_i \, d\tau}{\int \psi_i^* \psi_i \, d\tau}$$

The whole problem of the determination of the energy E_i and the c_{ij}, the linear coefficients, may be treated under the variational principle: the best estimate of the energy is obtained when the energy E_i is minimized with respect to the coefficients c_{ij}.

Substitute the expression for the LCAO MOs into the energy expression

$$E_i = \frac{\displaystyle\sum_k \sum_j c_{ik}^* c_{ij} \int \phi_k^* \mathfrak{K} \phi_j \, d\tau}{\displaystyle\sum_k \sum_j c_{ik}^* c_{ij} \int \phi_k^* \phi_j \, d\tau}$$

Let

$$H_{kj} = \int \phi_k^* \mathfrak{K} \phi_j \, d\tau$$

and

$$S_{kj} = \int \phi_k^* \phi_j \, d\tau$$

Then

$$E_i = \frac{\displaystyle\sum_k \sum_j c_{ik}^* c_{ij} H_{kj}}{\displaystyle\sum_k \sum_j c_{ik}^* c_{ij} S_{kj}}$$

Upon rearranging we find

$$\sum_k \sum_j c_{ik}^* c_{ij} (H_{kj} - E_i S_{kj}) = 0$$

Now we apply the variational principle, i.e., minimize the energy with respect to c_{kj}^*. The result is

$$\sum_j c_{ij}(H_{ij} - E_i S_{ij}) = 0 \tag{9.1}$$

The only nontrivial solution to this system of homogeneous equations requires that the determinant of the coefficients vanish:

$$|H_{ij} - E_i S_{ij}| = 0 \tag{9.2}$$

Equations (9.1) and (9.2) are a statement of the eigenvalue problem. Although there are standard methods for the solution of such problems, unless the above array is fairly simple, the amount of labor necessary to obtain the solution by hand is prohibitive.

In order to understand the part symmetry arguments may play in the reduction of the order of magnitude of this eigenvalue problem consider the following enlarged version of it.

$$
\begin{array}{c}
 \\
\phi_1 \\
\phi_2 \\
\phi_3 \\
\phi_4 \\
 \\
\phi_k \\
\phi_{k+1} \\
\phi_{k+2}
\end{array}
\begin{array}{c}
\phi_1 \\
\left[\begin{array}{c}
H_{11} - E_i S_{11} \\
H_{12} - E_i S_{12} \\
H_{13} - E_i S_{13} \\
H_{14} - E_i S_{14} \\
\cdots \\
H_{1,k} - E_i S_{1,k} \\
H_{1,k+1} - E_i S_{1,k+1} \\
H_{1,k+2} - E_i S_{1,k+2}
\end{array}\right.
\end{array}
\begin{array}{c}
\phi_2 \\
H_{21} - E_i S_{21} \\
H_{22} - E_i S_{22} \\
H_{23} - E_i S_{23} \\
H_{24} - E_i S_{24} \\
\cdots \\
H_{2,k} - E_i S_{2,k} \\
H_{2,k+1} - E_i S_{2,k+1} \\
H_{2,k+2} - E_i S_{2,k+2}
\end{array}
\begin{array}{c}
\phi_3 \\
H_{31} - E_i S_{31} \\
H_{32} - E_i S_{32} \\
H_{33} - E_i S_{33} \\
H_{34} - E_i S_{34} \\
\cdots \\
\cdots \\
\cdots \\
\cdots
\end{array}
\begin{array}{c}
 \\
\cdots \\
\cdots \\
\cdots \\
\cdots \\
 \\
\cdots \\
\cdots \\
\cdots
\end{array}\left.\right]
$$

Now, if by group-theoretical methods, the various AOs ϕ_i are arranged into linear combinations belonging to the same symmetry, certain matrix elements can be seen to be zero. That is, matrix elements between wave functions of different symmetries must vanish. Then, if all the wave functions of the same symmetry are grouped serially together, the matrix $[H_{ij} - E_i S_{ij}]$ takes on block-diagonal form as shown on page 219.

Thus, instead of the laborious problem of solving an $N \times N$ eigenvalue problem, a series of smaller determinants—perhaps with a 3×3 as the largest—may be solved.

We can make use of arguments presented earlier to show why the integrals involving orbitals from different irreducible representations are zero.

$$H_{kj} = \int \phi_k'^* \mathfrak{IC} \phi_j' \, d\tau$$

Since the hamiltonian operator must possess the full symmetry of the molecule, it belongs to the totally symmetric representation A_1. Thus,

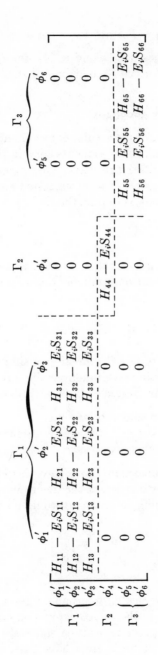

if ϕ'_k and ϕ'_j belong to different irreducible representations, the integrand above reduces as

$$\phi_k^{*'} \mathfrak{IC} \phi_j' \rightarrow \Gamma_\alpha \Gamma_{A_1} \Gamma_\beta \rightarrow \Gamma_\alpha \Gamma_\beta \neq \Gamma_{A_1} \qquad \alpha \neq \beta$$

Since the integrand does not belong to A_1, the integral vanishes. The same argument holds for the S_{kj} matrix elements.

9.2 THE SIMPLE HÜCKEL APPROACH

In the above expression for the secular determinant we see that all nonzero elements including off-diagonal elements contain the eigenvalue E_i. The problem is greatly simplified if the eigenvalue appears only on the diagonal of the secular determinant. Hückel suggested an approach to this problem: the zero-differential-overlap method.

Let

$$S_{kj} = \delta_{kj}$$

That is, the overlap integral is assumed to be zero between any two atoms. Then, the secular determinant takes on a simpler form

$$|H_{kj} - E_i \mathbb{I}| = 0$$

The symbol $\mathbb{I}$ stands for the unit matrix. The off-diagonal terms are only of the H_{kj} type.

In the evaluation of the H_{kj} integrals a similar assumption is introduced. Since the atomic wave functions die out fairly rapidly across a molecule, interactions are neglected between atoms which are not bonded:

$$H_{kk} = \alpha_k \qquad \text{the coulomb integral}$$
$$H_{kj} = \begin{cases} \beta_{kj} & k = j \pm 1; \text{ the resonance integral} \\ 0 & \text{nonbonded atoms} \end{cases}$$

Under these assumptions many zeros are introduced into the secular determinant, and the evaluation of the determinant is greatly simplified. For example, the following determinant would result for a linear (or bent) triatomic molecule:

$$\begin{vmatrix} \alpha_1 - E_i & \beta_{21} & 0 \\ \beta_{12} & \alpha_2 - E_i & \beta_{32} \\ 0 & \beta_{23} & \alpha_3 - E_i \end{vmatrix} = 0$$

The solution to the secular determinant gives the energy eigenvalues E_i. The coefficients c_{ij} in the LCAO expression for the MOs are obtained by solving the set of equations for each eigenvalue E_i.

Once the energies of the system have been determined, an energy-level diagram can be constructed. The energy levels may be filled with the available number of electrons according to the Pauli principle and by Hund's rules. The total energy of the system is then the sum of the energies of the filled molecular orbitals.

9.3 HÜCKEL THEORY AND THE PI-SYSTEM APPROXIMATION

A useful method of treating organic systems with double bonds—aromatic or not—involves the assumption that the pi electron system may be treated independently from the sigma electron system. Since this approximation simplifies the overall problem, we shall consider certain pi systems first. It must be remembered that simple Hückel theory is a crude approximation and the results must be judged accordingly.

Under the pi approximation the hamiltonian may be written as a sum

$$\mathcal{3C} = \mathcal{3C}_\sigma + \mathcal{3C}_\pi$$

and the wave function as a product

$$\Psi_{total} = \psi_\sigma \psi_\pi$$

Thus, the pi system is separable from the sigma system and mathematically may be treated completely independently. This assumption is equivalent to stating that all the pi electrons experience the same interaction with the sigma core electrons.

We must now evaluate the expressions for each energy level. We shall use the preceding definitions of the various integrals. The energy of the ith energy level is given as

$$E_i = \int \psi_i^* \mathcal{3C} \psi_i \, d\tau$$

Now use the LCAO definition of the wave function ψ_i

$$\psi_i = N_i \sum_j a_{ij} \phi_j \qquad (N_i \text{ is a normalization constant})$$

Then

$$E_i = \int N_i^* \sum_j a_{ij}^* \phi_j^* \mathcal{3C} N_i \sum_k a_{ik} \phi_k \, d\tau$$

This expression may be written in two terms, one for coulomb integrals and one for resonance (exchange) integrals

$$E_i = N_i^2 \sum_j a_{ij}^* a_{ij} \int \phi_j^* \mathcal{3C} \phi_j \, d\tau + N_i^2 \sum_j \sum_{\substack{k \\ j>k}} a_{ij}^* a_{ik} \int \phi_j^* \mathcal{3C} \phi_k \, d\tau$$

Let

$$\int \phi_j^* \mathcal{3C} \phi_j \, d\tau = \alpha_j$$

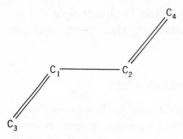

Fig. 9.1 The carbon skeleton of *trans*-1,2-butadiene showing the location of the two double bonds.

and

$$\int \phi_j^* \mathfrak{K} \phi_k \, d\tau = \beta_{jk}$$

Then

$$E_i = N_i^2 \sum_j |a_{ij}|^2 \alpha_j + N_i^2 \sum_{j>k} \sum_k |a_{ij} a_{ik}| \beta_{jk}$$

This is the energy expression under the so-called *one-electron approxima-tion*. Further simplification may be introduced for the organic pi sys-tem by setting all α_j equal; considering the same kind of p pi orbital to be contributed by each carbon atom.

Note that

$$N_i^2 \sum_j |a_{ij}|^2 = 1$$

then

$$E_i = \alpha + N_i^2 \sum_{j>k} \sum_k |a_{ij} a_{ik}| \beta_{jk}$$

Let us now consider ethylene and butadiene as specific examples.

BUTADIENE

Butadiene is most stable in the trans form, as shown in Fig. 9.1. It possesses C_{2h} point-group symmetry. The C_{2h} character table is

C_{2h}	E	C_2	i	σ_h
A_g	1	1	1	1
B_g	1	-1	1	-1
A_u	1	1	-1	-1
B_u	1	-1	-1	1

In order to factor the secular determinant the first step in the use of group theory is to determine the sets of symmetry orbitals. Then, the symmetries of the MOs are determined in the standard manner.

There are two sets of nonequivalent carbon atoms in butadiene: 1, 2 and 3, 4. Let us write both symmetric and antisymmetric combinations of the p pi orbitals centered on these two sets of atoms.

$$\chi_{1,2}{}^S = \phi_1 + \phi_2 \qquad \chi_{1,2}{}^A = \phi_1 - \phi_2$$
$$\chi_{3,4}{}^S = \phi_3 + \phi_4 \qquad \chi_{3,4}{}^A = \phi_3 - \phi_4$$

We now consider a representation based on these four p pi orbitals each of which is centered on a carbon atom. By considering the result of the various symmetry operations upon the p pi orbitals, a character system can be determined. Since no symmetry operation in the group interchanges 1 and 2 with 3 and 4, these two groups may be taken as independent basis sets.

C_{2h}	E	C_2	i	σ_h
$\Gamma_{\text{all } p\pi}$	4	0	0	-4
$\Gamma_{1,2}$	2	0	0	-2
$\Gamma_{3,4}$	2	0	0	-2

Note that the p pi orbital has a node in the molecular plane so that $\sigma_h p\pi = -p\pi$. Thus,

$$\Gamma_{\text{all } p\pi} = \Gamma_{1,2} + \Gamma_{3,4}$$

By the standard reduction process we find

$$\Gamma_{\text{all } p\pi} = 2A_u + 2B_g$$

and

$$\Gamma_{1,2} = \Gamma_{3,4} = A_u + B_g$$

We can now write out the MOs in terms of the various p pi orbitals (or symmetry orbitals) so that they conform to the symmetry of the allowed irreducible representations.

1. A_u orbitals must be symmetric upon C_2 rotation and antisymmetric to inversion and to reflection in the molecular plane. Thus

$$\psi_1(A_u) = \frac{1}{\sqrt{2}} (\phi_1 + \phi_2) = \frac{1}{\sqrt{2}} \chi_{1,2}{}^S$$

$$\psi_2(A_u) = \frac{1}{\sqrt{2}} (\phi_3 + \phi_4) = \frac{1}{\sqrt{2}} \chi_{3,4}{}^S$$

2. B_g orbitals must be antisymmetric under C_2 rotation and reflection in the molecular plane and symmetric to inversion. Thus

$$\psi_1(B_g) = \frac{1}{\sqrt{2}}(\phi_1 - \phi_2) = \frac{1}{\sqrt{2}}\chi_{1,2}{}^A$$

$$\psi_2(B_g) = \frac{1}{\sqrt{2}}(\phi_3 - \phi_4) = \frac{1}{\sqrt{2}}\chi_{3,4}{}^A$$

The next step is the calculation of the matrix elements. First, the A_u MOs:

$$H_{11} = \int \frac{1}{\sqrt{2}}(\phi_1 + \phi_2)\mathfrak{H} \frac{1}{\sqrt{2}}(\phi_1 + \phi_2)\, d\tau$$

$$= \tfrac{1}{2}\left(\int \phi_1\mathfrak{H}\phi_1\, d\tau + \int \phi_1\mathfrak{H}\phi_2\, d\tau + \int \phi_2\mathfrak{H}\phi_1\, d\tau + \int \phi_2\mathfrak{H}\phi_2\, d\tau\right)$$

$$= \tfrac{1}{2}(\alpha_1 + \beta_{12} + \beta_{21} + \alpha_2)$$

Let $\alpha_1 = \alpha_2 = \alpha$ and $\beta_{12} = \beta_{21} = \beta$, so that

$$H_{11} = \alpha + \beta$$

Similarly

$$H_{22} = \tfrac{1}{2}(\alpha_3 + \beta_{34} + \beta_{43} + \alpha_4) = \alpha$$

since $\beta_{34} = \beta_{43} = 0$, and

$$H_{12} = H_{21} = \tfrac{1}{2}(\beta_{13} + \beta_{14} + \beta_{23} + \beta_{24}) = \beta$$

since $\beta_{14} = \beta_{23} = 0$. Similarly for the B_g MOs:

$$H_{11} = \tfrac{1}{2}(\alpha_1 - \beta_{12} - \beta_{21} + \alpha_2) = \alpha - \beta$$
$$H_{22} = \tfrac{1}{2}(\alpha_3 - \beta_{34} - \beta_{43} + \alpha_4) = \alpha$$
$$H_{12} = H_{21} = \tfrac{1}{2}(\beta_{12} - \beta_{14} - \beta_{23} + \beta_{24}) = \beta$$

Let us write the secular determinant for the whole molecule and observe that it is in block-diagonal form because of the relation

$$\int \psi_i(A_u)\mathfrak{H}\psi_i(B_g)\, d\tau \equiv 0$$

$$\begin{vmatrix} \alpha + \beta - E_i & \beta & 0 & 0 \\ \beta & \alpha - E_i & 0 & 0 \\ 0 & 0 & \alpha - \beta - E_i & \beta \\ 0 & 0 & \beta & \alpha - E_i \end{vmatrix} = 0$$

We can thus consider the A_u and B_g determinants separately:

$$\begin{vmatrix} \alpha + \beta - E_i & \beta \\ \beta & \alpha - E_i \end{vmatrix} = 0 \quad \text{and} \quad \begin{vmatrix} \alpha - \beta - E_i & \beta \\ \beta & \alpha - E_i \end{vmatrix} = 0$$

Make the substitution $(\alpha - E_i)/\beta = x$.

$$\begin{vmatrix} x+1 & 1 \\ 1 & x \end{vmatrix} = 0 \qquad \begin{vmatrix} x-1 & 1 \\ 1 & x \end{vmatrix} = 0$$

The secular equations are easily obtained from these determinants.

$$x^2 + x - 1 = 0 \qquad x^2 - x - 1 = 0$$
$$x = \frac{-1 \pm \sqrt{5}}{2} \qquad x = \frac{1 \pm \sqrt{5}}{2}$$

or

$$E_1{}^A = \alpha + \beta \frac{-1 + \sqrt{5}}{2} \qquad E_1{}^B = \alpha + \beta \frac{1 + \sqrt{5}}{2}$$

$$E_2{}^A = \alpha + \beta \frac{-1 - \sqrt{5}}{2} \qquad E_2{}^B = \alpha + \beta \frac{1 - \sqrt{5}}{2}$$

$$E_1{}^A = \alpha + 0.618\beta \qquad E_1{}^B = \alpha + 1.618\beta$$
$$E_2{}^A = \alpha - 1.618\beta \qquad E_2{}^B = \alpha - 0.618\beta$$

An energy-level diagram for the butadiene pi system can now be constructed. It is shown in Fig. 9.2. Note that both α and β are negative.

Two electrons may be placed in each of the two lowest MOs. Since these two lowest MOs possess energy which is lower than the separated p pi orbitals, that is α, the system is binding. The total pi energy can be calculated by summing the energy of the four electrons.

$$E_T{}^\pi = 2(\alpha + 0.618\beta) + 2(\alpha + 1.618\beta) = 4\alpha + 4.472\beta$$

In order to compute the charge distribution and bond order we need the true MO wave function. The functions listed above are symmetry orbitals used to factorize the secular determinant. We must determine the combination of A_u symmetry orbitals which has an energy of $\alpha + 1.618\beta$. Let us write the true MO wave function, then, as follows:

$$\psi^{(1)}(A_u) = N_{A_u}[\psi_1(A_u) + a\psi_2(A_u)]$$

Let us normalize $\psi^{(1)}(A_u)$:

$$\int \psi^{(1)}(A_u)\psi^{(1)}(A_u) \, d\tau = 1$$
$$N_{A_u}{}^2 \int [\psi_1(A_u) + a\psi_2(A_u)][\psi_1(A_u) + a\psi_2(A_u)] \, d\tau = 1$$
$$= \int \psi_1(A_u)\psi_1(A_u) \, d\tau + 2a\int \psi_1(A_u)\psi_2(A_u) \, d\tau + a^2 \int \psi_2(A_u)\psi_2(A_u) \, d\tau$$
$$1 = N_{A_u}{}^2(1 + a^2)$$

So that

$$N_{A_u} = \frac{1}{(1 + a^2)^{\frac{1}{2}}}$$

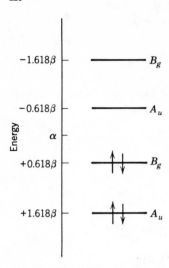

Fig. 9.2 The MO energy-level scheme for the pi system of *trans*-1,2-butadiene under the simple Hückel approximation showing the electron occupancy of the two lowest energy levels. The directions of the arrows indicate the relative spin of the electrons: the spin quantum numbers $\pm\frac{1}{2}$. The energy is given in units of α, the carbon $2p$ coulomb integral.

Thus

$$\psi^{(1)}(A_u) = \frac{1}{(1 + a^2)^{\frac{1}{2}}} [\psi_1(A_u) + a\psi_2(A_u)]$$

To determine a we write the energy expression as a function of a for $\psi^{(1)}(A_u)$. The energy must be equal to $\alpha + 1.618\beta$.

$$E_{A_u}^{(1)} = \int \psi^{(1)}(A_u) \mathcal{K} \psi^{(1)}(A_u)\, d\tau$$

$$\alpha + 1.618\beta = \frac{1}{1 + a^2} \{\int [\phi_1 + \phi_2 + a(\phi_3 + \phi_4)]\mathcal{K}[\phi_1 + \phi_2$$

$$+ a(\phi_3 + \phi_4)]\, d\tau\}$$

$$= \frac{1}{1 + a^2} (\alpha + \beta + a\beta + 0 + \beta + \alpha + 0 + a\beta + a\beta$$

$$+ 0 + a^2\alpha + 0 + 0 + a\beta + 0 + a^2\alpha)$$

$$= \alpha + \frac{2(1 + 2a)\beta}{2(1 + a^2)}$$

or

$$a^2 - 1.236a + 0.382 = 0$$

$$a = \frac{1.236 \pm \sqrt{1.528 - 1.528}}{2} = 0.618$$

so that

$$\psi^{(1)}(A_u) = \frac{\psi_1(A_u) + 0.618\psi_2(A_u)}{\sqrt{1 + 0.618^2}}$$

$$= \frac{1}{1.276}\left[\frac{1}{\sqrt{2}}(\phi_1 + \phi_2) + \frac{0.618}{\sqrt{2}}(\phi_3 + \phi_4)\right]$$

$$\psi^{(1)}(A_u) = 0.61\phi_1 + 0.61\phi_2 + 0.37\phi_3 + 0.37\phi_4$$

In the same manner the B_g MO is obtained:

$$\psi^{(1)}(B_g) = 0.37\phi_1 - 0.37\phi_2 + 0.61\phi_3 - 0.61\phi_4$$

Let us define the bond order b_{ij}:

$$b_{ij} = 2\sum_{k=1}^{N_{occ}} c_{ki}c_{kj}$$

where N_{occ} is the number of occupied orbitals, ij refer to the numbering of the atoms, and c_{ki}, c_{kj} are the coefficients in the MO.

Let us calculate b_{12} and b_{13}:

$$b_{12} = 2(0.61)(0.61) + 2(0.37)(-0.37) = 0.72 - 0.27 = 0.45$$
$$b_{13} = 2(0.37)(0.61) + 2(0.61)(0.37) = 0.45 + 0.45 = 0.90$$

The concept of the bond order (as defined originally by Coulson[1]) generally relates to the strength of the bond and, thus, to the bond length (see Streitweiser's book, listed in the references at the end of the chapter). In butadiene the above calculation shows that although there may be pi character in the C_1—C_2 bond, the outer bonds possess at least twice the pi character.

It is of interest to compare the energy of the butadiene pi system (two conjugated double bonds) with the energy of two isolated double bonds (as the total pi energy of two ethylene pi systems).

ETHYLENE

As shown in Fig. 9.3, in C_2H_4 there are two p pi orbitals on adjacent carbon atoms available for the formation of a double bond. These two

[1] C. A. Coulson, "Valence," 2d ed., Oxford University Press, Fair Lawn, N.J., 1961.

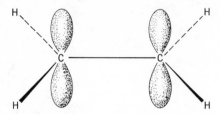

Fig. 9.3 The molecular structure of ethylene showing a $2p_z$ orbital centered on each carbon atom.

orbitals generate a 2×2 secular determinant as follows:

$$H_{11} = H_{22} = \int \phi_i \mathcal{3C} \phi_i \, d\tau = \alpha$$
$$H_{12} = H_{21} = \int \phi_i \mathcal{3C} \phi_j \, d\tau = \beta$$
$$\begin{vmatrix} \alpha - E_i & \beta \\ \beta & \alpha - E_i \end{vmatrix} = 0$$
$$\alpha^2 - 2\alpha E_i + E_i^2 - \beta^2 = 0$$
$$E_i^2 - 2\alpha E_i + \alpha^2 - \beta^2 = 0$$
$$E_i = \frac{2\alpha \pm \sqrt{4\alpha^2 - 4\alpha^2 + 4\beta^2}}{2} = \alpha \pm \beta$$

The energy-level diagram is shown in Fig. 9.4. The total pi energy is easily summed:

$$E_{total}^{\pi} = 2(\alpha + \beta) = 2\alpha + 2\beta$$

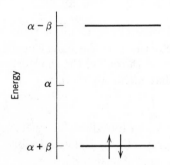

Fig. 9.4 The MO energy-level scheme for the pi system of ethylene showing the occupancy of the lowest energy level. Energy is given in units of α, the carbon $2p$ coulomb integral.

We may now compare the total pi energy of butadiene with twice that of ethylene:

$$E_{\text{total}}^{\text{but}} - 2E_{\text{total}}^{\text{eth}} = 4\alpha + 4.472\beta - 4\alpha - 4\beta$$
$$= 0.472\beta$$

That is, the conjugation of two double bonds lowers their energy relative to the separated state by 0.472β. Since β for this molecule should be 18 to 20 kcal/mole, this resonance stabilization energy is about 9 to 10 kcal/mole.

BENZENE

Let us now consider a cyclic pi system, C_6H_6, benzene. It will be assumed that the sigma system is composed of sp^2 hybrid bonds centered on the carbon atoms and $1s$ orbitals centered on the hydrogen atoms. There remains, then, one p pi orbital on each carbon atom, as shown in Fig. 9.5.

Let us first determine the symmetry of the MOs obtained using these six p pi orbitals as a basis set.

D_{6h}	E	$2C_6$	$2C_3$	C_2	$3C_2'$	$3C_2''$	i	$2S_3$	$2S_6$	σ_h	$3\sigma_d$	$3\sigma_v$
$\Gamma_{p\pi}$	6	0	0	0	-2	0	0	0	0	-6	0	2

By the standard reduction formula we find that this character system reduces as follows:

$$\Gamma_{p\pi} = A_{2u} + B_{2g} + E_{1g} + E_{2u}$$

However, we shall not need the full symmetry of the molecule for the purpose of obtaining the symmetry orbitals. We require only the sixfold rotation subgroup. Thus, we need only refer to the character table for C_6. The character system for the p pi orbitals is obtained in the usual manner and is shown together with the C_6 character table in Table 9.1.

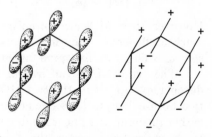

Fig. 9.5 The carbon skeleton of benzene showing the carbon $2p_z$ AOs of the benzene pi system with the signs of the atomic wave functions.

Table 9.1　Character table for point group C_6

$\epsilon = \exp{(2\pi i/6)}$; $\epsilon^* = \exp{(-2\pi i/6)}$

C_6	E	C_6	C_3	C_2	$C_3{}^2$	$C_6{}^5$
A	1	1	1	1	1	1
B	1	-1	1	-1	1	-1
E_1	1	ϵ	$-\epsilon^*$	-1	$-\epsilon$	ϵ^*
	1	ϵ^*	$-\epsilon$	1	$-\epsilon^*$	ϵ
E_2	1	$-\epsilon^*$	$-\epsilon$	1	$-\epsilon^*$	$-\epsilon$
	1	$-\epsilon$	$-\epsilon^*$	1	$-\epsilon$	$-\epsilon^*$
$\Gamma_{p\pi}$	6	0	0	0	0	0

In agreement with the result obtained for the full-symmetry point group D_{6h}, the standard reduction procedure yields the direct sum

$$\Gamma_{p\pi} = A + B + E_1 + E_2$$

The results obtained for cyclic pi systems under the rotation subgroup may be stated in a general manner: the direct sum for the rotation subgroup will contain each irreducible representation once and only once.

It may now be observed that the coefficients of the LCAO MOs are the character systems of the irreducible representations of the rotation subgroup. One may simply show by inspection of the resulting MOs that they conform to the appropriate symmetry. The symmetry orbitals are written out below. Note that, in general, each AO must appear in each MO since there are no independent subsets.

$A \to A_{2u}$:　　$\phi_1 + \phi_2 + \phi_3 + \phi_4 + \phi_5 + \phi_6$

$B \to B_{2g}$:　　$\phi_1 - \phi_2 + \phi_3 - \phi_4 + \phi_5 - \phi_6$

$E_1 \to E_{1g}$:　$\begin{cases} \phi_1 + \epsilon\phi_2 - \epsilon^*\phi_3 - \phi_4 - \epsilon\phi_5 + \epsilon^*\phi_6 \\ \phi_1 + \epsilon^*\phi_2 - \epsilon\phi_3 - \phi_4 - \epsilon^*\phi_5 + \epsilon\phi_6 \end{cases}$

$E_2 \to E_{2u}$:　$\begin{cases} \phi_1 - \epsilon^*\phi_2 - \epsilon\phi_3 + \phi_4 - \epsilon^*\phi_5 - \epsilon\phi_6 \\ \phi_1 - \epsilon\phi_2 - \epsilon^*\phi_3 + \phi_4 - \epsilon\phi_5 - \epsilon^*\phi_6 \end{cases}$

However, these MOs are not normalized, and four of them contain imaginary coefficients. The first problem is trivial once the second one is solved. Thus, we first give our attention to the imaginary coefficients.

The symbol E for an irreducible representation indicates a double degeneracy. That is, the two MOs which belong to the E_{1g} representation both belong to the same energy eigenvalue. Thus, according to an earlier theorem, any linear combination of these two MOs will also belong to the same energy eigenvalue. Since in the above MOs the imaginary coefficients occur in pairs, or complex conjugates, the simple sum and difference of the two degenerate wave functions will produce real coefficients.

First consider the E_1 wave functions: by adding the two we obtain

$$E_{1g}{}^1 = 2\phi_1 + (\epsilon + \epsilon^*)\phi_2 - (\epsilon + \epsilon^*)\phi_3 - 2\phi_4 - (\epsilon + \epsilon^*)\phi_5 \\ + (\epsilon + \epsilon^*)\phi_6$$

Subtraction yields

$$E_{1g}{}^2 = +(\epsilon - \epsilon^*)\phi_2 - (\epsilon - \epsilon^*)\phi_3 - (\epsilon - \epsilon^*)\phi_5 - (\epsilon - \epsilon^*)\phi_6$$

In the group C_6 the definition of ϵ is

$$\epsilon = \exp\left(i\,\frac{2\pi}{6}\right) = \cos\frac{2\pi}{6} - i\sin\frac{2\pi}{6} \qquad i = \sqrt{-1}$$

Thus

$$\epsilon + \epsilon^* = \cos\frac{2\pi}{6} - i\sin\frac{2\pi}{6} + \cos\frac{2\pi}{6} + i\sin\frac{2\pi}{6} = 2\cos\frac{2\pi}{6} = 1$$

and

$$\epsilon - \epsilon^* = \cos\frac{2\pi}{6} - i\sin\frac{2\pi}{6} - \cos\frac{2\pi}{6} - i\sin\frac{2\pi}{6} = -2i\sin\frac{2\pi}{6} = -i\sqrt{3}$$

The first MO reduces to

$$E_{1g}{}^1 = 2\phi_1 + \phi_2 - \phi_3 - 2\phi_4 - \phi_5 + \phi_6$$

The second is obtained after division by i:

$$E_{1g}{}^2 = \phi_2 + \phi_3 - \phi_5 - \phi_6$$

Expressions for the E_{2u} wave functions are obtained in a similar fashion:

$$E_{2u}{}^1 = 2\phi_1 - \phi_2 - \phi_3 + 2\phi_4 - \phi_5 - \phi_6$$
$$E_{2u}{}^2 = \phi_2 - \phi_3 + \phi_5 - \phi_6$$

The expressions may be normalized by using the expression

$$\int \phi_i \phi_j \, d\tau = \delta_{ij}$$

The normalized symmetry orbitals are then

$$\chi(A_{2u}) = \frac{1}{\sqrt{6}}(\phi_1 + \phi_2 + \phi_3 + \phi_4 + \phi_5 + \phi_6)$$

$$\chi(B_{2g}) = \frac{1}{\sqrt{6}}(\phi_1 - \phi_2 + \phi_3 - \phi_4 + \phi_5 - \phi_6)$$

$$\chi(E_{1g}{}^1) = \frac{1}{\sqrt{12}}(2\phi_1 + \phi_2 - \phi_3 - 2\phi_4 - \phi_5 + \phi_6)$$

$$\chi(E_{1g}{}^2) = \tfrac{1}{2}(\phi_2 + \phi_3 - \phi_5 - \phi_6)$$

$$\chi(E_{2u}{}^1) = \frac{1}{\sqrt{12}}(2\phi_1 - \phi_2 - \phi_3 + 2\phi_4 - \phi_5 - \phi_6)$$

$$\chi(E_{2u}{}^2) = \tfrac{1}{2}(\phi_2 - \phi_3 + \phi_5 - \phi_6)$$

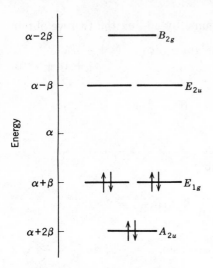

Fig. 9.6   The MO energy-level scheme
for the pi system of benzene showing
the symmetry species of each level
along with its electron occupancy.
The energy is given in units of α, the
carbon $2p$ coulomb integral.

Since there is only one MO for each symmetry (except for the degeneracies), the MOs must be equivalent to the above symmetry orbitals.

Let us now calculate the energy of each MO:

$$A_{2u}: \quad H_{11} = \tfrac{1}{6}\int (\phi_1 + \phi_2 + \phi_3 + \phi_4 + \phi_5 + \phi_6)\mathfrak{IC}(\phi_1 + \phi_2 + \phi_3$$
$$+ \phi_4 + \phi_5 + \phi_6)\, d\tau = \tfrac{1}{6}(\alpha + \beta + \beta)6$$
$$= \alpha + 2\beta$$

The other energy levels are obtained in the same way as follows:

$$B_{2g}: \qquad \alpha - 2\beta$$
$$E_{1g}{}^1 = E_{1g}{}^2: \quad \alpha + \beta$$
$$E_{2u}{}^1 = E_{2u}{}^2: \quad \alpha - \beta$$

The energy-level diagram can now be constructed; it is shown in
Fig. 9.6.

Let us now review briefly the steps in the method of obtaining LCAO
MOs and their corresponding energies under group theory:

1. Determine the point group of the molecular system.
2. Decide on the set of basis orbitals.

3. By standard reduction techniques determine the symmetries of the MOs.

4. Determine the symmetry orbitals.

5. Compute the elements of the various secular determinants (approximations may be introduced at this point).

6. Solve the secular determinants for the energy eigenvalues.

7. Determine the correct MOs as linear combinations of the symmetry orbitals (if necessary).

8. Compute molecular properties based on the LCAO MO coefficients.

So that the student may practice this method on hydrocarbons, the following tables have been constructed from various sources.

Table 9.2 Cyclobutadiene, C_4H_4

i	x_i	E_i	c_1	c_2	c_3	c_4	Γ
1	-2	$\alpha + 2\beta$	$\frac{1}{2}$	$\frac{1}{2}$	$\frac{1}{2}$	$\frac{1}{2}$	A
2	0	α	$\frac{1}{2}$	0	$-\frac{1}{2}$	0	E
3	0	α	0	$\frac{1}{2}$	0	$-\frac{1}{2}$	E
4	$+2$	$\alpha - 2\beta$	$\frac{1}{2}$	$-\frac{1}{2}$	$\frac{1}{2}$	$-\frac{1}{2}$	B

Table 9.3 Cyclopentadienyl radical, C_5H_5

i	x_i	E_i	c_1	c_2	c_3	c_4	c_5	Γ
1	-2	$\alpha + 2\beta$	$\dfrac{1}{\sqrt{5}}$	$\dfrac{1}{\sqrt{5}}$	$\dfrac{1}{\sqrt{5}}$	$\dfrac{1}{\sqrt{5}}$	$\dfrac{1}{\sqrt{5}}$	A
2	$-2C$	$\alpha + 2\beta \cos\dfrac{2\pi}{5}$	$\sqrt{\dfrac{2}{5}}$	$\sqrt{\dfrac{2}{5}}\cos\dfrac{2\pi}{5}$	$\sqrt{\dfrac{2}{5}}\cos\dfrac{4\pi}{5}$	$\sqrt{\dfrac{2}{5}}\cos\dfrac{4\pi}{5}$	$\sqrt{\dfrac{2}{5}}\cos\dfrac{2\pi}{5}$	E_1
3	$-2C$	$\alpha + 2\beta \cos\dfrac{2\pi}{5}$	0	$\sqrt{\dfrac{2}{5}}\sin\dfrac{2\pi}{5}$	$\sqrt{\dfrac{2}{5}}\sin\dfrac{4\pi}{5}$	$-\sqrt{\dfrac{2}{5}}\sin\dfrac{4\pi}{5}$	$-\sqrt{\dfrac{2}{5}}\sin\dfrac{2\pi}{5}$	E_1
4	$2C$	$\alpha - 2\beta \cos\dfrac{2\pi}{5}$	$\sqrt{\dfrac{2}{5}}$	$\sqrt{\dfrac{2}{5}}\cos\dfrac{4\pi}{5}$	$\sqrt{\dfrac{2}{5}}\cos\dfrac{2\pi}{5}$	$\sqrt{\dfrac{2}{5}}\cos\dfrac{2\pi}{5}$	$\sqrt{\dfrac{2}{5}}\cos\dfrac{4\pi}{5}$	E_2
5	$2C$	$\alpha - 2\beta \cos\dfrac{2\pi}{5}$	0	$\sqrt{\dfrac{2}{5}}\sin\dfrac{4\pi}{5}$	$-\sqrt{\dfrac{2}{5}}\sin\dfrac{2\pi}{5}$	$\sqrt{\dfrac{2}{5}}\sin\dfrac{2\pi}{5}$	$-\sqrt{\dfrac{2}{5}}\sin\dfrac{4\pi}{5}$	E_2

$$C = \cos\frac{2\pi}{5}$$

Table 9.4 Allyl radical, C_3H_5

i	x_i	E_i	c_1	c_2	c_3	Γ
1	-2	$\alpha - 2\beta$	$\frac{1}{2}$	$\frac{1}{2}$	$\frac{1}{2}$	B_1
2	0	α	$\frac{1}{2}$	0	$-\frac{1}{2}$	A_2
3	2	$\alpha + 2\beta$	$\frac{1}{2}$	$-\frac{1}{2}$	$\frac{1}{2}$	B_1

Table 9.5 Cyclopropenyl, C_3H_3

i	x_i	E_i	c_1	c_2	c_3	Γ
1	-2	$\alpha + 2\beta$	$\frac{1}{3}$	$\frac{1}{3}$	$\frac{1}{3}$	A_1'
2	1	$\alpha + \beta$	$\frac{1}{6}$	$\frac{1}{6}$	$-\frac{2}{6}$	E''
3	1	$\alpha + \beta$	$\frac{1}{2}$	$-\frac{1}{2}$	0	E''

Table 9.6 Bicyclohexatriene, C_6H_6

i	x_i	E_i	c_1	c_2	c_3	c_4	c_5	c_6	Γ
1	-2.414	$\alpha + 2.414\beta$	0.354	0.500	0.354	0.354	0.500	0.354	A_1
2	-1.000	$\alpha + \beta$	0.500	0	-0.500	-0.500	0	0.500	B_2
3	-0.414	$\alpha + 0.414\beta$	0.354	0.500	0.354	-0.354	-0.500	-0.354	B_1
4	$+0.414$	$\alpha - 0.414\beta$	0.354	-0.500	0.354	0.354	-0.500	0.354	B_1
5	1.000	$\alpha - \beta$	0.500	0	-0.500	0.500	0	-0.500	A_2
6	2.414	$\alpha - 2.414\beta$	0.354	-0.500	0.354	-0.354	0.500	-0.354	A_1

9.4 THE TECHNIQUES FOR HETEROATOMS

When "heavy" atoms of more than one type appear in the molecular system, certain simplifications in definitions may be introduced in order to reduce the algebra. The problem is treated in the same manner as described previously for hydrocarbons except for the definition of the various integrals.

For molecules which contain carbon-carbon bonds as well as bonds between carbon and other atoms (boron, nitrogen, oxygen, sulfur, chlorine, etc.) we use the following definitions:

$$\beta_{C-X} = k_X\beta_{C-C} = k_X\beta$$
$$\alpha_X = \alpha_C + h_X\beta_{C-C} = \alpha + h_X\beta$$

The parameters k_X and h_X depend upon the atom X and may be arbitrarily specified or determined in a manner such that a certain physical property of the molecule is matched by the chosen values of k_X and h_X. A table of such parameters is given in Table 9.7.

Let us take pyridine as an example. We shall consider only the pi

Table 9.7 Suggested parameter values for heteroatoms for use with simple LCAO theory

Element	Coulomb integral	Bond integral
Boron	$h_B = -1$	$k_{C-B} = 0.7$
Carbon		$k_{C-C} = 0.9\ddagger$
		$k_{C-C} = 1.0\S$
		$k_{C=C} = 1.1\P$
Nitrogen	$h_{\dot{N}} = 0.5$	$k_{C-N} = 0.8$
	$h_{\ddot{N}} = 1.5$	$k_{C-N} = 1$
	$h_{N^+} = 2$	$k_{N-O} = 0.7$
Oxygen	$h_{\dot{O}} = 1$	$k_{C-O} = 0.8$
	$h_{\ddot{O}} = 2$	$k_{C-O} = 1$
	$h_{O^+} = 2.5$	
Fluorine	$h_F = 3$	$k_{C-F} = 0.7$
Chlorine	$h_{Cl} = 2$	$k_{C-Cl} = 0.4$
Bromine	$h_{Br} = 1.5$	$k_{C-Br} = 0.3$
Methyl (conjugation		
model $\equiv$ C—Y—Z)	$h_C = -0.1$	$k_{C-Y} = 0.8$
	$h_Z = -0.5$	$k_{Y-Z} = 3$

$\ddagger$ For single sp^2sp^2 of 1.47 Å length.
$\S$ For an aromatic bond of 1.40 Å length.
$\P$ For a double bond of 1.34 Å length.
Source: Taken by permission from A. Streitwieser, "Molecular Orbital Theory for Organic Chemists," p. 135, John Wiley & Sons, Inc., New York, 1961.

system and the p pi orbitals which will be used as a basis set, as shown in Fig. 9.7.

The point group is C_{2v}. The character table and the character system for the p pi orbitals are shown in Table 9.8. By the standard reduc-

Table 9.8 Character table for point group C_{2v}

C_{2v}	E	C_2	σ_v	σ_v'
A_1	1	1	1	1
A_2	1	1	-1	-1
B_1	1	-1	1	-1
B_2	1	-1	-1	1
$\Gamma_{p\pi}$	6	-2	-6	2

tion formula the direct sum for $\Gamma_{p\pi}$ is shown to be

$$\Gamma_{p\pi} = 2A_2 + 4B_2$$

The symmetry orbitals can now be determined by considering the various independent subsets of p pi orbitals. Since no symmetry operation interchanges ϕ_1 with any other orbital, ϕ_1 must be a symmetry orbital.

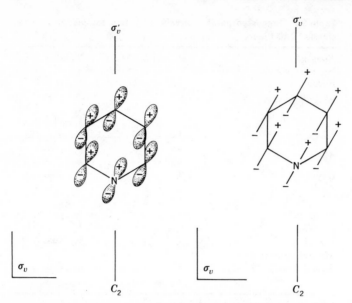

Fig. 9.7 The carbon-nitrogen skeleton of pyridine showing the $2p_z$ AOs which contribute to the pi bonding system. The signs of the AOs are shown along with the symmetry elements of point group C_{2v}.

Likewise, for the same reason, ϕ_6 is a symmetry orbital. Symmetry operations such as $C_2{}^1$ and σ_v' interchange ϕ_2 with ϕ_3 and ϕ_4 with ϕ_5 but never mix ϕ_2 with either ϕ_4 or ϕ_5. Thus, the remaining symmetry orbitals must be $\phi_2 \pm \phi_3$ and $\phi_4 \pm \phi_5$, and the normalized symmetry orbitals are

$$\chi_1 = \phi_1$$

$$\chi_2{}^{a,b} = \frac{1}{\sqrt{2}} (\phi_2 \pm \phi_3)$$

$$\chi_3{}^{a,b} = \frac{1}{\sqrt{2}} (\phi_4 \pm \phi_5)$$

$$\chi_4 = \phi_6$$

The symmetry of these orbitals can be determined by applying the various symmetry operations of C_{2v}:

$$\chi_1 = \phi_1$$
$$E\phi_1 = \phi_1$$
$$C_2{}^1\phi_1 = -\phi_1$$
$$\sigma_v\phi_1 = -\phi_1$$
$$\sigma_v'\phi_1 = \phi_1$$

Therefore, χ_1 belongs to B_2.

The same result is obtained for ϕ_6.

$$\chi_2{}^a = \frac{1}{\sqrt{2}} (\phi_2 + \phi_3)$$

$$E\left[\frac{1}{\sqrt{2}} (\phi_2 + \phi_3)\right] = \frac{1}{\sqrt{2}} (\phi_2 + \phi_3) = \chi_2{}^a$$

$$C_2{}^1\left[\frac{1}{\sqrt{2}} (\phi_2 + \phi_3)\right] = \frac{1}{\sqrt{2}} (-\phi_3 - \phi_2) = -\frac{1}{\sqrt{2}} (\phi_2 + \phi_3) = -\chi_2{}^a$$

$$\sigma_v\left[\frac{1}{\sqrt{2}} (\phi_2 + \phi_3)\right] = \frac{1}{\sqrt{2}} (-\phi_2 - \phi_3) = -\frac{1}{\sqrt{2}} (\phi_2 + \phi_3) = -\chi_2{}^a$$

$$\sigma_v'\left[\frac{1}{\sqrt{2}} (\phi_2 + \phi_3)\right] = \frac{1}{\sqrt{2}} (\phi_3 + \phi_2) = \frac{1}{\sqrt{2}} (\phi_2 + \phi_3) = \chi_2{}^a$$

Therefore, $\chi_2{}^a$ belongs to B_2. A similar result may be obtained for $\chi_3{}^a$. Let us now consider $\chi_2{}^b$:

$$\chi_2{}^b = \frac{1}{\sqrt{2}} (\phi_2 - \phi_3)$$

$$E\left[\frac{1}{\sqrt{2}} (\phi_2 - \phi_3)\right] = \frac{1}{\sqrt{2}} (\phi_2 - \phi_3) = \chi_2{}^b$$

$$C_2{}^1\left[\frac{1}{\sqrt{2}} (\phi_2 - \phi_3)\right] = \frac{1}{\sqrt{2}} (-\phi_3 + \phi_2) = \chi_2{}^b$$

$$\sigma_v\left[\frac{1}{\sqrt{2}} (\phi_2 - \phi_3)\right] = \frac{1}{\sqrt{2}} (-\phi_2 + \phi_3) = -\chi_2{}^b$$

$$\sigma_v'\left[\frac{1}{\sqrt{2}} (\phi_2 - \phi_3)\right] = \frac{1}{\sqrt{2}} (-\phi_2 + \phi_3) = -\chi_2{}^b$$

Therefore, $\chi_2{}^b$ belongs to A_2.

Thus, we can list the symmetry orbitals as follows:

A_2	B_2
$\chi_1{}^A = \frac{1}{\sqrt{2}} (\phi_2 - \phi_3)$	$\chi_1{}^B = \phi_1$
$\chi_2{}^A = \frac{1}{\sqrt{2}} (\phi_4 - \phi_5)$	$\chi_4{}^B = \phi_6$
	$\chi_2{}^B = \frac{1}{\sqrt{2}} (\phi_2 + \phi_3)$
	$\chi_3{}^B = \frac{1}{\sqrt{2}} (\phi_4 + \phi_5)$

Let us now evaluate the elements of the secular determinants using the following definitions:

$$\int \phi_6 \mathfrak{IC} \phi_6 \, d\tau = \alpha$$
$$\int \phi_5 \mathfrak{IC} \phi_6 \, d\tau = \beta$$
$$\int \phi_1 \mathfrak{IC} \phi_1 \, d\tau = \alpha + h_{\tilde{N}} \beta$$
$$\int \phi_1 \mathfrak{IC} \phi_2 \, d\tau = k_{\tilde{N}} \beta$$
$$H_{11}{}^A = \int \chi_1{}^A \mathfrak{IC} \chi_1{}^A \, d\tau = \tfrac{1}{2}(\int \phi_2 \mathfrak{IC} \phi_2 \, d\tau - \int \phi_2 \mathfrak{IC} \phi_3 \, d\tau$$
$$\qquad\qquad - \int \phi_3 \mathfrak{IC} \phi_2 \, d\tau + \int \phi_3 \mathfrak{IC} \phi_3 \, d\tau) = \tfrac{1}{2}(\alpha - 0 - 0 + \alpha)$$
$$H_{11}{}^A = \alpha$$
$$H_{22}{}^A = \int \chi_1{}^A \mathfrak{IC} \chi_2{}^A \, d\tau = \tfrac{1}{2}(\alpha - 0 - 0 + \alpha) = \alpha$$
$$H_{12} = H_{21} = \int \chi_1{}^A \mathfrak{IC} \chi_2{}^A \, d\tau = \tfrac{1}{2}(0 + \beta + \beta + 0) = \beta$$

In a similar manner the following are found:

$$H_{11}{}^B = \alpha + h_{\tilde{N}} \beta \qquad H_{12}{}^B = \sqrt{2}\, k_{\tilde{N}} \beta \qquad H_{23}{}^B = \beta \qquad H_{34}{}^B = \sqrt{2}\, \beta$$
$$H_{22}{}^B = \alpha \qquad\qquad H_{13}{}^B = 0 \qquad\qquad H_{24}{}^B = 0$$
$$H_{33}{}^B = \alpha \qquad\qquad H_{14}{}^B = 0$$
$$H_{44}{}^B = \alpha$$

The two secular determinants are then

$$\begin{vmatrix} \alpha - E_i & \beta \\ \beta & \alpha - E_i \end{vmatrix} = 0$$

$$\begin{vmatrix} \alpha + h_{\tilde{N}} \beta - E_i & \sqrt{2}\, k_{\tilde{N}} \beta & 0 & 0 \\ \sqrt{2}\, k_{\tilde{N}} \beta & \alpha - E_i & \beta & 0 \\ 0 & \beta & \alpha - E_i & \sqrt{2}\, \beta \\ 0 & 0 & \sqrt{2}\, \beta & \alpha - E_i \end{vmatrix} = 0$$

Dividing by β and making the standard substitution $x = (\alpha - E_i)/\beta$, we find

$$A_2 \qquad\qquad\qquad\qquad B_2$$

$$\begin{vmatrix} x & 1 \\ 1 & x \end{vmatrix} = 0 \qquad \begin{vmatrix} x + h_{\tilde{N}} & \sqrt{2}\, k_{\tilde{N}} & 0 & 0 \\ \sqrt{2}\, k_{\tilde{N}} & x & 1 & 0 \\ 0 & 1 & x & \sqrt{2} \\ 0 & 0 & \sqrt{2} & x \end{vmatrix} = 0$$

The A_2 secular determinant can easily be solved by hand, but the B_2 determinant cannot, even when values are chosen for $h_{\tilde{N}}$ and $k_{\tilde{N}}$. A computer program will be employed in this case to provide the eigenvalues and eigenvectors.

The solution to the A_2 secular determinant is

$$\begin{vmatrix} x & 1 \\ 1 & x \end{vmatrix} = 0 \qquad x = \frac{\alpha - E_i}{\beta} \qquad E_i = \alpha - x\beta$$
$$x^2 - 1 = 0 \qquad \text{or} \qquad x = \pm 1$$

thus

$$E = \alpha \pm \beta$$

To obtain the true MO of A_2 symmetry having energy corresponding to $\alpha + \beta$ (or $\alpha - \beta$) we write the true MO as a linear combination of the two A_2 symmetry orbitals in normalized form

$$\psi^{\alpha+\beta}(A_2) = \frac{1}{\sqrt{1 + x^2}} (\chi_1{}^A + x\chi_2{}^A)$$

By calculating the energy of $\psi(A_2)$ and setting the expression equal to $\alpha + \beta$ we can solve for x:

$$E = \alpha + \beta = \frac{\int \psi^{\alpha+\beta}(A_2)\mathcal{K}\psi^{\alpha+\beta}(A_2)\, d\tau}{\int \psi^{\alpha+\beta}(A_2)\psi^{\alpha+\beta}(A_2)\, d\tau}$$

$$= \frac{1}{1 + x^2}\frac{1}{2}\left\{ \int [\phi_2 - \phi_3 + x(\phi_4 - \phi_5)]\mathcal{K}[\phi_2 \right.$$

$$\left. - \phi_3 + x(\phi_4 - \phi_5)]\, d\tau \right\}$$

$$= \frac{1}{2(1 + x^2)} [2(1 - x^2)\alpha + 4x\beta]$$

$$\alpha + \beta = \alpha + \frac{2x\beta}{1 + x^2}$$

$$x^2 - 2x + 1 = 0$$

$$(x - 1)^2 = 0$$

$$x = 1$$

Thus, the A_2 MO of lowest energy, $\alpha + \beta$, is given as

$$\psi^{\alpha+\beta}(A_2) = \frac{1}{\sqrt{1 + x^2}} (\chi_1 + x\chi_2) = \frac{1}{\sqrt{2}} (\chi_1 + \chi_2)$$

$$= \frac{1}{\sqrt{2}}\left[\frac{1}{\sqrt{2}} (\phi_2 - \phi_3) + \frac{1}{\sqrt{2}} (\phi_4 - \phi_5) \right]$$

$$\psi^{\alpha+\beta}(A_2) = \tfrac{1}{2}(\phi_2 - \phi_3 + \phi_4 - \phi_5)$$

In order to evaluate the B_2 secular determinant, values must be given to both $h_{\ddot{N}}$ and $k_{\ddot{N}}$. Let us take those suggested by Streitweiser in Table 9.7:

$$h_{\ddot{N}} = 1.5 \quad \text{and} \quad k_{\ddot{N}} = 1.0$$

The B_2 determinant, then, is given as

$$\begin{vmatrix} x + 1.5 & 1.414 & 0 & 0 \\ 1.414 & x & 1 & 0 \\ 0 & 1 & x & 1.414 \\ 0 & 0 & 1.414 & x \end{vmatrix} = 0$$

The determinant eigenvalue problem was solved on a IBM 1460 computer (see Appendix III), and the results are

Table 9.9

i	x_i	E_i	c_1'	c_2'	c_3'	c_4'
1	0.5940	$\alpha - 0.5940\beta$	0.4430	−0.6560	−0.2367	0.5634
2	1.8624	$\alpha - 1.8624\beta$	−0.2183	0.5191	−0.6581	0.4997
3	−1.4306	$\alpha + 1.4306\beta$	−0.4321	0.0212	0.6412	0.6338
4	−2.5258	$\alpha + 2.5258\beta$	0.7546	0.5474	0.3157	0.1767

The true MOs are given by the following linear combination of the symmetry orbitals χ_j:

$$\psi_i = \sum_j c_{ij}' \chi_j = \sum_j c_{ij} \phi_j$$

In order to determine the occupied MOs we must construct the energy-level diagram, as shown in Fig. 9.8.

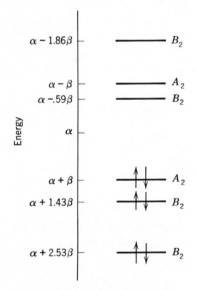

Fig. 9.8 The MO energy-level scheme for the pi system of pyridine showing the symmetry species of each level along with its electron occupancy. The energy is given in units of α, the carbon $2p$ coulomb integral.

We can then construct a table of the atomic orbital coefficients, c_{ij}, for the occupied MOs as shown in Table 9.10.

Table 9.10 MO coefficients and energy levels for pyridine

i	E_i	c_1	c_2	c_3	c_4	c_5	c_6	Γ
1	$\alpha + \beta$	0.000	0.500	-0.500	0.500	-0.500	0.000	A_2
2	$\alpha + 1.43\beta$	-0.432	0.015	0.015	0.453	0.453	0.634	B_2
3	$\alpha + 2.53\beta$	0.755	0.383	0.383	0.223	0.223	0.177	B_2

We can now calculate the Coulson bond orders b_{ij} and the pi-electron-system charges q_i as given by the following formulas:

$$q_i = N_i - l_i$$
$$\left. \begin{array}{l} b_{ij} = \sum_k n_k c_{ki} c_{kj} \\[2mm] l_i = \sum_k n_k c_{ki}{}^2 \end{array} \right\} \quad \text{sums performed over occupied orbitals}$$

where n_k is the number of electrons in the kth occupied MO and N_i is the number of electrons contributed to the pi system by the ith atom. We need only to calculate b_{12}, b_{24}, and b_{46} and q_1, q_2, q_4, and q_6.

$$b_{12} = 2(0.0)(0.5) + 2(-0.432)(0.015) + 2(0.755)(0.383) = 0.591$$
$$b_{24} = 2(0.5)(0.5) + 2(0.015)(0.453) + 2(0.383)(0.223) = 0.684$$
$$b_{46} = 2(0.5)(0.0) + 2(0.453)(0.634) + 2(0.223)(0.177) = 0.653$$
$$q_1 = 1. - [2(0.0)^2 + 2(-0.432)^2 + 2(0.755)^2] = 1. - 1.513$$
$$q_2 = 1. - [2(0.5)^2 + 2(0.015)^2 + 2(0.383)^2] = 1. - 0.795$$
$$q_4 = 1. - [2(0.5)^2 + 2(0.453)^2 + 2(0.223)^2] = 1. - 1.010$$
$$q_6 = 1. - [2(0.0)^2 + 2(0.634)^2 + 2(0.177)^2] = 1. - 0.867$$

Table 9.11 Pi-system bond orders in pyridine

	b_{ij}
b_{12}	0.591
b_{24}	0.684
b_{46}	0.653

Table 9.12 Atomic charges in pyridine

	q_i
q_1	- 0.513
q_2	0.205
q_4	- 0.010
q_6	0.133

Other molecular properties of the molecule pyridine can now be determined: ionization potential, dipole moment, and electronic spectral transitions. A value of β must be obtained in order to calculate the first and last of these quantities. (The student must carefully consider the contribution to various molecular properties by the system of sigma electrons. Sigma effects may be very important in the overall bond orders and in the dipole moment.)

9.5 LCAO MO AND SIMPLE HÜCKEL CALCULATIONS ON SIGMA SYSTEMS

Before discussing coordination compounds and use of computers in MO calculations, let us consider methods for doing LCAO MO calculations on the sigma electron systems of molecules. This section will apply to nonaromatic molecules as well, and in fact, we shall deal only with nonaromatic molecules in this section by considering two molecules, BH_3 and C_2H_6.

The method is essentially the same as that used for pi electron systems:

1. Determine the character system for the set of basis orbitals to be used (in this case all the valence-shell orbitals).
2. Reduce the character system to the direct sum by standard techniques.
3. List the symmetry-independent sets of orbitals (use will be made of hybridized orbitals).
4. Determine the symmetry orbitals of the types found in the direct sum.
5. Decide upon symbols (or numerical values) for the various integrals which will be encountered. (There will be several types of integrals, and careful attention must be given to their evaluation.)
6. Write down and solve (perhaps by high-speed digital computer) the secular determinants for the energy eigenvalues and the MO eigenvectors.
7. Plot the energy levels and determine the occupied MOs.
8. Determine the coefficients of the AOs in the MOs.

BH₃, BORANE

Table 9.13 Character table for point group D_{3h}

D_{3h}	E	$2C_3$	$3C_2$	σ_h	$2S_3$	$3\sigma_v$
A_1'	1	1	1	1	1	1
A_2'	1	1	-1	1	1	-1
E'	2	-1	0	2	-1	0
A_1''	1	1	1	-1	-1	-1
A_2''	1	1	-1	-1	-1	1
E''	2	-1	0	-2	1	0
Γ	7	1	1	5	-1	3

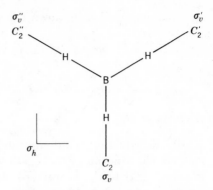

Fig. 9.9 The molecular structure of borane, BH_3, showing orientations of the symmetry elements. The three-fold proper and improper axes are perpendicular to the plane of the paper through the boron atom.

The molecular structure and symmetry elements for borane are shown in Fig. 9.9.

$$\Gamma = 2A_1' + 2E' + A_2''$$

The character system which serves as a basis for Γ may be computed using the hydrogen $1s$ functions and the $2s$, $2p_x$, $2p_y$, and $2p_z$ of boron. However, for the remainder of the calculation sp^2 hybrids will be used in place of $2s$, $2p_x$, and $2p_y$ of boron. It is seen that Γ is the same when one uses sp^2 hybrid AOs since the sp^2 AOs were designed to possess D_{3h} symmetry.

Let us now list the independent sets of orbitals using the following symbols:

Hydrogen $1s$ H_i
Boron sp^2 Tr_i
Boron $2p_z$ B_{p_z}

The independent sets of orbitals are

B_{p_z}
H_1, H_2, H_3
Tr_1, Tr_2, Tr_3

We may now write down the various symmetry orbitals as follows:

A_1': $\chi_1 = \dfrac{1}{\sqrt{3}}(Tr_1 + Tr_2 + Tr_3)$

$\chi_2 = \dfrac{1}{\sqrt{3}}(H_1 + H_2 + H_3)$

A_2'': $\chi_1 = B_{p_z}$

In determining the doubly degenerate orbitals of E' symmetry we may use the same idea as was used for the E_{1g} and E_{2u} orbitals in benzene. We shall refer to the character system for the E representation in point group C_3 and write a preliminary set of orbitals as follows:

$$\omega_1 = Tr_1 + \epsilon Tr_2 + \epsilon^* Tr_3 + H_1 + \epsilon H_2 + \epsilon^* H_3$$
$$\omega_2 = Tr_1 + \epsilon^* Tr_2 + \epsilon Tr_3 + H_1 + \epsilon^* H_2 + \epsilon H_3$$

By taking the sum and difference and making use of the following identities we can arrive at a more useful form:

$$\epsilon = \exp\frac{2\pi i}{3} = \cos\frac{2\pi}{3} + i\sin\frac{2\pi}{3}$$

$$\epsilon + \epsilon^* = 2\cos\frac{2\pi}{3} = -1$$

$$\epsilon - \epsilon^* = 2i\sin\frac{2\pi}{3} = i\sqrt{3}$$

Thus

E': $\chi_1 = \dfrac{1}{\sqrt{12}}(2Tr_1 - Tr_2 - Tr_3 + 2H_1 - H_2 - H_3)$

$\chi_2 = \dfrac{3}{\sqrt{12}}(Tr_2 - Tr_3 + H_2 - H_3) = \frac{1}{2}(Tr_2 - Tr_3 + H_2 - H_3)$

$\chi_3 = \dfrac{1}{\sqrt{12}}(2Tr_1 - Tr_2 - Tr_3 - 2H_1 + H_2 + H_3)$

$\chi_4 = \dfrac{3}{\sqrt{12}}(Tr_2 - Tr_3 - H_2 + H_3) = \frac{1}{2}(Tr_2 - Tr_3 - H_2 + H_3)$

Now, we must decide upon values of various atomic integrals. We shall make the following choices:

$$\int Tr_i \mathcal{3C} Tr_j \, d\tau = \begin{cases} \alpha_T & i = j \\ t\alpha_t & i \neq j; \, 0 < t \ll 1 \end{cases}$$

$$\int H_i \mathcal{3C} H_j \, d\tau = \begin{cases} \alpha_H & i = j \\ 0 & i \neq j \end{cases}$$

$$\int Tr_i \mathcal{3C} H_j \, d\tau = \begin{cases} \beta & i = j \\ 0 & i \neq j \text{ (nonbonded)} \end{cases}$$

The calculation of the elements of the various secular determinants now proceeds in a straightforward manner.

A_2'': $H_{11} = \int B_{p_z} \mathfrak{IC} B_{p_z}\, d\tau = \alpha_{B_{2p}}$

A_1': $H_{11} = \frac{1}{3} \int (Tr_1 + Tr_2 + Tr_3)\mathfrak{IC}(Tr_1 + Tr_2 + Tr_3)\, d\tau$
$= \frac{1}{3}[3(\alpha_T + 2t\alpha_T)] = \alpha_T(1 + 2t)$

$H_{22} = \frac{1}{3} \int (H_1 + H_2 + H_3)\mathfrak{IC}(H_1 + H_2 + H_3)\, d\tau$
$= \frac{1}{3}(\alpha_H + 0 + 0 + 0 + \alpha_H + 0 + 0 + 0 + \alpha_H) = \alpha_H$

$H_{21} = H_{12} = \frac{1}{3}\int(Tr_1 + Tr_2 + Tr_3)\mathfrak{IC}(H_1 + H_2 + H_3)\, d\tau$
$= \frac{1}{3}(\beta + 0 + 0 + 0 + \beta + 0 + 0 + 0 + \beta) = \beta$

For E' we find

$H_{11} = \frac{1}{4}\int(Tr_2 - Tr_3 + H_2 - H_3)\mathfrak{IC}(Tr_2 - Tr_3 + H_2 - H_3)\, d\tau$
$= \frac{1}{4}(\alpha_T - t\alpha_T + \beta + 0 - t\alpha_T + \alpha_T + 0 + \beta + \beta + 0 + \alpha_H$
$\qquad\qquad\qquad\qquad + 0 + 0 + \beta + 0 + \alpha_H)$
$= \frac{1}{4}[2(1 - t)\alpha_T + 2\alpha_H + 4\beta] = \dfrac{(1 - t)\alpha_T + \alpha_H}{2} + \beta$

$H_{11} = \frac{1}{4}\int(Tr_2 - Tr_3 - H_2 + H_3)\mathfrak{IC}(Tr_2 - Tr_3 - H_2 + H_3)\, d\tau$
$= \frac{1}{4}(\alpha_T - t\alpha_T - \beta + 0 - t\alpha_T + \alpha_T + 0 - \beta - \beta + 0 + \alpha_H$
$\qquad\qquad\qquad\qquad + 0 + 0 - \beta + 0 + \alpha_H)$
$= \dfrac{(1 - t)\alpha_T + \alpha_H}{2} - \beta$

Thus, the energies are determined directly for the A_2'' and E' states:

$E(A_2'') = \alpha_{B_{2p}}$

$E(E') = \dfrac{\alpha_T(1 - t) + \alpha_H}{2} \pm \beta$

A 2×2 determinant must be solved for the A_1' states:

$$\begin{vmatrix} \alpha_T(1 + 2t) - E_i & \beta \\ \beta & \alpha_H - E_i \end{vmatrix} = 0$$

The secular (characteristic) equation of this determinant is easily found:

$$E^2 - [\alpha_T(1 + 2t) + \alpha_H]E + \alpha_H\alpha_T(1 + 2t) - \beta^2 = 0$$

and the roots are obtained from the quadratic formula

$$E(A_1') = E = \frac{\alpha_T(1 + 2t) + \alpha_H \pm \sqrt{[\alpha_T(1 + 2t) - \alpha_H]^2 + 4\beta^2}}{2}$$

Thus, the expressions for the energy are

$$E(A_1') = \frac{\alpha_T(1 + 2t) + \alpha_H \pm \sqrt{[\alpha_T(1 + 2t) - \alpha_H]^2 + 4\beta^2}}{2}$$

$$E(A_2'') = \alpha_{B_{2p}}$$

$$E(E') = \frac{\alpha_T(1 - t) + \alpha_H}{2} \pm \beta$$

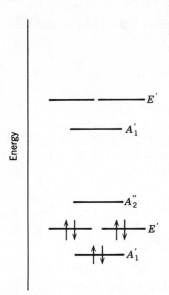

Fig. 9.10 The MO energy-level scheme for borane, BH₃, showing the symmetry species of each level and its electron occupancy. The energy is given in arbitrary units and is based on an approximate simple Hückel calculation.

Since there are six bonding (valence) electrons in BH₃, there are three bonding MOs. Thus, we need to find only the three lowest-lying energy states. Trial calculations will show that the lowest state is of A_1' symmetry and the next two are a doubly degenerate pair of E' symmetry. The values for the various parameters in the above energy expressions determine the order of the excited states. The energy-level diagram in Fig. 9.10 indicates the results of a typical calculation.

In order to obtain the coefficients of the atomic orbitals we must now find the true MOs of the A_1' and E' symmetry which correspond to the energies

$$\frac{\alpha_T(1 + 2t) + \alpha_H + \sqrt{[\alpha_T(1 + 2t) - \alpha_H]^2 + 4\beta^2}}{2}$$

and

$$\frac{\alpha_T(1 - t) + \alpha_H}{2} + \beta$$

respectively. We shall use here the same method as was used for the A_2 MO in the pi-system calculation of pyridine.

$$\psi(A_1') = \frac{1}{\sqrt{1 + x^2}}\,(\chi_1{}^{A_1'} + x\chi_2{}^{A_1'})$$

$$E(A_1') = \frac{\alpha_T(1 + 2t) + \alpha_H + \sqrt{[\alpha_T(1 + 2t) - \alpha_H]^2 + 4\beta^2}}{2}$$

$$= \frac{1}{3(1 + x^2)}\int (Tr_1 + Tr_2 + Tr_3 + xH_1 + xH_2 + xH_3)\mathfrak{K}(Tr_1 + Tr_2 + Tr_3 + xH_1 + xH_2 + xH_3)\,d\tau$$

$$= \frac{1}{3(1 + x^2)}\,[3(\alpha_T + t\alpha_T + t\alpha_T + x\beta) + 3(x\beta + x^2\alpha_H)]$$

$$= \frac{1}{1 + x^2}\,[\alpha_T(1 + 2t) + x^2\alpha_H + 2x\beta]$$

Thus,

$$\frac{\alpha_T(1 + 2t) + \alpha_H + \sqrt{[\alpha_t(1 + 2t) - \alpha_H]^2 + 4\beta^2}}{2}$$

$$= \frac{1}{1 + x^2}\,[\alpha_T(1 + 2t) + x^2\alpha_H + 2x\beta]$$

In order to simplify the algebra let us introduce the further assumption that $[\alpha_T(1 + 2t) - \alpha_H] < 4\beta^2$. The above equation then becomes

$$\frac{\alpha_T(1 + 2t) + \alpha_H + 2\beta}{2} = \frac{1}{1 + x^2}\,[\alpha_T(1 + 2t) + x^2\alpha_H + 2x\beta]$$

$$x = \frac{2\beta \pm \sqrt{4\beta^2 + [\alpha_T(1 + 2t) - \alpha_H + 2\beta][\alpha_T(1 + 2t) - \alpha_H - 2\beta]}}{\alpha_T(1 + 2t) - \alpha_H + 2\beta}$$

$$= \frac{2\beta \pm [\alpha_T(1 + 2t) - \alpha_H]}{\alpha_T(1 + 2t) - \alpha_H + 2\beta}$$

$$x = 1$$

because under the above approximation, $\{2\beta - [\alpha_T(1 + 2t) - \alpha_H]\}/\{2\beta + [\alpha_T(1 + 2t) - \alpha_H]\} = 1$. Thus

$$\psi(A_2) = \frac{1}{\sqrt{2}}\left[\frac{1}{\sqrt{3}}\,(Tr_1 + Tr_2 + Tr_3 + H_1 + H_2 + H_3)\right]$$

We can now construct a table of coefficients of the orbitals used in this calculation on BH_3.

Table 9.14   Table of MO coefficients for BH_3 using boron trigonal orbitals

Orbital designation of the coefficients		Γ						
		A_1'	E'	E'	A_2''	A_1'	E'	E'
H_1	C_1'	1.000	2.000	0.000	0.000	−1.000	−2.000	0.000
H_2	C_2'	1.000	−1.000	1.000	0.000	−1.000	1.000	−1.000
H_3	C_3'	1.000	−1.000	−1.000	0.000	−1.000	1.000	1.000
Tr_1	C_4'	1.000	2.000	0.000	0.000	1.000	2.000	1.000
Tr_2	C_5'	1.000	−1.000	1.000	0.000	1.000	−1.000	−1.000
Tr_3	C_6'	1.000	−1.000	−1.000	0.000	1.000	−1.000	0.000
B_{2P_z}	C_7'	0.000	0.000	0.000	1.000	0.000	0.000	0.000
N:		$\dfrac{1}{\sqrt{6}}$	$\dfrac{1}{\sqrt{12}}$	$\dfrac{1}{2}$	1.000	$\dfrac{1}{\sqrt{6}}$	$\dfrac{1}{\sqrt{12}}$	$\dfrac{1}{2}$

From the chapter on hybrid orbitals we obtain the following list of linear combinations for the boron sp^2 trigonal orbitals Tr_i. From these it is possible to construct a list of the coefficients of the atomic orbitals.

$$Tr_1 = \frac{1}{\sqrt{3}} S + \frac{1}{\sqrt{6}} P_x$$

$$Tr_2 = \frac{1}{\sqrt{3}} S - \frac{1}{\sqrt{6}} P_x + \frac{1}{\sqrt{2}} P_y$$

$$Tr_3 = \frac{1}{\sqrt{3}} S - \frac{1}{\sqrt{6}} P_x - \frac{1}{\sqrt{2}} P_y$$

Table 9.15   Table of coefficients using hydrogen $1s$ and boron $2s, 2p_x, 2p_y, 2p_z$

Orbital designation of the coefficients		Γ						
		A_1'	E'	E'	A_2''	A_1'	E'	E'
H_{1s_1}	C_1	0.408	0.000	0.578	0.000	−0.408	−0.578	0.000
H_{1s_2}	C_2	0.408	0.500	−0.289	0.000	−0.408	0.289	−0.500
H_{1s_3}	C_3	0.408	−0.500	−0.289	0.000	−0.408	0.289	0.500
B_{2s}	C_4	0.706	0.000	0.000	0.000	0.706	0.000	0.000
B_{2p_x}	C_5	0.000	0.709	−0.283	0.000	0.000	−0.283	0.707
B_{2p_y}	C_6	0.000	−0.707	−0.283	0.000	0.000	−0.283	−0.707
B_{2p_z}	C_7	0.000	0.000	0.000	1.000	0.000	0.000	0.000

C₂H₆ (STAGGERED, D_{3d})

The molecular structure for ethane is shown in Fig. 9.11. The basis set of atomic orbitals is H_{1s}, C_{2s}, C_{2p_x}, C_{2p_y}, C_{2p_z}, or H_{1s} and tetrahedral sp^3 on carbon $(T_{h_j}{}^i)$. We shall use the following symbols and notations:

H^i H_{1s}
$T_{h_j}{}^i$ C hybrid orbitals pointing toward the hydrogen atoms
$T_y{}^i$ C hybrid orbital pointing toward another carbon atom

Table 9.16 Character table for point group D_{3d}

D_{3d}	E	$2C_3$	$3C_2$	i	$2S_6$	$3\sigma_d$
A_{1g}	1	1	1	1	1	1
A_{2g}	1	1	-1	1	1	-1
E_g	2	-1	0	2	-1	0
A_{1u}	1	1	1	-1	-1	-1
A_{2u}	1	1	-1	-1	-1	1
E_u	2	-1	0	-2	1	0
Γ	14	2	0	0	0	6

In the standard manner we find the direct sum for the sigma system in ethane

$$\Gamma = 3A_{1g} + 2E_g + 2E_u + 3A_{2u}$$

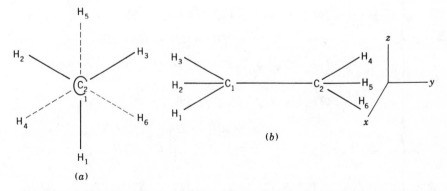

(a)

(b)

Fig. 9.11 Two views of molecular structure of ethane showing the cartesian coordinate system used to describe the atomic positions and the atomic numbering scheme. (*a*) A view down the C—C bond showing hydrogen atoms 1, 2, and 3 closest to the viewer; (*b*) a view perpendicular to the C—C bond. See also the stereoscopic drawings in Chap. 2.

The following groups of orbitals are the independent sets of orbitals:

1. $T_y{}^1$, $T_y{}^2$
2. $T_{h_1}{}^1$, $T_{h_2}{}^1$, $T_{h_3}{}^1$, $T_{h_4}{}^2$, $T_{h_5}{}^2$, $T_{h_6}{}^2$
3. H^1, H^2, H^3, H^4, H^5, H^6

The symmetry orbitals may then be written as follows:

A_{1g}: $\chi_1 = \dfrac{1}{\sqrt{2}} (T_y{}^1 - T_y{}^2)$

$\chi_2 = \dfrac{1}{\sqrt{6}} (T_{h_1}{}^1 + T_{h_2}{}^1 + T_{h_3}{}^1 + T_{h_4}{}^2 + T_{h_5}{}^2 + T_{h_6}{}^2)$

$\chi_3 = \dfrac{1}{\sqrt{6}} (H^1 + H^2 + H^3 + H^4 + H^5 + H^6)$

A_{2u}: $\chi_1 = \dfrac{1}{\sqrt{2}} (T_y{}^1 + T_y{}^2)$

$\chi_2 = \dfrac{1}{\sqrt{6}} (T_{h_1}{}^1 + T_{h_2}{}^1 + T_{h_3}{}^1 - T_{h_4}{}^2 - T_{h_5}{}^2 - T_{h_6}{}^2)$

$\chi_3 = \dfrac{1}{\sqrt{6}} (H^1 + H^2 + H^3 - H^4 - H^5 - H^6)$

E_g:

$\chi_1 = \dfrac{1}{\sqrt{24}} (2T_{h_1}{}^1 - T_{h_2}{}^1 - T_{h_3}{}^1 + 2T_{h_4}{}^2 - T_{h_5}{}^5 - T_{h_6}{}^2$
$+ 2H^1 - H^2 - H^3 + 2H^4 - H^5 - H^6)$

$\chi_2 = \dfrac{1}{\sqrt{8}} (T_{h_2}{}^1 - T_{h_3}{}^1 + T_{h_5}{}^2 - T_{h_6}{}^2 + H^2 - H^3 + H^5 - H^6)$

$\chi_1' = \dfrac{1}{\sqrt{24}} (2T_{h_1}{}^1 - T_{h_2}{}^1 - T_{h_3}{}^1 + 2T_{h_4}{}^2 - T_{h_5}{}^2 - T_{h_6}{}^2$
$- 2H^1 + H^2 + H^3 - 2H^4 + H^5 + H^6)$

$\chi_2' = \dfrac{1}{\sqrt{8}} (T_{h_2}{}^1 - T_{h_3}{}^1 + T_{h_5}{}^2 - T_{h_6}{}^2 - H^2 + H^3 - H^5 + H^6)$

E_u:

$\chi_1 = \dfrac{1}{\sqrt{24}} (2T_{h_1}{}^1 + T_{h_2}{}^1 - T_{h_3}{}^1 - 2T_{h_4}{}^2 - T_{h_5}{}^2 + T_{h_6}{}^2$
$+ 2H^1 + H^2 - H^3 - 2H^4 - H^5 + H^6)$

$\chi_2 = \dfrac{1}{\sqrt{8}} (T_{h_2}{}^1 - T_{h_3}{}^1 - T_{h_5}{}^2 + T_{h_6}{}^2 + H^2 - H^3 - H^5 + H^6)$

$\chi_1' = \dfrac{1}{\sqrt{24}} (2T_{h_1}{}^1 + T_{h_2}{}^1 - T_{h_3}{}^1 - 2T_{h_4}{}^2 - T_{h_5}{}^2 + T_{h_6}{}^2 - 2H^1$
$- H^2 + H^3 + 2H^4 + H^5 - H^6)$

$\chi_2' = \dfrac{1}{\sqrt{8}} (T_{h_2}{}^1 + T_{h_3}{}^1 - T_{h_5}{}^2 - T_{h_6}{}^2 - H^2 - H^3 + H^5 + H^6)$

Let us now use the following symbols for the various integrals:

$$\int T_{h_j}{}^{i}\mathfrak{IC}T_{h_l}{}^{k}\,d\tau = \begin{cases} \alpha_T & i = k, j = l \\ \alpha_T + t\alpha_t & i = k, j \neq l \\ 0 & i \neq k \end{cases}$$

$$\int T_{y}{}^{i}\mathfrak{IC}T_{y}{}^{j}\,d\tau = \begin{cases} \alpha_T & i = j \\ \beta_{C-C} & i \neq j \end{cases}$$

$$\int T_{y}{}^{i}\mathfrak{IC}T_{h_j}{}^{k}\,d\tau = \begin{cases} \alpha_T & i = k \\ 0 & i \neq k \end{cases}$$

$$\int H^{i}\mathfrak{IC}H^{j}\,d\tau = \begin{cases} \alpha_H & i = j \\ 0 & i \neq j \end{cases}$$

$$\int T_{h_j}{}^{i}\mathfrak{IC}H^{k}\,d\tau = \begin{cases} \beta_{C-H} & j = k \\ 0 & j \neq k \end{cases}$$

$$\int T_{y}{}^{i}\mathfrak{IC}H^{j}\,d\tau = 0$$

The calculation of the various matrix elements is now performed in a straightforward manner using the above symbols.

A_{1g}: $H_{11} = \frac{1}{2}[2(\alpha_T - \beta)] = \alpha_T - \beta_{C-C}$
$\quad\quad H_{22} = \frac{1}{6}[6(\alpha_T + 2t\alpha_T)] = \alpha_T(1 + 2t)$
$\quad\quad H_{33} = \frac{1}{6}[6(\alpha_H)] = \alpha_H$
$\quad\quad H_{12} = \frac{1}{12}(3\alpha_T - 3\alpha_T) = 0$
$\quad\quad H_{13} = 0$
$\quad\quad H_{23} = \frac{1}{6}[6(\beta_{C-H})] = \beta_{C-H}$

A_{2u}: $H_{11} = \frac{1}{2}[2(\alpha_T + \beta_{C-C})] = \alpha_T + \beta_{C-C}$
$\quad\quad H_{22} = \frac{1}{6}[6(\alpha_T + 2t\alpha_T)] = \alpha_T(1 + 2t)$
$\quad\quad H_{33} = \frac{1}{6}[6(\alpha_H)] = \alpha_H$
$\quad\quad H_{12} = \frac{1}{12}(3\alpha_T - 3\alpha_T) = 0$
$\quad\quad H_{13} = 0$
$\quad\quad H_{23} = \frac{1}{6}[6(\beta_{C-H})] = \beta_{C-H}$

E_g: $H_{11} = \frac{1}{8}[4(\alpha_T - t\alpha_T \pm \beta_{C-H}) + 4(\pm\beta_{C-H} \pm \alpha_H)]$
$\quad\quad = \dfrac{\alpha_T(1 - t) \pm \alpha_H}{2} \pm \beta_{C-H}$

E_u: $H_{11} = \frac{1}{8}[4(\alpha_T + t\alpha_T \pm \beta_{C-H}) + 4(\pm\beta_{C-H} \pm \alpha_H)]$
$\quad\quad = \dfrac{\alpha_T(1 + t) \pm \alpha_H}{2} \pm \beta_{C-H}$

Only the A_{1g} secular determinant need be solved since, as can be seen below, two roots are in common with those of the A_{2u} determinant:

$$A_{1g}: \begin{vmatrix} \alpha_T - \beta_{C-C} - E_i & 0 & 0 \\ 0 & \alpha_T(1 + 2t) - E_i & \beta_{C-H} \\ 0 & \beta_{C-H} & \alpha_H - E_i \end{vmatrix} = 0$$

$$A_{2u}: \quad \begin{vmatrix} \alpha_T + \beta_{C-C} - E_i & 0 & 0 \\ 0 & \alpha_T(1 + 2t) - E_i & \beta_{C-H} \\ 0 & \beta_{C-H} & \alpha_H - E_i \end{vmatrix} = 0$$

The A_{1g} determinant reduces as follows:

$$(\alpha_T - \beta_{C-C} - E_i) \begin{vmatrix} \alpha_T(1 + 2t) - E_i & \beta_{C-H} \\ \beta_{C-H} & \alpha_H - E_i \end{vmatrix} = 0$$

The roots are easily determined to be

$$A_{1g}: \quad E_1 = \alpha_T - \beta_{C-C}$$

$$E_{2,3} = \frac{\alpha_T(1 + 2t) + \alpha_H \pm \sqrt{[\alpha_T(1 + 2t) - \alpha_H]^2 + 4\beta_{C-H}{}^2}}{2}$$

$$A_{2u}: \quad E_1 = \alpha_T + \beta_{C-C}$$

$$E_{2,3} = \frac{\alpha_T(1 + 2t) + \alpha_H \pm \sqrt{[\alpha_T(1 + 2t) - \alpha_H]^2 + 4\beta_{C-H}{}^2}}{2}$$

$$E_g: \quad E_{1,2} = \frac{\alpha_T(1 - t) \pm (\alpha_H + 2\beta_{C-H})}{2}$$

$$E_u: \quad E_{1,2} = \frac{\alpha_T(1 + t) \pm (\alpha_H + 2\beta_{C-H})}{2}$$

Once values are chosen for the various parameters in the energy expressions, an energy-level scheme can be drawn and MO coefficients determined for the true wave functions of the occupied MOs. Here, however, the preceding information will instead be applied to an understanding of the energy levels and MO wave functions determined by a high-speed computer program.

9.6 THE LCAO MO METHOD APPLIED TO COORDINATION COMPOUNDS

In compounds which contain transition metals the number of electrons is considerably larger than in molecules we have considered earlier. In addition to s and p orbitals we must also consider d and even f orbitals. With this increase in number and complexity of AOs comes an even greater increase in the difficulties of solving (even approximately) the Schrödinger equation for such systems. Hence, whatever labor may be saved by the use of group-theoretic methods is most welcomed. Of course, the lower the symmetry of the molecule or ion, the less useful the methods of group theory. However, as in other cases, much can often be learned from a treatment of a more symmetric idealized structure.

The MO approach to metal-ligand binding is useful because it can be discussed qualitatively in terms of orbital overlap. Hence, the crystal-field concept on the one hand can be discussed in terms of zero or small overlap, whereas the MO theory can be discussed as a covalent theory with variable overlap.

Although a complete approximate treatment of coordination compounds such as those mentioned earlier would represent a huge amount of labor, the qualitative features of the MO scheme presented here lend a great deal of understanding to the electronic structure of coordination compounds. A discussion of electronic spectra and of such properties as paramagnetism must await the development of crystal-field theory in the final chapter.

We shall take up here a detailed discussion of both sigma and pi bonding in octahedral cases, a short presentation of the tetrahedral case, and a development of the electronic structure of ferrocene.

OCTAHEDRAL COMPLEXES, MX₆

Let us consider a coordination compound in which six ligands X surround a transition metal M in an octahedral configuration as in $FeF_6{}^{3-}$. Each ligand is considered to contribute one sigma-type orbital each to the bonding system in addition to one or more pi-type orbitals. The AOs available from the first transition series metal atom may be contributed from $3d$, $4s$, and $4p$ orbitals. We shall first consider sigma bonding.

Figure 9.12 shows the coordinate system we shall use, along with the designations of the sigma orbitals from the ligands. Using methods

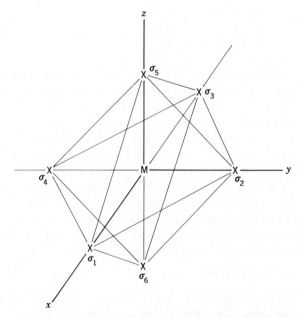

Fig. 9.12 The coordinate system for an octahedral complex MX_6 showing the designations of the ligand sigma orbitals.

developed in Chap. 8, it can be shown that the $3d_{z^2}$, $3d_{x^2-y^2}$, $4s$, $4p_x$, $4p_y$, and $4p_z$ orbitals possess the appropriate symmetry for sigma bonding. The $3d_{xy}$, $3d_{xz}$, and $3d_{yz}$ in addition to the $4p$ orbitals may participate in pi bonding. Hence, in an octahedral complex there are 12 orbitals available for combination in the MO scheme. The number of electrons which may be assigned to the various levels depends upon the transition-metal atom; 12 electrons are contributed by the ligands.

Let us now consider the six ligand sigma orbitals as basis functions for a representation of the octahedral point group O_h. The character system may be determined as follows and then reduced in the standard manner.

O_h	E	$8C_3$	$6C_2$	$6C_4$	$3C_2$	i	$6S_4$	$8S_6$	$3\sigma_h$	$6\sigma_d$
Γ_σ	6	0	0	2	2	0	0	0	4	2

$$\Gamma_\sigma = A_{1g} + E_g + T_{1u}$$

By a similar procedure, the six atomic orbitals of the metal atom may be shown to belong to the same irreducible representations as follows:

$$4p \ (p_x, \ p_y, \ p_z) \quad T_{1u}$$
$$4s \qquad\qquad\qquad A_{1g}$$
$$3d \ (d_{z^2}, \ d_{x^2-y^2}) \quad E_g$$

The problem now is to prepare linear combinations of the ligand sigma orbitals which correspond to the above irreducible representations. There is no simple set of rules for this task. However, a kind of pictorial approach can be used to simplify the procedure.

Let us first consider the linear combinations of T_{1u} symmetry. Figure 9.13 shows the p_x orbital of the metal atom which also belongs to the T_{1u} irreducible representation. Also included in Fig. 9.13 are two ligand orbitals, σ_1 and σ_3, with their relative signs as positive. It is now clear that only orbitals σ_1 and σ_3 can contribute to the linear combination of T_{1u} which matches the symmetry of the p_x orbital. Further, σ_3 must be entered with a negative sign. Hence, we may write one of the combination ligand orbitals of T_{1u} symmetry as

$$\phi_x(T_{1u}) = \sigma_1 - \sigma_3$$

As written here ϕ_x is unnormalized. Using procedures established earlier, we obtain a normalization constant of $1/\sqrt{2}$.

By making use of our knowledge of the symmetry of the various AOs, the pictorial approach may be used to construct the other five com-

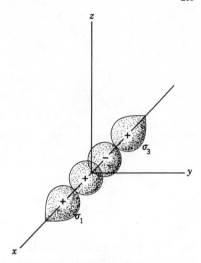

Fig. 9.13 The metal atom p_x orbital and two ligand sigma orbitals, σ_1 and σ_3, which may be combined to form a symmetry orbital of T_{1u} symmetry.

bination ligand orbitals. Figures 9.14 and 9.15 may be used to obtain orbitals of A_{1g} and of E_g symmetry. The symmetry orbitals are listed in Table 9.17.

Table 9.17 Ligand symmetry orbitals and metal atomic orbitals in an octahedral complex

Metal orbital	Ligand symmetry orbitals	Representation
s	$\dfrac{1}{\sqrt{6}}(\sigma_1 + \sigma_2 + \sigma_3 + \sigma_4 + \sigma_5 + \sigma_6)$	A_{1g}
d_{z^2}	$\dfrac{1}{\sqrt{12}}(2\sigma_5 + 2\sigma_6 - \sigma_1 - \sigma_2 - \sigma_3 - \sigma_4)$	E_g
$d_{x^2-y^2}$	$\tfrac{1}{2}(\sigma_1 - \sigma_2 + \sigma_3 - \sigma_4)$	E_g
p_x	$\dfrac{1}{\sqrt{2}}(\sigma_1 - \sigma_3)$	T_{1u}
p_y	$\dfrac{1}{\sqrt{2}}(\sigma_2 - \sigma_4)$	T_{1u}
p_z	$\dfrac{1}{\sqrt{2}}(\sigma_5 - \sigma_6)$	T_{1u}

Caution must be exercised in the use of the pictorial approach, particularly in construction of the E_g symmetry orbitals. It must be remem-

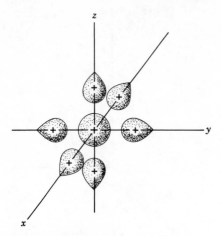

Fig. 9.14   The metal atom s orbital shown
with the ligand sigma orbitals which may
be combined to yield a symmetry orbital
of A_{1g} symmetry.

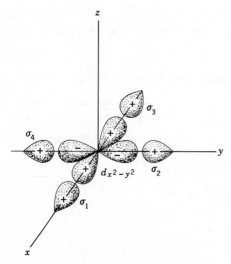

Fig. 9.15   The metal atom $d_{x^2-y^2}$ orbital
shown with the ligand sigma orbitals which
may be combined to yield a symmetry
orbital of E_g symmetry.

Metal
Atomic orbitals

Octahedral complex
Molecular orbitals

Ligand
Sigma orbitals
donated

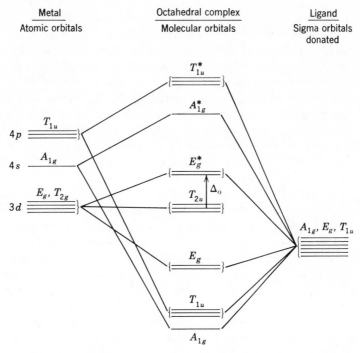

Fig. 9.16 The qualitative MO energy-level diagram showing approximate relative ordering of levels and their degree of degeneracy. This diagram is valid in the case of no pi bonding for first transition-series metals. The arrow labeled Δ_o is called the crystal-field splitting.

bered that in the d_{z^2} AO the probability along the z axis is twice that in the xy plane.

In order to complete the problem we must set up and solve the various secular determinants, and to do this we must decide upon (approximate) values for the various integrals involved. The problem, however, has been reduced from a 12 × 12 determinant to one 6 × 6, one 4 × 4, and one 2 × 2 determinant. The methods used to set up these secular equations are somewhat beyond the scope of this book. However, one may obtain a qualitative picture of the MO scheme in an octahedral complex by observing the usual order of energy levels in the atomic ion and the ligand orbitals: $\sigma_{\text{ligand}} < 3d < 4s < 4p$. Remember that each combination of symmetry orbitals produces a low-energy bonding MO and a high-energy antibonding MO. Figure 9.16 shows an approximate scheme for a typical octahedral complex when pi bonding is ignored. In this case, the d_{xy}, d_{xz}, and d_{yz} metal orbitals (T_{2g}) become nonbonding in the complex.

According to the general rule of thumb of MO theory, when two symmetry orbitals of very different energy (2 to 3 ev difference) are combined, the two resulting MOs are quite different in character. The lower-energy, or bonding, MO takes on the character primarily of the lower-energy symmetry orbital. Hence, in the octahedral complex the bonding MOs are primarily of ligand character, and we may think of these 6 MOs as being filled with the 12 "donated" ligand electrons. The metal-ion electrons then are placed in the scheme beginning with the nonbonding T_{2g} orbitals. The energy gap Δ_o between the T_{2g} level and the E_g^* level is most important in coordination chemistry. Chapter 11 is devoted to a discussion of the influence and determination of Δ_o. We shall concern ourselves here with the overall MO scheme.

The influence of pi bonding on the properties of coordination compounds may be dramatic. Many ligands possess the appropriate orbitals for pi bonding. In halide ions if we consider the p_z orbital as taking part in the sigma bonding, both the lone-pair electron pairs in the p_x and p_y orbitals are available for pi overlap. (Of course, one may wish to use hybrid orbitals on the ligand. The possibility of pi bonding is not changed because hybrid orbitals are chosen to preserve the atomic symmetry.)

Figure 9.17 shows the coordinate system for the pi bonding scheme in an octahedral complex. Once the coordinate system is chosen, one may

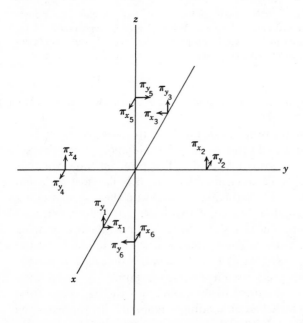

Fig. 9.17   The coordinate system for the description of pi bonding in octahedral complexes showing the designations of the AOs which are possible for pi bonding.

again use the pictorial method for obtaining expressions for the linear-combination symmetry orbitals.

The appropriate expressions for the symmetry orbitals used in pi bonding are listed in Table 9.18 along with the proper metal orbitals.

Table 9.18   Pi symmetry orbitals for octahedral bonding

Metal orbitals	Symmetry orbitals	Representation
p_x	$\frac{1}{2}(\pi_{y_2} + \pi_{x_5} - \pi_{x_4} - \pi_{y_6})$	T_{1u}
p_y	$\frac{1}{2}(\pi_{x_1} + \pi_{y_5} - \pi_{y_3} - \pi_{x_6})$	T_{1u}
p_z	$\frac{1}{2}(\pi_{y_1} + \pi_{x_2} - \pi_{x_3} - \pi_{y_4})$	T_{1u}
d_{xy}	$\frac{1}{2}(\pi_{y_1} + \pi_{y_5} + \pi_{x_3} + \pi_{y_6})$	T_{2g}
d_{xz}	$\frac{1}{2}(\pi_{x_2} + \pi_{y_5} + \pi_{y_4} + \pi_{x_6})$	T_{2g}
d_{yz}	$\frac{1}{2}(\pi_{x_1} + \pi_{y_2} + \pi_{y_3} + \pi_{x_4})$	T_{2g}

The effect of the available pi orbitals on the MO scheme may now be considered.   The final scheme depends upon the relative ordering of the metal T_{2g} orbitals and the ligand pi orbitals.   The situation may be further complicated when the ligands possess antibonding as well as bonding (or filled as well as unfilled) pi orbitals: there is then a competition in the determination of the orbital energy-level scheme.

Ligands such as oxygen and fluorine possess filled pi-type orbitals which are generally lower in energy than other pi orbitals; whereas, phosphines and arsines generally possess empty pi-type orbitals of high energy. However, carbon monoxide and the cyanide ion possess both types.   Figure 9.18 shows a qualitative scheme for the two simple types.

Some qualitative calculations have been performed on carbon monoxide and cyanide ligand systems.   The competition between the bonding and nonbonding pi-type ligand orbitals is clearly demonstrated here. Figure 9.19 shows a sample energy-level scheme for $M(CO)_6$ or $M(CN)_6{}^{n-}$ Hence, although the gross features of the electronic structure of octahedral complexes do emerge from the foregoing treatment, the details depend upon much more complex calculations.

TETRAHEDRAL AND OTHER LOWER-SYMMETRY COMPLEXES

The high symmetry of the octahedral complex allows for great reduction in the size of the computational problem, partly because of the clean separation of the various symmetry types of AOs involving sigma and pi bonding.   Such is not the case in lower-symmetry cases.   We have already referred to such a problem, viz., in the designation of pi orbitals for hybridized AOs for tetrahedral geometry.   The orbitals p_x, p_y, and p_z are of appropriate symmetry for both sigma and pi bonding.   This

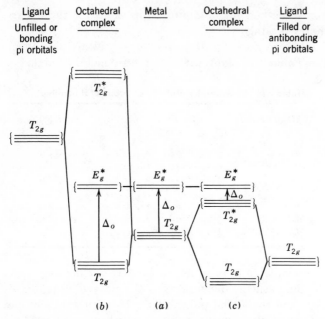

Fig. 9.18 MO energy-level diagrams for certain of the levels in an octahedral complex depicting the effect of pi-type orbitals in the ligands upon the crystal-field splitting. (*a*) No pi-type orbitals available; (*b*) high-energy (unfilled or bonding) pi-type ligand orbitals; (*c*) low-energy (filled or antibonding) pi-type ligand orbitals. Notice the relative size of the crystal-field splittings Δ_o in these three cases.

problem is illustrated in Table 9.19, which gives the AOs appropriate for sigma and pi bonding for several geometries as summarized from Chap. 8.

Table 9.19 Bonding designations for AOs in some common metal-complex geometries

Bonding type	Geometry			
	Octahedral	*Tetrahedral*	*Square planar*	*Trigonal bipyramidal*
Sigma	d_{z^2}, $d_{x^2-y^2}$, s, p_x p_y, p_z	s, p_x, p_y, p_z or s, d_{xy}, d_{xz}, d_{yz}	s, $d_{x^2-y^2}$, p_x, p_y or d_{z^2}, $d_{x^2-y^2}$, p_x, p_y	d_{z^2}, s, p_x, p_y, p_z
Pi	d_{xy}, d_{xz}, d_{yz}	p_x, p_y, p_z d_{xy}, d_{xz}, d_{yz} and d_{z^2}, $d_{x^2-y^2}$	p_z, d_{xz}, d_{yz}	$d_{x^2-y^2}$, d_{xy} p_x, p_y, p_z d_{xz}, d_{yz}

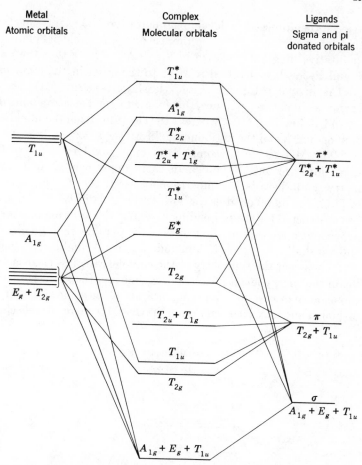

Metal
Atomic orbitals

Complex
Molecular orbitals

Ligands
Sigma and pi
donated orbitals

Fig. 9.19 MO energy-level scheme based on qualitative calculations for an octahedral complex with two types of ligand pi orbitals as in some metal carbonyls and cyanides. [*From H. B. Gray and N. A. Beach, J. Am. Chem. Soc.*, **85**:2922(1963).]

Thus, although the MO method may be applied to lower-symmetry complexes with success, the results may not be so simply obtained. In the tetrahedral case, for example, the p_x, p_y, and p_z orbitals and the d_{xy}, d_{xz}, and d_{yz} orbitals belong to the T_2 representation. Hence, the T_2 symmetry orbitals must be written as a linear combination of both sets, thereby increasing the computational problem. The linear-combination symmetry orbital may be written

$$\chi_{\text{tetra}}(T_2) = P + aD$$
$$= (c_1 p_x + c_2 p_y + c_3 p_z) + a(c_4 d_{xy} + c_5 d_{xz} + c_6 d_{yz})$$

We can then proceed to develop a qualitative MO energy-level scheme for that tetrahedral case in which there is no appreciable pi bonding. Such a qualitative diagram is shown in Fig. 9.20. (Note that the order of the E and T_2 levels is inverted relative to the order in the octahedral case.)

As in the octahedral case, the lowest-energy MOs are primarily ligandlike in nature. Hence, the donated ligand electron pairs occupy the A_1 and T_2 bonding MOs, whereas the electrons from the metal occupy the nonbonding E and the antibonding T_2^* MOs.

The MO scheme becomes even more involved when pi bonding is taken into account. The ligands then supply orbitals of E and T_2 symmetry, and there is a competition between the T_2 (p_x, p_y, p_z) and T_2 (d_{xy}, d_{xz}, d_{yz}) metal orbitals for both sigma and pi MOs. A diagram could be constructed for the pi-bonding case, but the ordering of levels is highly dependent upon the specific values of the parameters for a given complex, and we shall not attempt to include a general qualitative diagram here.

The lower the symmetry of the complex, the less clear-cut the ordering of the energy levels in the MO scheme and the less certain the relative importance of various competing orbitals of the same symmetry. Hence, although one may construct a qualitative MO energy-level scheme by the

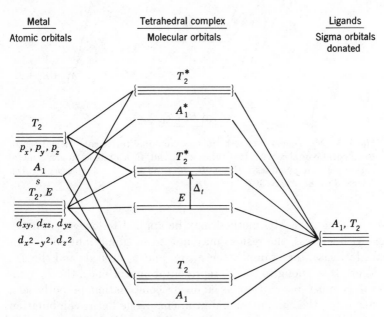

Fig. 9.20 A qualitative MO energy-level scheme for a tetrahedral complex with no pi bonding, showing the crystal-field splitting Δ_t. Note the competition between the two sets of metal T_2 symmetry orbitals for the one set of ligand T_2 symmetry orbitals.

use of rule-of-thumb estimations, caution must be exercised in the detailed interpretation of such diagrams.

ORGANOMETALLIC SANDWICH COMPOUNDS

Since 1951, when the (accidental) synthesis of the first sandwich compound was published,[1] and since 1956, when the sandwich structure was confirmed by x-ray diffraction,[2] there has been much interest in the electronic structure of sandwich compounds such as dicyclopentadienyliron, commonly called ferrocene. There is still some question whether the two cyclopentadiene rings are in a staggered or eclipsed conformation. Most of the ferrocene derivatives show an eclipsed conformation in the solid state. Other sandwich compounds such as dicyclopentadieneosmium and ruthenocene are eclipsed in the solid state. There is some evidence indicating that ferrocene may be staggered in the liquid and gaseous states. The two possible molecular geometries for ferrocene are shown in Fig. 9.21.

We shall use ferrocene as an example in demonstrating the application of MO methods to organometallic sandwich compounds. We shall use the staggered D_{5d} structure in setting up the MO energy-level scheme. The reader may ponder the possible differences between D_{5d} and D_{5h} geometries in the energy-level scheme as an exercise (in Prob. 9.16).

First, we must decide which orbitals of the metal and of the hydrocarbon rings are involved in the organometallic bonding system. For the iron atom we shall assume that the five $3d$, the one $4s$, and the three $4p$ orbitals may participate in the bonding. The planar cyclopentadienyl rings consist of a sigma-bonded hydrocarbon skeleton plus a double-doughnut pi-bonded system. Here, we shall assume that only the p pi carbon orbitals are involved in the organometallic system. To at least a

[1] T. J. Kealy and P. L. Pauson, *Nature*, **168**:103 (1951).
[2] J. D. Dunitz, L. E. Orgel, and A. Rich, *Acta Cryst.*, **9**:373 (1956).

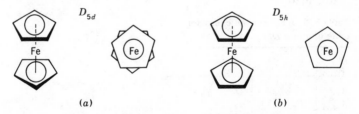

Fig. 9.21 The two conformations for the molecular geometry of ferrocene (hydrogen atoms not included). (*a*) The staggered conformation of symmetry D_{5d} shown in perspective (*left*) and in a view down the fivefold axis (*right*); (*b*) the eclipsed conformation of symmetry D_{5h} shown in perspective (*left*) and in a view down the fivefold axis (*right*). See also the stereoscopic illustrations in Chap. 2.

first approximation the sigma orbitals of the hydrocarbon ring systems are unaffected. Hence, some of the negative charge of the cyclopentadienyl ions is transferred to the ferrous ion in the synthesis of ferrocene

$$2C_5H_5^- + Fe^{++} = (C_5H_5)_2Fe$$

At this point let us review the general method of MO energy-level scheme construction by summarizing the technique for ferrocene:

1. Determine the irreducible representations to which the iron-atom AOs belong in point group D_{5d}.
2. Construct linear combinations of the cyclopentadiene p pi orbitals (symmetry orbitals) which possess the same symmetry as the irreducible representations of the iron-atom orbitals.
3. Combine the cyclopentadiene and iron symmetry orbitals into MOs in bonding and antibonding pairs (taking into account any competition between symmetry orbitals belonging to the same irreducible representation).
4. Symmetry orbitals of a unique symmetry species in the bonding system become nonbonding MOs.
5. On the basis of quantitative computations or on the basis of qualitative rule-of-thumb estimates order the bonding, nonbonding, and antibonding MOs in the energy-level scheme. The approximate order and spacing of the metal-orbital energy levels can be obtained from the electronic spectra of the metal ion, and similar information for the hydrocarbon rings can be obtained from the ultraviolet spectrum.
6. Place electrons into the MOs starting with the lowest-energy MO and observing Hund's rule in the case of degeneracies.

In order to determine the symmetry species of the iron atom in point group D_{5d} let us refer to a condensed version of the D_{5d} character table in Table 9.20.

Table 9.20 A condensed character table of group D_{5d}

D_{5d}		
A_{1g}		$x^2 + y^2$, z^2
A_{2g}	R_z	
E_{1g}	(R_x, R_y)	(xz, yz)
E_{2g}		$(x^2 - y^2, xy)$
A_{1u}		
A_{2u}	z	
E_{1u}	(x, y)	
E_{2u}		

Table 9.20 gives the right-hand portion of the D_{5d} character table which is used to identify the AO symmetry species directly, as shown here:

A_{1g}	E_{1g}	E_{2g}	A_{2u}	E_{1u}
$4s, 3d_{z^2}$	$3d_{xz}, 3d_{yz}$	$3d_{x^2-y^2}, 3d_{xy}$	$4p_z$	$4p_x, 4p_y$

For the two cyclopentadiene rings we examine the reducible representation for which the two sets of five p pi atomic orbitals serve as basis functions. The character system for these 10 p pi orbitals in group D_{5d} along with the direct sum for the totally reduced representation are given below. The reader may wish to refer to Fig. 9.22 in the determination of this character system. The signs of the carbon $2p_z$ atomic orbitals are indicated, and consideration must be given to these signs in the determination of $\Gamma_{p\pi}$.

D_{5d}	E	$2C_5$	$2C_5{}^2$	$5C_2$	i	$2S_{10}{}^3$	$2S_{10}$	$5\sigma_d$
$\Gamma_{p\pi}$	10	0	0	0	0	0	0	2

$$\Gamma_{p\pi} = A_{1g} + E_{1g} + E_{2g} + A_{2u} + E_{1u} + E_{2u}$$

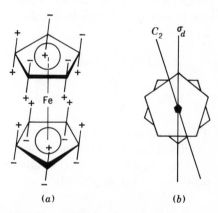

(a)   (b)

Fig. 9.22 (a) The molecular structure of the skeleton of ferrocene (staggered) showing the signs of the carbon $2p_z$ atom orbitals arranged by the convention which places the positive lobe between atoms which are bonded; (b) a view down the fivefold axis in the D_{5d} geometry showing the relative geometry of one dihedral mirror plane and one twofold rotation axis.

Notice that these symmetry species occur in pairs, one of which is symmetric to inversion and the other antisymmetric to inversion.

$$\Gamma_{p\pi} \begin{cases} A_{1g}, \ A_{2u} \\ E_{1g}, \ E_{1u} \\ E_{2g}, \ E_{2u} \end{cases}$$

The procedure for the construction of the ring symmetry orbitals can be simplified when we realize that use can be made of the pi-system wave functions tabulated in Sec. 9.5. The $C_5H_5^-$ ion possesses MOs of A, E_1, and E_2 symmetry, and these may be used directly in this present case as appropriate linear combinations of the two sets of ring orbitals.

From the tables at the end of Sec. 9.5 we can write wave functions of A symmetry, ϕ_1, for the two rings as follows:

$$\phi_1(A) = \frac{1}{\sqrt{5}} (p_1 + p_2 + p_3 + p_4 + p_5)$$

and

$$\phi_2(A) = \frac{1}{\sqrt{5}} (p_1' + p_2' + p_3' + p_4' + p_5')$$

where p_i represents the $2p_z$ carbon AO centered on carbon atom i. It can be seen by inspection that the A_{1g} and A_{2u} ring symmetry orbitals may be written

$$\chi(A_{1g}) = \frac{1}{\sqrt{2}} [\phi_1(A) + \phi_2(A)]$$

$$\chi(A_{2u}) = \frac{1}{\sqrt{2}} [\phi_1(A) - \phi_2(A)]$$

The reader may wish to write out $\chi(A_{1g})$ and $\chi(A_{2u})$ and verify that these two linear combinations possess the appropriate symmetry.

By the same method of direct inspection the remaining symmetry orbitals (doubly degenerate) can be determined and tabulated as follows:

$$\chi_a(E_{1g}) = \frac{1}{\sqrt{2}} [\phi_1{}^a(E_1{}^a) + \phi_2{}^a(E_1{}^a)]$$

$$\chi_b(E_{1g}) = \frac{1}{\sqrt{2}} [\phi_1{}^b(E_1{}^b) + \phi_2{}^b(E_1{}^b)]$$

$$\chi_a(E_{1u}) = \frac{1}{\sqrt{2}} [\phi_1{}^a(E_1{}^a) - \phi_2{}^a(E_1{}^a)]$$

$$\chi_b(E_{1u}) = \frac{1}{\sqrt{2}} [\phi_1{}^b(E_1{}^b) - \phi_2{}^b(E_1{}^b)]$$

$$\chi_a(E_{2g}) = \frac{1}{\sqrt{2}} [\phi_1{}^a(E_2{}^a) + \phi_2{}^a(E_2{}^a)]$$

$$\chi_b(E_{2g}) = \frac{1}{\sqrt{2}} [\phi_1{}^b(E_2{}^b) + \phi_2{}^b(E_2{}^b)]$$

$$\chi_a(E_{2u}) = \frac{1}{\sqrt{2}} [\phi_1{}^a(E_2{}^a) - \phi_2{}^a(E_2{}^a)]$$

$$\chi_b(E_{2u}) = \frac{1}{\sqrt{2}} [\phi_1{}^b(E_2{}^b) - \phi_2{}^b(E_2{}^b)]$$

Thus, there are nine AOs of the iron atom to be combined with the ten symmetry orbitals of the cyclopentadiene rings. One of the ring symmetry orbitals must be nonbonding in the organometallic system; it is the pair of E_{2u} orbitals, since there are no iron AOs of E_{2u} symmetry.

In order to obtain the final MO wave functions we must solve the 19×19 order set of secular equations. However, by the use of symmetry the order of these equations has been reduced by the preceding factorization procedure to the following set of smaller secular determinants:

Number	Size	Symmetry of MO
1	3×3	A_{1g}
1	2×2	A_{2u}
2	2×2	E_{1g}
1	1×1	E_{1u}
2	2×2	E_{2g}
2	2×2	E_{2u}

Once these smaller secular determinants are solved, the coefficients in the MOs can be tabulated and the relative energies of the MOs determined. Because of the complexities involved in the evaluation of the necessary integrals, rather gross approximations are used to give values for the integrals in this case, and we shall not deal with that aspect of the problem here in detail. Dyatkina[1] has given the results of a self-consistent-field (SCF) calculation which shows the MO energy-level scheme given in Fig. 9.23. Notice that the 18 valence electrons just fill the available bonding orbitals.

The energy-level diagram in Fig. 9.23 may also correspond, at least qualitatively, to the energy-level scheme for other dicyclopentadienyl-metal sandwich compounds. However, because many of the levels are quite closely spaced, the exact sequence of states depends upon the details of quantitative calculations.

[1] E. M. Shustorovich and M. E. Dyatkina, *Dokl. Akad. Nauk. SSSR*, **128**:1234 (1959).

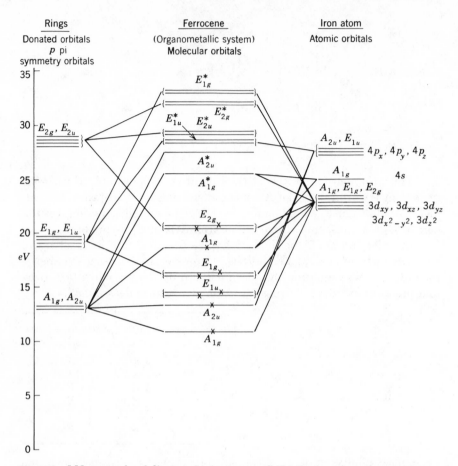

Fig. 9.23 MO energy-level diagram for ferrocene, $(C_5H_5)_2Fe$, based on an approximate self-consistent-field calculation by Dyatkina. The zero of the energy scale has been chosen arbitrarily. Energy levels occupied by electron pairs have been indicated by small x's. Notice that the ring symmetry orbitals are grouped in pairs of the same rotational symmetry but opposite symmetry with respect to inversion.

A few words concerning the evaluation of some of the integrals are in order here. At least three semiempirical integral estimation formulas have been commonly used. The three methods are

$$\mathbf{H}_{ij} = \int \phi_i \mathcal{K} \phi_j \, d\tau = \begin{cases} KS_{ij} & (9.1) \\ \frac{1}{2}K(H_{ii} + H_{jj})S_{ij} & (9.2) \\ \frac{1}{2}K(H_{ii} + H_{jj})(1 + |S_{ij}|)S_{ij} & (9.3) \end{cases}$$

All these formulas are based upon the notion that the interaction between orbitals centered on different atoms varies with distance between the atoms in much the same way that the overlap integral between the two AOs varies with distance. In Eq. (9.1) the dependence is a direct proportion. The second formula is known as the *Wolfsberg-Helmholz*[1] formula and the third as *Cusachs' formula*.[2] Although various values for K have been used, a value of about 2.0 ev is often taken. The reader may wish to employ a set of overlap-integral tables in some trial calculations. The work may be long and tedious, but much useful experience can be gained in the process.

Using the above procedure the MO energy-level schemes have been worked out for dicyclobutadiene and dibenzene organometallic sandwich compounds and tabulated below.

1. $(C_4H_4)_2M$; point group $= D_{4h}$

Metal orbitals

A_{1g}	B_{1g}	B_{2g}	E_g	A_{2u}	E_u
s, d_{z^2}	$d_{x^2-y^2}$	d_{xy}	d_{xz}, d_{yz}	p_z	p_x, p_y

Cyclobutadiene p pi symmetry orbitals

D_{4h}	E	$2C_4$	C_2	$2C_2'$	$2C_2''$	i	$2S_4$	σ_h	$2\sigma_v$	$2\sigma_d$
$\Gamma_{p\pi}$	8	0	0	0	0	0	0	0	0	4

$$\Gamma_{p\pi} = A_{1g} + B_{2g} + E_g + A_{2u} + B_{1u} + E_u$$

The MO energy-level scheme is shown in Fig. 9.24.

2. $(C_6H_6)_2M$; point group $= D_{6h}$

Metal orbitals

A_{1g}	E_{1g}	E_{2g}	A_{2u}	E_{1u}
s, d_{z^2}	d_{xz}, d_{yz}	$d_{xy}, d_{x^2-y^2}$	p_z	p_x, p_y

Benzene p pi symmetry orbitals

D_{6h}	E	$2C_6$	$2C_3$	C_2	$3C_2'$	$3C_2''$	i	$2S_3$	$2S_6$	σ_h	$3\sigma_d$	$3\sigma_v$
$\Gamma_{p\pi}$	12	0	0	0	0	0	0	0	0	0	0	4

$$\Gamma_{p\pi} = A_{1g} + B_{2g} + E_{1g} + E_{2g} + A_{2u} + B_{1u} + E_{1u} + E_{2u}$$

The MO energy-level scheme is shown in Fig. 9.25.

[1] M. Wolfsberg and L. Helmholz, *J. Chem. Phys.*, **20**:837 (1952).
[2] L. C. Cusachs, *J. Chem. Phys.*, **43**:S157 (1965).

Rings	Dicyclobutadiene metal	Metal atom
Donated p pi symmetry orbitals	(Organometallic system) Molecular orbitals	Atomic orbitals

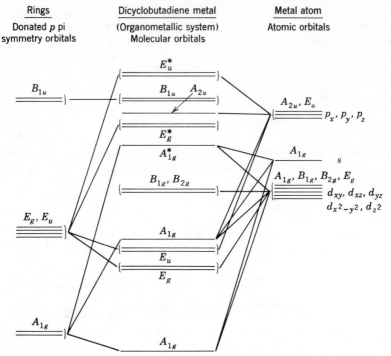

Fig. 9.24 MO energy-level diagram for dicyclobutadiene-metal sandwich compounds, $(C_4H_4)_2M$, based on qualitative estimates of energy-level spacings.

9.7 USE OF HIGH-SPEED DIGITAL COMPUTERS

From the discussions of the previous section it can be seen that for large molecules or sophisticated conditions hand calculations rapidly become prohibitive. Thus, many investigators are now using high-speed digital computers. Computer programs are now available for simple Hückel, extended Hückel, and even more sophisticated calculations. It is appropriate to make some comments here on the interpretation of the output of such computer programs.

We have indicated in earlier sections that symmetry considerations are not only useful in performing calculations leading to MO coefficients but are also necessary in the proper interpretation of electronic spectra and in understanding other chemical problems. This section shows how to determine from the computer output the irreducible representation to which each MO belongs. We shall make use of the results from Sec. 9.5 in discussing computer calculations on BH_3 and C_2H_6.

Energy levels and MOs are given in Tables 9.21 and 9.22 for BH_3 and C_2H_6. The extended Hückel program of R. Hoffmann[1] was used.

[1] R. Hoffmann and W. N. Lipscomb, *J. Chem. Phys.*, **36**:2179, 3489 (1962).

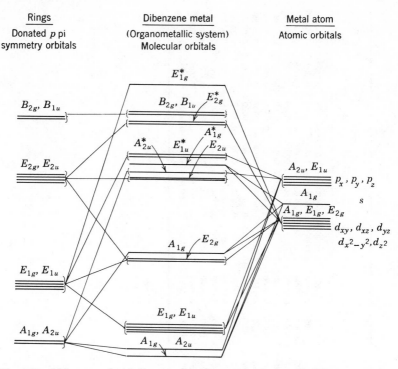

Rings
Donated p pi
symmetry orbitals

Dibenzene metal
(Organometallic system)
Molecular orbitals

Metal atom
Atomic orbitals

Fig. 9.25 MO energy-level diagram for dibenzene-metal sandwich compounds, $(C_6H_6)_2M$, based on an approximate SCF calculation on $(C_6H_6)_2Cr$ by Dyatkina. (See footnote on page 267.)

Table 9.21 Energy levels and MO coefficients for BH₃

No.	Energy, ev	$H_{1s}{}^1$	$H_{1s}{}^2$	$H_{1s}{}^3$	B_{2s}	B_{2p_x}	B_{2p_y}	B_{2p_z}
1	39.737	0.9012	0.9012	0.9012	−1.8713	0.0000	0.0000	0.0000
2	15.930	1.2072	0.6036	0.6036	0.0000	−1.3815	0.0000	0.0000
3	15.930	0.0000	−1.0454	1.0454	0.0000	0.0000	1.3815	0.0000
4	−8.630	0.0000	0.0000	0.0000	0.0000	0.0000	0.0000	1.0000
5	−13.968	−0.5620	0.2553	0.3068	0.0000	0.4586	−0.0243	0.0000
6	−13.968	−0.0297	0.5016	−0.4719	0.0000	0.0243	0.4586	0.0000
7	−20.305	0.2700	0.2700	0.2700	0.4833	0.0000	0.0000	0.0000

The symmetry of each MO wave function is reflected in the signs and relative values of the coefficients. However, as we shall see, we need not examine every AO coefficient in each MO in order to determine the irreducible representation to which the wave function belongs.

Table 9.22 Energy levels and MO coefficients for C_2H_6

No.	Energy, ev	H_{1s}^1	H_{1s}^2	H_{1s}^3	H_{1s}^4	H_{1s}^5	H_{1s}^6	C_{2s}^1	C_{2s}^2	$C_{2p_z}^1$	$C_{2p_z}^2$	$C_{2p_y}^1$	$C_{2p_y}^2$	$C_{2p_x}^1$	$C_{2p_x}^2$
1	43.792	0.5045	0.5045	0.5045	-0.5045	-0.5045	-0.5045	-1.3570	1.3570	0.0000	0.0000	0.1768	0.1768	0.0000	0.0000
2	26.366	0.5158	0.5158	0.5158	0.5158	0.5158	0.5158	-1.0295	-1.0295	0.0000	0.0000	-0.4027	0.4027	0.0000	0.0000
3	10.677	-0.2452	-0.5408	0.7860	-0.5408	-0.2452	0.7860	0.0000	0.0000	0.2646	-0.2646	0.0000	0.0000	-0.8266	0.8266
4	10.677	0.7661	-0.5954	-0.1707	-0.5954	0.7661	-0.1707	0.0000	0.0000	-0.8266	0.8266	0.0000	0.0000	-0.2646	0.2646
5	7.246	0.6442	0.0894	-0.7336	-0.0894	-0.6442	0.7336	0.0000	0.0000	-0.6091	0.6091	0.0000	0.0000	-0.4492	0.4492
6	7.246	0.4751	-0.7955	0.3204	0.7955	-0.4751	-0.3204	0.0000	0.0000	-0.4492	-0.4492	0.0000	0.0000	-0.6091	-0.6091
7	3.131	0.2638	0.2638	0.2638	-0.2638	-0.2638	-0.2638	0.1152	-0.1152	0.0000	0.0000	-1.0503	-1.0503	0.0000	0.0000
8	-13.759	0.3687	-0.2500	-0.1187	-0.2500	0.3678	-0.1187	0.0000	0.0000	0.4529	-0.4529	0.0000	0.0000	-0.4529	-0.0931
9	-13.759	0.0758	0.2814	-0.3572	0.2814	0.0758	-0.3572	0.0000	0.0000	0.0931	-0.0931	0.0000	0.0000	-0.0931	-0.4529
10	-14.111	0.1177	0.1177	0.1177	0.1177	0.1177	0.1177	-0.0788	-0.0788	0.0000	0.0000	0.5618	-0.5618	0.0000	0.0000
11	-15.857	-0.3112	0.1201	0.1911	-0.1201	0.3112	-0.1911	0.0000	0.0000	-0.3954	-0.3954	0.0000	0.0000	0.0521	0.0521
12	-15.857	0.0410	-0.2901	0.2490	0.2901	-0.0410	-0.2490	0.0000	0.0000	0.0521	0.0521	0.0000	0.0000	0.3954	0.3954
13	-21.823	-0.1885	-0.1885	-0.1885	0.1885	0.1885	0.1885	-0.4011	0.4011	0.0000	0.0000	-0.1036	0.1036	0.0000	0.0000
14	-26.671	0.0847	0.0847	0.0847	0.0847	0.0847	0.0847	0.4608	0.4608	0.0000	0.0000	-0.0201	0.0201	0.0000	0.0000

We shall consider BH_3 first. In Sec. 9.5 we showed that the direct sum for BH_3 for all valence electrons is

$$\Gamma_{BH_3} = 2A_1' + 2E' + A_2''$$

The symmetry orbitals determined in Sec. 9.5 are shown here in terms of the AOs.

$A_1':$ $\chi_1 = B_{2s}$

      $\chi_2 = (\frac{1}{3})^{\frac{1}{2}}(H_{1s}^{~1} + H_{1s}^{~2} + H_{1s}^{~3})$

$A_2'':$ $\chi_1 = B_{2p_z}$

$E':$ $\chi_1 = 2^{-\frac{1}{2}}B_{2p_x} + (\frac{1}{12})^{\frac{1}{2}}(2H_{1s}^{~1} - H_{1s}^{~2} - H_{1s}^{~3})$

      $\chi_1' = 2^{-\frac{1}{2}}B_{2p_x} - (\frac{1}{12})^{\frac{1}{2}}(2H_{1s}^{~1} - H_{1s}^{~2} - H_{1s}^{~3})$

      $\chi_2 = 2^{-\frac{1}{2}}B_{2p_y} + \frac{1}{2}(H_{1s}^{~2} - H_{1s}^{~3})$

      $\chi_2' = 2^{-\frac{1}{2}}B_{2p_y} - \frac{1}{2}(H_{1s}^{~2} - H_{1s}^{~3})$

We may readily observe the following facts concerning the BH_3 MOs shown in Table 9.21 and the symmetry orbitals shown above:

1. There are two pairs of energy levels with the same energy (levels 2, 3 and 5, 6). They are degenerate and must belong to the E' representation.
2. Only the boron $2p_z$ orbital contributes to the A_2'' MOs. Thus, orbital 4 $(-8.630$ ev$)$ must belong to the A_2'' representation.
3. Coefficients of the hydrogen orbitals in A_1' MOs must all be equal. There must be no contributions from $2p$ orbitals. Thus, energy levels 1 and 7 must belong to the A_1' representation.

Thus, the examination of a few of the coefficients in the symmetry orbitals and in the computed MOs allows identification of the irreducible representation to which each MO belongs.

Let us examine this problem further by considering the MOs for ethane and the symmetry orbitals in Sec. 9.5. Once again the degenerate energy levels are easily identified. We shall find that the various symmetry species can be identified by examination of only the coefficients of the hydrogen AOs. We may observe the following:

1. The six hydrogen $1s$ coefficients are all equal in A_{1g} representations.
2. Three hydrogen $1s$ coefficients (those belonging to hydrogen atoms bonded to one carbon atom) must have opposite signs from the other three hydrogen coefficients in the A_{2u} representation.
3. In the E_g orbitals there is an even number of minus signs on the hydrogen $1s$ coefficients whereas in the E_u orbitals there is an odd number of minus signs.

We can then identify all the energy levels as follows:

No.	Energy, ev	Γ
1	43.792	A_{2u}
2	26.366	A_{1g}
3, 4	10.677	E_g
5, 6	7.246	E_u
7	3.131	A_{2u}
8, 9	−13.759	E_g
10	−14.111	A_{1g}
11, 12	−15.857	E_u
13	−21.823	A_{2u}
14	−26.671	A_{1g}

A similar strategy can be used to determine the symmetry species of the MOs of larger molecules. The following suggestions may be helpful:

1. Identify the doubly and triply degenerate energy levels.
2. Determine the pi orbitals (if any). Pi MOs are orthogonal to other MOs and may be treated independently, as shown in Sec. 8.3.
3. Examine the symmetry orbitals. Often certain atoms may not contribute orbitals to certain MOs, i.e., boron $2p_z$ in A_1 and E' orbitals in BH_3. Sometimes one need examine only the hydrogen $1s$ orbitals.
4. Remember that a pair of doubly degenerate MOs may be replaced with linear combinations of the pair. Thus, the values of coefficients in degenerate MOs computed by a program need not be the same as those in symmetry orbitals.
5. Direct reference to character tables and the direct sum for the electrons involved may often be a simpler procedure than reference to symmetry orbitals.

PROBLEMS (Use Appendix III in many of these problems.)

9.1. Consider the molecules benzene, naphthalene, phenanthrene, and tetracene (see Fig. 9.26).

(a) For each molecule determine the symmetries of MO wave functions for the pi systems.

(b) Use simple Hückel theory to determine the energy of each MO. Draw the energy-level scheme for each molecule.

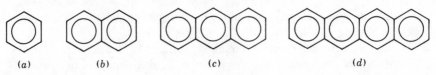

(a)   (b)   (c)   (d)

Fig. 9.26 The carbon-skeleton geometries for (a) benzene, (b) naphthalene, (c) phenanthrene, (d) tetracene.

(c) Determine the bond order for each symmetry-independent bond. Compare similar bonds in the series.

9.2. Phthalic anhydride and phthalimide are isoelectronic and belong to the same point group (see Fig. 9.27).

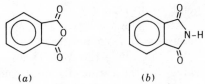

(a)   (b)

Fig. 9.27 The molecular-skeleton geometries for (a) phthalic anhydride and (b) phthalimide.

(a) What is the point-group symmetry of these two molecules?

(b) Determine the symmetry of their MOs.

(c) Using simple Hückel theory, obtain expressions for the pi-system energy levels and draw the energy-level diagram.

(d) Obtain the MO wave-function coefficients using the symmetry orbital method as outlined for pyridine. Write them in table form.

(e) Compute the pi bond orders and pi atomic charges. Compare the pi-system electronic distribution of these two molecules.

9.3. Consider the molecule tetracyanoethylene, $C_2(CN)_4$ (see Fig. 9.28).

(a) What is its point group? Determine the symmetries of the MOs for the pi system consisting of the 10 p_z orbitals which are perpendicular to the molecular plane (compare ψ_1, ψ_2, ψ_3, and ψ_4, etc.).

(b) Calculate the MO coefficients for the occupied orbitals and compute bond order and charges.

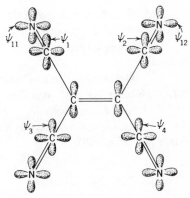

Fig. 9.28 The molecular geometry of tetracyanoethylene showing the $2p_y$ (in the molecular plane) and $2p_z$ orbitals centered on appropriate atoms.

(c) What effect do the triple bonds of the cyano groups have on the energy-level scheme in the simple Hückel approximation (compare ψ_{11}, ψ_{12}, etc., in Fig. 9.28).

9.4. Consider homonuclear diatomic molecules such as N_2, O_2, F_2, etc., of point group $D_{\infty h}$.

(a) Using the $2s$, $2p_x$, $2p_y$, and $2p_z$ orbitals as basis functions for MOs, determine the symmetries of the MOs.

(b) Arrange the MOs in an energy-level scheme using appropriate values for the various coulomb and exchange integrals.

(c) What are the possible electronic spectral transitions?

9.5. For heteronuclear diatomic molecules of the first-row elements such as NO and CO, the symmetry is lower than the homonuclear diatomics.

(a) What is the point group of heteronuclear diatomic molecules?

(b) Show how the MOs and the energy-level scheme are affected by comparing homonuclear and heteronuclear diatomics.

9.6. Consider the planar ring systems cyclobutadiene, C_4H_4, and the cyclopentadiene anion, $C_5H_5^-$ (see Fig. 9.29).

(a)   (b)

Fig. 9.29 The carbon-skeleton geometries for (a) cyclobutadiene and the (b) cyclopentadienyl anion, both planar systems.

(a) What are the point groups of these molecules? Determine the symmetries of the pi-system MOs.

(b) Using simple Hückel theory, compute the MO energy-level scheme.

(c) Determine the coefficients in the occupied MOs.

9.7. Compare the carbonyl bond order and pi atomic charges in ketene, H_2CCO, and formaldehyde, H_2CO, using simple Hückel theory and the LCAO MO approximations by computing the coefficients of the occupied MOs (see Fig. 9.30).

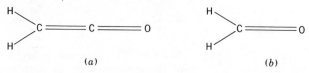

(a)   (b)

Fig. 9.30 The molecular geometry of (a) ketene and (b) formaldehyde.

9.8. Consider the two molecules pyridine and symmetric triazine (see Fig. 9.31).

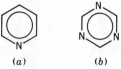

(a)   (b)

Fig. 9.31 The skeleton geometry for (a) pyridine and (b) symmetric triazine.

(a) What are the point groups of these two molecules? Determine the number and symmetries of the pi-system MOs.

(b) Using simple Hückel theory, compute the coefficients of the occupied MOs.

(c) Compare the C—N pi-bond orders in the two molecules.

9.9. Using simple Hückel theory for the pi systems of naphthalene and azulene, compare the bond order and pi atomic charges (see Fig. 9.32).

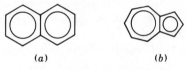

(a)   (b)

Fig. 9.32 The carbon-skeleton geometries for (a) naphthalene and (b) azulene.

9.10. (a) What is the point group of maleic anhydride? Determine the symmetries of the pi-system MOs (see Fig. 9.33).

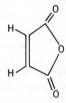

Fig. 9.33 The molecular structure of maleic anhydride.

(b) Using simple Hückel theory, compute the coefficients of occupied MOs.

(c) Using the results of Prob. 9.2, compare the bond orders in maleic anhydride with the corresponding ones in phthalic anhydride.

9.11. Consider the molecule quinone, OC_6H_4O, and the phenoxide ion, $C_6H_5O^-$ (see Fig. 9.34).

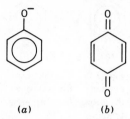

(a)   (b)

Fig. 9.34 The atomic skeletal geometries of (a) the phenoxide ion and (b) quinone.

(a) What are the point groups of these two molecules? Determine the symmetries of the pi-system MOs. (Oxygen contributes a p_z orbital perpendicular to the molecular plane in $C_6H_5O^-$.)

(b) Using simple Hückel theory and the method of symmetry orbitals, determine the coefficients in the occupied MOs.

(c) Compare bond orders and pi atomic charges between these two molecules.

9.12. Consider the symmetric unmetallated form of porphine in Fig. 9.35.

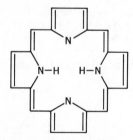

Fig. 9.35 The molecular skeleton of symmetric porphine.

(a) What is the symmetry of this molecule (ignoring the two hydrogen atoms on two of the pyrrole nitrogen atoms)?

(b) Determine the symmetries of the pi-system MOs.

(c) Using simple Hückel theory, determine the pi-system energy-level scheme and the coefficients of the occupied MOs.

(d) In the simple Hückel approximation what would be the effect on the energy-level scheme if ethylene groups were symmetrically attached to all the outer carbon atoms (eight $H_2C\!\!=\!\!CH$ groups in all)?

9.13. Figure 9.36 shows the two diazine molecules imidazole and pyrazole.

Fig. 9.36 The molecular skeleton geometries for (*a*) symmetric diazine, imidiazole, and (*b*) asymmetric diazine, pyrazole.

(*a*) What are the point groups of these two molecules? Determine the symmetries of the pi-system MOs.

(*b*) Using simple Hückel theory, determine the energy-level scheme and the coefficients in the occupied MOs.

(*c*) Compare the bond orders and pi-system atomic charges for corresponding bonds and atoms.

9.14. Consider the molecule BH_2 in a nonlinear form.

(*a*) What is its point group? For the valence atomic orbitals determine the symmetries of the MOs.

(*b*) The following table represents the output of a computer program which uses the LCAO MO method in a SCF treatment.

The entries in the following table under the AO designations are the MO coefficients, and the energies are given in atomic units (1 a.u. = 27.205 ev). Construct the energy-level diagram.

State	B_{2s}	B_{2p_x}	B_{2p_y}	B_{2p_z}	$H_{1s}{}^1$	$H_{1s}{}^2$	*Energy*, a.u.
1	0.6994	−0.1005	0.1741	0.0000	0.4850	0.4850	−0.9096
2	0.0000	0.5749	0.3319	0.0000	−0.5288	0.5288	−0.6974
3	−0.4819	−0.4207	0.7286	0.0000	0.1731	0.1731	−0.4365
4	0.0000	0.0000	0.0000	1.0000	0.0000	0.0000	0.0798
5	−0.5279	0.2510	−0.4345	0.0000	0.4846	0.4846	0.2862
6	−0.0000	−0.6476	−0.3740	0.0000	−0.4694	0.4694	0.3197

(*c*) Determine the symmetry of each MO.

(*d*) Using these MO symmetry designations, determine the symmetries of the ground state and excited state in which only one electron is excited. What are the possible transitions?

9.15. In the description of some of the compounds of beryllium, boron, and aluminum, for example, $Be_2(CH_3)_6$, B_2H_6, and $Al_2(CH_3)_6$, three-center MOs have been introduced by Eberhardt.[1] A total of two electrons are contributed to the bonding scheme from three atoms each of which supplies one AO: 1s for hydrogen, an sp^3 hybrid orbital for carbon,

[1] W. H. Eberhardt, B. L. Crawford, and W. N. Lipscomb, *J. Chem. Phys.*, **22**:989 (1954).

and a $2p$ orbital (or hybrid sigma orbital) for boron.   In all cases, atoms A_2 and A_3 are the same.

(a) For the atomic arrangement shown in Fig. 9.37a solve the LCAO MO problem for the three AOs obtaining MO coefficients and energies using the simple Hückel approximation.   (In Fig. 9.37 A_1 means atom

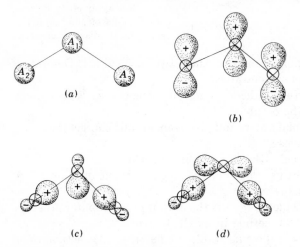

Fig. 9.37   (a) The geometry and numbering scheme for a three-atom two-electron system; (b) to (d) the orientations of the atomic p orbitals in three possible arrangements.

number 1.)   Consider three possible AO arrangements as in Fig. 9.37b to d in three separate calculations.   In each case the interaction between atoms 2 and 3 is considered to be zero: $\beta_{23} = 0$.   This case is called *open* three-center bonding.

(b) Now consider the case in which $\beta_{23} \neq 0$; this is called *closed* three-center bonding.   Construct tables showing the change in the various MO energy levels as a function of β_{23} between the values of $\beta_{23} = 0$ and $\beta_{23} = \beta_{13} = \beta_{12}$.

9.16. Determine the differences between the MO energy-level schemes for staggered and eclipsed ferrocene, $(C_5H_5)_2Fe$, of point groups D_{5d} and D_{5h}, respectively (see Fig. 9.21).

9.17. Consider the square planar complex $Ni(CO)_4$.

(a) What is its point group?

(b) Find the irreducible representations to which the $3d$, $4s$, and $4p$ orbitals belong and those to which the ligand orbitals belong.

(c) Considering only sigma bonding, construct the ligand symmetry orbitals of appropriate symmetry.

(d) Construct the MO energy-level diagram for sigma bonding only.

(e) Determine the irreducible representations to which the carbonyl ligand pi orbitals belong.

(f) Add the ligand pi-symmetry orbital energy levels to the MO energy-level diagram (approximately) and discuss their effect on the over-all energy-level scheme.

9.18. Consider the complex cobalt tricarbonylnitrosyl, $Co(CO)_3NO$. The four ligands are arranged about the cobalt atom in a tetrahedral configuration.

(a) What is the point group of this complex? (Remember that NO is not equivalent to CO.)

(b) Construct the MO energy-level scheme for this complex for sigma bonding only.

(c) Compare this scheme to that for a tetrahedral complex of point group T_d.

9.19. Consider trigonal planar complexes of the type $Ag(R_3P)_3^+$ and $Ag(R_2S)_3^+$.

(a) What is the point group of the system composed of the silver ion and the ligand sulfur or phosphorus atoms.

(b) Construct the MO energy-level diagram for the sigma bonding system of these complexes.

9.20. The spectrochemical series lists ligands according to their usual crystal-field splitting Δ. Use MO theory to show why cyanide ion has a large splitting (at the head of the series), iodide ion has a small splitting (at the bottom of the series), and ammonia lies somewhere in between.

REFERENCES

Cartmell, E., and G. W. A. Fowles: "Valency and Molecular Structure," D. Van Nostrand Company, Inc., Princeton N.J., 1966.

Coulson, C. A.: "Valence," 2d ed., Oxford University Press, Fair Lawn, N.J., 1961.

Daudel, R., R. Lefebvre, and C. Moser: "Quantum Chemistry: Methods and Applications," Interscience Publishers, Inc., New York, 1960.

Eyring, H., J. Walter, and G. E. Kimball: "Quantum Chemistry," John Wiley & Sons, Inc., New York, 1947.

Gray, Harry B.: "Electrons and Chemical Bonding," W. A. Benjamin, Inc., New York, 1964.

Kauzman, W.: "Quantum Chemistry," Academic Press Inc., New York, 1957.

Murrell, J. N., S. F. A. Kettle, and J. M. Tedder: "Valence Theory," John Wiley & Sons, Inc., New York, 1965.

Pauling, L., and E. B. Wilson: "Introduction to Quantum Mechanics," McGraw-Hill Book Company, New York, 1935.

Sandorfy, C.: "Electronic Spectra and Quantum Chemistry," Prentice-Hall, Inc., Englewood Cliffs, N.J., 1964.

Schiff, L. I.: "Quantum Mechanics," 2d ed., McGraw-Hill Book Company, New York, 1955.

Streitweiser, A.: "Molecular Orbital Theory for Organic Chemists," John Wiley & Sons, Inc., New York, 1961.

10
selection rules for electronic spectra

Let us now consider the possible transitions which might take place between the electronic ground state of a molecule or ion and the series of available excited states. Figure 10.1 shows a typical arrangement of an electronic ground state and two excited states. Each state is described by a potential-energy curve which possesses a stable-equilibrium configuration of the atomic nuclei of the molecule.[1] Hence, for each electronic state there is a set of vibrational levels which describes the ground and excited states for vibrational motion. The molecular system may absorb electromagnetic radiation (usually in the ultraviolet or visible regions) and undergo a quantum transition to an excited electronic state (indicated by arrows in Fig. 10.1). The energy absorbed, that is, ΔE_1 or ΔE_2, may be related to the spectral frequency or wavelength as follows:[2]

$$\Delta E = h\nu = \frac{hc}{\lambda} = hc\bar{\nu} \tag{10.1}$$

[1] Certain excited states are repulsive and hence do not possess a stable equilibrium. We shall not discuss transitions to such states.

[2] Symbols for the spectral frequency ν: wavelength $= \lambda$ and wave number $= \bar{\nu}$.

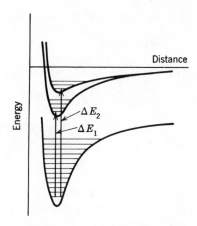

Fig. 10.1 A qualitative diagram schematically representing three electronic states of a molecule. Vibrational states are superimposed on each electronic state. Two possible electronic transitions are shown, with the corresponding energy changes labeled ΔE_1 and ΔE_2. Each of these transitions originates and terminates in a vibrational ground state.

We have shown earlier that the intensity of a spectral transition is proportional to integrals of the following type, which are called *transition moments*,

$$M_x = \int \Psi_i \mu_x \Psi_j \, d\tau \qquad M_y = \int \Psi_i \mu_y \Psi_j \, d\tau \qquad M_z = \int \Psi_i \mu_z \Psi_j \, d\tau \qquad (10.2)$$

The quantities μ_x, μ_y, and μ_z are the components of the electric dipole moment. Ψ_i and Ψ_j are the *total* wave functions of the systems for the two states involved in the transition. We shall consider here only transitions in which the initial state is the molecular ground state.

10.1 SPIN SELECTION RULES

In the nonrelativistic case the total wave function may be written as a product of a spin function S and a function ϕ of all other molecular coordinates, electronic and vibrational

$$\Psi_i = \phi_i S_i \qquad (10.3)$$

An important rule arises here because the dipole-moment operators μ_x, μ_y, and μ_z have no effect on the spin wave functions S. Hence, the transition moments of Eq. (10.2) may be rewritten

$$M_k = \int \Psi_i \mu_k \Psi_j \, d\tau = \int_{\tau_1} \phi_i \mu_k \phi_j \, d\tau_1 \int_{\tau_2} S_i S_j \, d\tau_2 \qquad k = x, y, z \qquad (10.4)$$

However, the spin functions form an orthonormal set.

$$\int_\tau S_i S_j \, d\tau = \delta_{ij} \qquad (10.5)$$

Thus, the transition moments are all zero unless the initial and final states possess the same spin functions

$$\int \Psi_i \mu_k \Psi_j \, d\tau = 0 \qquad \Delta S \neq 0 \qquad (10.6)$$

In a later section we shall interpret this rule in terms of the spin multiplicities of the various electronic states. Because the treatment of electronic transition theory here is only approximate, the spin selection rule may be violated. However, the spin approximation is quite good, and transitions which violate the ΔS rule are generally quite weak in molecular systems.

10.2 VIBRATIONLESS TRANSITIONS

To the extent that vibrational motions, i.e., motions of the nuclei, interact, or *couple*, with electronic motions the total wave function may *not* be written as a product of an electronic wave function and a vibrational wave function. As a first approximation we can ignore any possible coupling and use the Born-Oppenheimer[1] approximation. In this treatment the wave function for the electrons is computed for a given (motionless) configuration of the nuclei. The ground-state wave function is computed for the position of stable equilibrium of the nuclei. One may compute the electronic wave function for a series of nuclear configurations and thus obtain the electronic energy as a function of internuclear distances. The resulting function of energy and nuclear positions may then be used as the vibrational potential-energy function. This was the basis for our approach in Chap. 7.

Under this kind of approximation we can write the total wave function as a product of electronic and vibrational wave functions

$$\Psi_i = \Psi_i(E)\Psi_i(V) \qquad (10.7)$$

The wave function $\Psi_i(E)$ is a function of electronic coordinates, and the wave function $\Psi_i(V)$ is a function of the normal modes (coordinates) of vibration. Under this product-function approximation there can be no change in vibrational quantum number accompanying an electronic transition because of the orthonormal properties of the vibrational wave

[1] M. Born and J. R. Oppenheimer, *Ann. Phys. (Paris)*, vol. 84, 1927.

function: $\Delta v = 0$. This is the basis of the so-called *symmetry selection rule* for electronic spectra. Equation (10.4) may now be written

$$M_k = \int \Psi_i \mu_k \Psi_j \, d\tau = \int \Psi_i(E) \mu_k \Psi_j(E) \, d\tau \qquad \begin{matrix} \Delta S = 0 \\ \Delta v = 0 \end{matrix} \qquad k = x, y, z$$

$$(10.8)$$

The wave functions $\Psi_i(E)$ are electronic functions.

In a later section we shall take up the question of *vibronic* transitions, in which a vibrational mode may be excited simultaneously with electronic excitation. Vibronic transitions are quite important because the coupling of a vibrational excitation of the appropriate symmetry type may permit an electronic transition which by itself is forbidden by the symmetry selection rules.

10.3 SYMMETRY SELECTION RULES

Under the Born-Oppenheimer approximation transition moments may now be written as Eq. (10.8). Thus, an intensity is zero when all the transition-moment integrals vanish. At least one of the three product representations must contain the totally symmetric irreducible representation. That is,

$$M_x \rightarrow \Gamma_{\Psi_i} \Gamma_{\mu_x} \Gamma_{\Psi_j} = \Gamma_{\Psi_i} \Gamma_x \Gamma_{\Psi_j} = \Gamma_{A_1} \tag{10.9}$$

or·

$$M_y \rightarrow \Gamma_{\Psi_i} \Gamma_{\mu_y} \Gamma_{\Psi_j} = \Gamma_{\Psi_i} \Gamma_y \Gamma_{\Psi_j} = \Gamma_{A_1} \tag{10.10}$$

or

$$M_z \rightarrow \Gamma_{\Psi_i} \Gamma_{\mu_z} \Gamma_{\Psi_j} = \Gamma_{\Psi_i} \Gamma_z \Gamma_{\Psi_j} = \Gamma_{A_1} \tag{10.11}$$

Note that we have dropped the designation E from $\Psi_i(E)$: Ψ_i.

Let us now proceed to the determination of the symmetry representations for the various states of molecules. We shall continue to use the MO approximation. Each state—ground or excited—is represented by a product wave function, one MO function for each occupied MO. Let us return to *trans*-butadiene for a specific example. The energy-level diagram for the ground and a first few excited states in which only one electron is excited at a time is shown in Fig. 10.2. Each state is labeled with a symmetry symbol. The other symbols, N and V_i, were suggested by Mulliken but have not been universally adopted. They are simply labels to identify the order of increasing energy of transition.

The symmetry of each state is determined from the product represen-

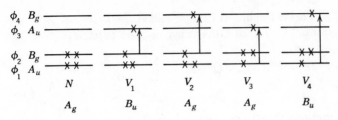

Fig. 10.2 MO energy-level schemes for the pi system of *trans*-butadiene showing four possible electronic transitions, their usual symbols V_i, and the symmetry of the excited-state wave function.

tations of the MO wave functions, which may be written

$$\Psi_N = \phi_1(A_u)^2\phi_2(B_g)^2 \tag{10.12}$$
$$\Psi_{V_1} = \phi_1(A_u)^2\phi_2(B_g)^1\phi_3(A_u)^1 \tag{10.13}$$
$$\Psi_{V_2} = \phi_1(A_u)^2\phi_2(B_g)^1\phi_4(B_g)^1 \tag{10.14}$$
$$\Psi_{V_3} = \phi_1(A_u)^1\phi_2(B_g)^2\phi_3(A_u)^1 \tag{10.15}$$
$$\Psi_{V_4} = \phi_1(A_u)^1\phi_2(B_g)^2\phi_4(B_g)^1 \tag{10.16}$$

The symbol $\phi_1(A_u)^2$ means that the MO ϕ_1 with A_u symmetry is doubly occupied—two electrons with opposite spins. The symmetry of each total wave function is the symmetry of the product representations, as shown in Table 10.1. The symmetry of any doubly occupied MO is the totally symmetric irreducible representation.

Table 10.1 Symmetries of the product functions in *trans*-butadiene

Wave function	Product	Product representation
Ψ_N	$A_u \times A_u \times B_g \times B_g$	A_g
Ψ_{V_1}	$A_u \times A_u \times B_g \times A_u$	B_u
Ψ_{V_2}	$A_u \times A_u \times B_g \times B_g$	A_g
Ψ_{V_3}	$A_u \times B_g \times B_g \times A_u$	A_g
Ψ_{V_4}	$A_u \times B_g \times B_g \times B_g$	B_u

We are now in a position to determine whether the transition moments are zero for the various transitions listed in Fig. 10.2. Since the ground state for *trans*-butadiene is totally symmetric (the usual situation in closed-shell molecules), the transition moments may now be written

$$M_x = \int\Psi_N\mu_x\Psi_{V_i}\,d\tau \rightarrow \Gamma_{A_g}\Gamma_{\mu_x}\Gamma_{V_i} \rightarrow \Gamma_{\mu_x}\Gamma_{V_i} \rightarrow \Gamma_x\Gamma_{V_i} \tag{10.17}$$
$$M_y = \int\Psi_N\mu_y\Psi_{V_i}\,d\tau \rightarrow \Gamma_{A_g}\Gamma_{\mu_y}\Gamma_{V_i} \rightarrow \Gamma_{\mu_y}\Gamma_{V_i} \rightarrow \Gamma_y\Gamma_{V_i} \tag{10.18}$$
$$M_z = \int\Psi_N\mu_z\Psi_{V_i}\,d\tau \rightarrow \Gamma_{A_g}\Gamma_{\mu_z}\Gamma_{V_i} \rightarrow \Gamma_{\mu_z}\Gamma_{V_i} \rightarrow \Gamma_z\Gamma_{V_i} \tag{10.19}$$

Thus, in order that the integral not vanish and the intensity not be zero, the excited-state product functions must belong to an irreducible representation which transforms as does one of the cartesian components x, y, or z. Further, the type of polarization is also indicated by the cartesian components. A_u transforms as z, and the polarization would be along z, whereas B_g transforms as both x and y and, hence, V_1 and V_4 are allowed transitions with polarization in the xy plane (the molecular plane). The results are summarized in Table 10.2.

Table 10.2   Spectral transitions in *trans*-butadiene

Transition	Symmetry of excited state	Activity	Polarization
$N \leftarrow V_1$	B_u	Allowed	(x, y)
$N \leftarrow V_2$	A_g	Forbidden	
$N \leftarrow V_3$	A_g	Forbidden	
$N \leftarrow V_4$	B_u	Allowed	(x, y)

Let us now consider a second example, the pi system of benzene. We determined the symmetries of the MOs as a direct sum earlier.

$$\Gamma_\pi(C_6H_6) = B_{2g} + E_{1g} + A_{2u} + E_{2u} \tag{10.20}$$

The energy-level diagram is reproduced in Fig. 10.3, along with schematic diagrams representing possible excited states for only one electron excited.

The symmetry of each excited-state wave function is determined from the representation based on the product of the occupied MOs.

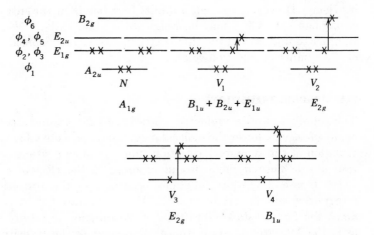

Fig. 10.3 MO energy-level schemes for the pi system of benzene showing four possible electronic transitions along with their symmetry designations.

$$\Psi_N = \phi_1(A_{2u})^2\phi_2(E_{1g})^2\phi_3(E_{1g})^2$$
$$\Psi_{V_1} = \phi_1(A_{2u})^2\phi_2(E_{1g})^2\phi_3(E_{1g})^1\phi_4(E_{2u})^1$$
$$\Psi_{V_2} = \phi_1(A_{2u})^2\phi_2(E_{1g})^2\phi_3(E_{1g})^1\phi_6(B_{2g})^1 \qquad (10.21)$$
$$\Psi_{V_3} = \phi_1(A_{2u})^1\phi_2(E_{1g})^2\phi_3(E_{1g})^2\phi_4(E_{2u})^1$$
$$\Psi_{V_4} = \phi_1(A_{2u})^1\phi_2(E_{1g})^2\phi_3(E_{1g})^2\phi_6(B_{2g})^1$$

Because of the presence of doubly degenerate MOs some of the product functions are not single terms but instead must be written as a sum of terms. In the simplest theories these terms correspond to three states all possessing the same energy. However, it is known that these energy levels are split. A more sophisticated theory would determine the amount of splitting. Hence, transitions are possible but not necessarily allowed to all three states. Table 10.3 summarizes the spectral analysis for the pi system of benzene.

Table 10.3 Spectral transitions in benzene

Transition	Symmetry of excited state	Activity	Polarization
$N \leftarrow V_1$	B_{1u}	Forbidden	
$N \leftarrow V_1$	B_{2u}	Forbidden	
$N \leftarrow V_1$	E_{1u}	Allowed	(x, y)
$N \leftarrow V_2$	E_{2g}	Forbidden	
$N \leftarrow V_3$	E_{2g}	Forbidden	
$N \leftarrow V_4$	B_{1u}	Forbidden	

Thus, there is only one symmetry-allowed transition in the pi system of benzene. However, benzene exhibits four bands in the ultraviolet; one strong band at 1830 Å may be assigned the allowed $A_{1g} \leftarrow E_{1u}$ transition. In order to understand the three extra bands we must consider violations of the symmetry selection rules.

10.4 VIBRONIC TRANSITIONS

The coupling of an asymmetric vibration to the ground electronic state could effectively lower the molecular symmetry so as to allow an apparent violation of the symmetry selection rule. In such a situation an excitation of the normal mode would accompany the electronic excitation. In that case, the wave functions occurring in the transition-moment integrals would be products of MOs and vibrational wave functions. Since the ground-state vibrational wave function is totally symmetric, as is the MO ground state, the x component of the transition moment may be written as Eq. (10.22).

$$M_x = \int \Psi_N \Psi_0(\text{vib}) \mu_x \Psi_{V_i} \Psi_j(\text{vib})\, d\tau \rightarrow \Gamma_{\mu_x} \Gamma_{V_i} \Gamma_{\text{vib}} \qquad (10.22)$$

Thus, for a nonvanishing transition moment the product representation $\Gamma_{V_i}\Gamma_{\text{vib}}$ must transform as one of the cartesian components x, y, or z. Perhaps a simpler statement of this requirement is that the product $\Gamma_\mu\Gamma_{V_i}$ must contain one of the allowed Γ_{vib} ($3N - 6 = 3 \times 12 - 6 = 30$ modes, 24 active; see Prob. 7.11). In order to determine whether the symmetry-forbidden $N \leftarrow V_1$ transitions might be vibronically active, let us determine $\Gamma_\mu\Gamma_{V_1}$ for the two states. For benzene, $\Gamma_\mu = A_{2u} + E_{1u}$.

$$\Gamma_\mu\Gamma_{V_1} = (A_{2u} + E_{1u}) \times B_{1u} = B_{2g} + E_{2g}$$
$$\Gamma_\mu\Gamma_{V_1} = (A_{2u} + E_{1u}) \times B_{2u} = B_{1g} + E_{2g}$$

Both B_{2g} and E_{2g} are among the symmetry species for normal vibrations in benzene. Hence, the $N \leftarrow V_1$ (B_{2u}) and the $N \leftarrow V_1$ (B_{1u}) transitions are vibronically allowed and are assigned to the two weak bands at 2550 and 2050 Å, respectively. The three strongest bands in the ultraviolet spectrum of benzene may now be assigned as shown in Table 10.4.

Table 10.4   Spectral assignments in the benzene ultraviolet spectrum

Transition	Symmetry of excited state	Activity	Polarization	λ, Å
$N \leftarrow V_1$	B_{1u}	Vibronic ($B_{2g} + E_{2g}$)		2050
$N \leftarrow V_1$	B_{2u}	Vibronic (E_{2g})		2550
$N \leftarrow V_1$	E_{1u}	Allowed	(x, y)	1830

A similar treatment may be performed on *trans*-butadiene. The $N \leftarrow V_2$ and $N \leftarrow V_3$ transitions are symmetry-forbidden. The excited-state representation Γ_{V_i} for both of these transitions is A_g. Hence

$$\Gamma_\mu\Gamma_{V_2} = (A_u + B_u) \times A_g = A_u + B_u$$
$$\Gamma_\mu\Gamma_{V_3} = (A_u + B_u) \times A_g = A_u + B_u$$

The vibrational representation for *trans*-butadiene was to be determined in Prob. 7.15. Since

$$\Gamma_{\text{vib}} = 9A_g + 3B_g + 4A_u + 8B_u$$

both symmetry-forbidden transitions are vibronically allowed. In general, the larger the molecule and the lower the symmetry, the greater the number of symmetry-allowed transitions and the greater the number of vibronically allowed (symmetry-forbidden) transitions.

10.5   VIOLATIONS OF THE SPIN RULE

In the ultraviolet spectrum of benzene there still remains one unassigned transition, the very weak band at 3600 Å. It is believed that this transi-

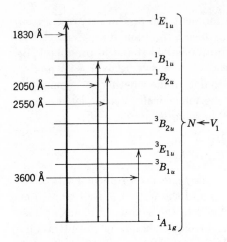

Fig. 10.4 The energy-level scheme for the pi system of benzene (including spin states) showing the possible transitions. The broadest arrow is both spin- and symmetry-allowed, the two intermediate width arrows are spin-allowed symmetry-forbidden, and the final arrow represents a transition which is both spin- and symmetry-forbidden.

tion arises out of a weak violation of the $\Delta S = 0$ rule. There are many causes for the breakdown of spin rule. The spin angular momentum of the electron may tend to couple with its orbital angular momentum. The greater the extent of the spin-orbit coupling, the less meaningful becomes the concept of the classification of spin states independent of their orbital angular momentum.

Let us now proceed to consider the $N \leftarrow V_1$ transition in somewhat more detail. Figure 10.3 shows this transition schematically. There are two questions to consider: (1) there are three different symmetry states involved here: $B_{1u} + B_{2u} + E_{1u}$ and (2) the excited electron and the unexcited electron may either be paired or unpaired, producing both singlet and triplet states. There are then six possible excited states associated with the $N \leftarrow V_1$ transition as shown in Fig. 10.4. We shall not show here how to calculate the relative ordering but simply indicate that the scheme shown in Fig. 10.4 is consistent with experimental measurements. The symbol $^3E_{1u}$ indicates the excited state of E_{1u} symmetry with unpaired spins is a triplet state.

The 3600-Å band has been assigned to the symmetry-allowed, spin-forbidden transition $^1A_{1g} \leftarrow {}^3E_{1u}$. Spin-forbidden transitions are usually the weakest bands in molecular spectra.

10.6 A CLASSIFICATION OF ELECTRONIC SPECTRA

There are no universally adopted schemes of classification and labeling for electronic transitions. However, we present here a brief outline of the symbols often used by many chemical spectroscopists.

1. $\pi \to \pi^*$. These transitions arise between different pi-type states and occur in the ultraviolet or visible regions. In the language of MO theory the transition takes place from a (predominantly) bonding orbital π to a (predominantly) antibonding orbital π^*.

2. $n \to \pi^*$. These bands also occur in the ultraviolet and visible and are ascribed to transitions from a nonbonding (perhaps lone-pair) orbital to an antibonding π^* orbital.

3. $\sigma \to \sigma^*$. These far-ultraviolet bands arise from transitions of bonding sigma-system electrons into antibonding sigma orbitals.

4. $n \to \sigma^*$. Transitions from nonbonding orbitals to antibonding sigma orbitals occur in the ultraviolet region.

5. *Charge transfer.* A band (of any of the preceding or other type) is called a *charge-transfer band* if the transition brings about an internal transfer of electronic charge. Such charge transfer is said to occur whenever the difference between the two states involved represents a significant rearrangement of the electronic distribution. Charge-transfer bands occur in a wide variety of compounds including organic, inorganic, and coordination compounds.

6. *Ligand field.* In Chap. 11 we shall discuss the electronic structure of metallic coordination compounds. Very interesting spectral transitions may occur because of the splitting of the degenerate metal-atom atomic states.

PROBLEMS

10.1. Compare the electronic spectra of *cis*- and *trans*-butadiene (see Fig. 10.5).

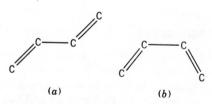

(a)   (b)

Fig. 10.5 The geometry of the molecular skeletons of (a) *trans*-1,2-butadiene and (b) *cis*-1,2-butadiene.

(a) Determine the symmetry-allowed transitions and the polarization of each transition.

(b) Determine whether any symmetry-forbidden transitions may be vibronically allowed.

10.2. Using the results of Prob. 9.2, determine the allowed spectral transitions for phthalic anhydride and phthalimide.

(a) Compare the allowed transitions and their polarizations and relative frequencies.

(b) Are the vibronically allowed transitions different for the two molecules?

10.3. Consider symmetry selection rules for centrosymmetric molecules.

(a) What general statement may be made about the irreducible representations to which x, y, and z (Γ_μ) belong?

(b) Derive the Laporte rule, which states that only $g \to u$ and $u \to g$ transitions are allowed, $g \to g$ and $u \to u$ transitions being forbidden; that is, $A_{1g} \to A_{2u}$ is allowed, but $A_{1g} \to A_{2g}$ is forbidden in D_{3d}.

10.4. (a) Using the results of Prob. 9.11, determine the symmetries of all the excited states in which only one electron is excited in quinone and in the phenoxide ion. Take into account singlet, triplet, or other spin states. Draw an energy-level scheme in which the states of highest multiplicity are lower in energy than the corresponding low-multiplicity states.

(b) Determine the transitions which are both spin- and symmetry-allowed.

(c) Compare the expected electronic spectra of these two compounds as to frequency and polarization.

10.5. Using the results of Prob. 9.9, compare the spectral transitions of naphthalene and azulene.

10.6. Compare the electronic spectra, in terms of frequency and polarization, of the cyclopentadienyl anion, $C_5H_5^-$, and cyclopentadiene, C_5H_6, in a *planar* form.

10.7. Refer to Prob. 9.13 for energy-level schemes and MO symmetry designations for imidazole and pyrazole. Compare the electronic spectra of these two molecules.

REFERENCES

Eyring, H., J. Walter, and G. E. Kimball: "Quantum Chemistry," John Wiley & Sons, Inc., New York, 1947.

Herzberg, G.: "Molecular Spectra and Molecular Structure, III: Electronic Structure," D. Van Nostrand Company, Inc., Princeton N.J., 1966.

Kauzman, W.: "Quantum Chemistry," Academic Press Inc., New York, 1957.

Sandorfy, C.: "Electronic Spectra and Quantum Chemistry," Prentice-Hall, Inc., Englewood Cliffs, N.J., 1964.

11
crystal field theory and transition metal chemistry

We have divided our treatment of molecular electronic structure into two sections. For small molecules of the first two rows of the periodic table we used the MO method. Although we also gave a preliminary treatment of transition-metal compounds using the LCAO MO method, we pointed out that additional techniques must be used for the study of the interaction of the ligands with the d and f orbitals of the metal ions.

By combining the formalism of MO theory with the techniques of crystal-field theory we can obtain a fairly complete theory of metal complexes. Hence, in this chapter we shall focus our attention on the d orbital of the metal atom and its interaction with the ligands. Crystal-field theory treats the ligands as point charges or point dipoles and considers the interaction between the ligands and the metal atoms to be purely electrostatic. Such treatment gave rise to the term *ligand-field theory*.[1] However, Hans Bethe first applied the theory to the spectra

[1] L. E. Orgel, *J. Chem. Soc.*, vol. 4756, 1952; *J. Chem. Phys.*, **23**:1004, 1819, 1824 (1955).

of metal ions in a crystal lattice, and the theory was then called *crystal-field theory*.[1] The term ligand-field theory is now usually applied to a modification of crystal-field theory which semiempirically takes into account the partial covalent character of the metal-ligand bond. In recent times ligand-field theory has been used to mean an MO treatment which may include crystal-field theory.

We shall find that crystal-field theory gives a useful account of the spectral and magnetic properties of transition-metal complexes and, further, that group theory is most useful in the application of crystal-field theory to the study of coordination compounds.

By way of review let us briefly set forth the manner in which the electronic structure of atoms is described under quantum mechanics. The solutions of the Schrödinger equation

$$\mathcal{3C}\psi_i = E_i\psi_i$$

consist of a set of wave functions ψ_i and the allowed energies E_i to which each wave function belongs. For the hydrogen atom the wave functions are written as product functions:

$$\psi_{n,l,m,s}(r, \theta, \phi) = R_{n,l}(r)Y_{l,m}(\theta, \phi)S_s$$

(see Fig. 8.1 for definition of the polar coordinates r, θ, ϕ). The energy is dependent only upon the principal quantum number n for hydrogen-like atoms but becomes dependent upon l also for many-electron atoms. The secondary quantum number l determines the orbital angular momentum in units of Planck's constant divided by 2π, or $lh/2\pi$, where l may have values from $n - 1$ to zero. The magnetic quantum number m (sometimes written m_l) describes the orientation of the orbital angular momentum in space. The values of m range from $-l$ to $+l$ in integer steps and are related to the orientation of the momentum vector relative to a given direction in space, as shown in Fig. 11.1. This spin wave function S_s is characterized by the spin quantum number s, which may take on only the two values $+\frac{1}{2}$ or $-\frac{1}{2}$, thus restricting values of spin angular momentum to $\pm\frac{1}{2}h/2\pi$.

11.1 SPECTROSCOPIC STATES AND TERM SYMBOLS FOR POLYELECTRONIC ATOMS: THE VECTOR MODEL

In the usual notation for electronic structure we write the electronic configuration of a hydrogen atom in the $2p$ (excited) state as $2p^1$, and for the boron atom in the ground state we write $1s^2 2s^2 2p^1$. In either case we usually think of each configuration as representing a single electronic energy state. Hence, in hydrogen an electronic transition from the $1s^1$ ground state to the $2p^1$ excited state should correspond to a single sharp

[1] H. A. Bethe, *Ann. Physik.*, **3**:133–206 (1929).

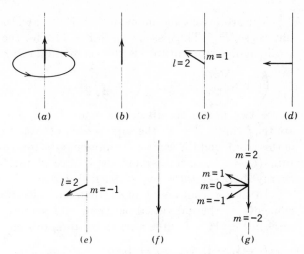

(a)　　　　(b)　　　　(c)　　　　(d)

(e)　　　　(f)　　　　(g)

Fig. 11.1 Vector representations of orbital angular momentum used in the vector model of spin-orbit coupling. (a) A vector represents the direction and magnitude of the orbital angular momentum of a "classical circulating" electron; (b) to (f) the various possible orientations of an orbital-angular-momentum vector relative to an arbitrary direction in space along with the corresponding values of m, the magnetic quantum number; (g) a summary of the possible orientations of the angular-momentum vector for $l = 2$.

spectral line. Under high resolution, however, two lines are observed. This splitting has been attributed to a coupling of the electron's orbital angular momentum, characterized by the l quantum number, to the electron's spin angular momentum, characterized by the s quantum number.

A simple model may be used to understand this splitting of states. On the basis of this model we may advance a method for deriving the various states of a given electronic configuration. Figure 11.2 gives a classical representation of orbital and spin angular momentum. Although we need not take this picture literally, we may use it as a convenient model. The vectors represent the angular momentum associated with the electron charge cloud described by the wave function ψ.

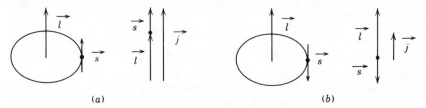

(a)　　　　　　　　　　　　(b)

Fig. 11.2 A vector model for the coupling of orbital and spin angular momentum of a single electron. (a) $\mathbf{j} = \mathbf{l} + \mathbf{s}$, and (b) $\mathbf{j} = \mathbf{l} - \mathbf{s}$.

The orbital angular momentum is $lh/2\pi$, and the spin angular momentum is $\frac{1}{2}sh/2\pi$. Thus, as shown in Fig. 11.2 for the one-electron case, the total angular momentum j is the vector sum of l and s, either

$$\left(l + \frac{1}{2}\right)\frac{h}{2\pi} \quad \text{or} \quad \left(l - \frac{1}{2}\right)\frac{h}{2\pi}$$

These two states are given the symbols $^2P_{\frac{3}{2}}$ and $^2P_{\frac{1}{2}}$. The subscripts are the j values $(l + s)$, the superscript is the spin multiplicity (a doublet in this case), and the capital P represents the total orbital angular momentum $(L = 2)$. Spectroscopic data have shown that the difference in energy[1] between these two states is 0.3651 cm^{-1}.

In atoms containing more than one electron the orbital angular momenta of the individual electrons add vectorially, as shown for two cases in Fig. 11.3, to give a resultant total orbital angular momentum L.

$$L = l_1 + l_2 + \cdots + l_N$$

[1] Note that 1 cm^{-1} = 1.230×10^{-4} ev = 2.859×10^{-3} kcal/mole.

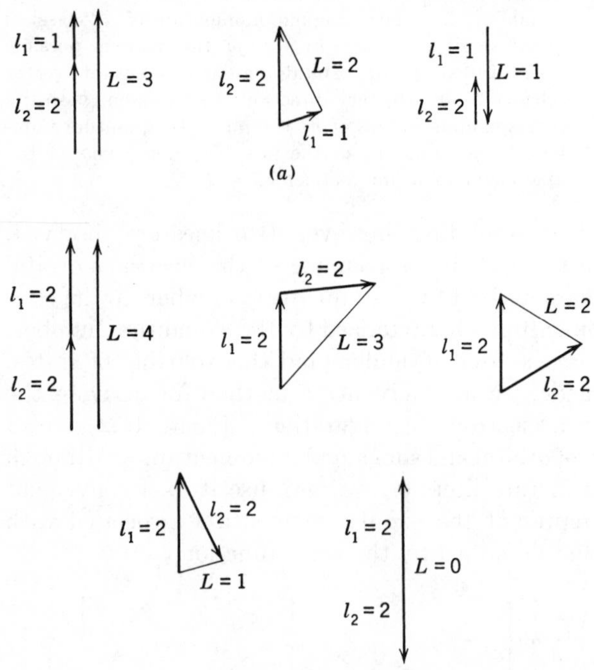

(a)

(b)

Fig. 11.3 The vector-model representation for the coupling of orbital angular momenta by the Russell-Saunders or L-S scheme. (a) Two electrons with $l_1 = 1$ and $l_2 = 2$ and (b) two electrons with $l_1 = 2$ and $l_2 = 2$.

Likewise individual spin angular momenta combine to yield a resultant S.

$$S = s_1 + s_2 + \cdots + s_N$$

Thus, L may take on values between the smallest difference in l values to the largest sum of l values. Similarly, S may range from 0 or $\frac{1}{2}$ to $n/2$, depending upon whether the number of electrons n is even or odd. The magnetic quantum number M for the system may take on values of $-L, -L + 1, \ldots, L - 1, L$. Hence, there are $2L + 1$ possible values for M just as there are $2S + 1$ possible values for M_s, the total spin angular momentum of the system. Finally, the L and S values combine vectorially to yield J, the quantum-mechanically allowed states of total angular momentum for the system. J may have values from $L - S$ to $L + S$ in integer steps. This coupling scheme is generally called *Russell-Saunders* or *L-S coupling*.

The various energy states which may arise from a given electronic configuration are designated by spectroscopic terms of the form $n^{2S+1}T_J$. The superscript represents the value of the spin multiplicity, the subscript is the value of the total angular momentum, and the prefix n stands for the principal quantum number (or even an electronic configuration as in $2p^2\,^3P_2$, where $n = 2p^2$, $2S + 1 = 3$, and $J = 2$).[1]

Let us now consider briefly the problem of determining the spectroscopic states of a given electronic configuration. For nonequivalent electrons (electrons with different n or l values) one can simply write out all the possible combinations of values of l and s and thereby determine all the possible states. Consider the $2p^1 3p^1$ state for example.

$$L = \begin{cases} 2 & l_1 + l_2 \\ 1 & \\ 0 & l_1 - l_2 \end{cases} \qquad S = \begin{cases} 1 & s_1 + s_2 \\ 0 & s_1 - s_2 \end{cases}$$

The possible combinations are shown in Table 11.1.

In the case of equivalent electrons the restrictions of the Pauli principle allow fewer spectroscopic term states. For example, in the $2p^2$ configuration in order for L to equal 2, l_1 and l_2 must be parallel, and since the magnetic quantum number m describes the orientation in space, $m_1 = m_2$. To satisfy the Pauli principle the electrons must have opposite spin, and thus $S = s_1 + s_2 = +\frac{1}{2} + (-\frac{1}{2}) = 0$ and only the singlet state is permitted: $^1D_2$.

---

[1] The symbol T is determined by the value of L as follows:

L	0	1	2	3	4	5	6
T	S	P	D	F	G	H	I

Table 11.1 The possible states and spectroscopic terms for a $2p^1 3p^1$ configuration

L	S	J	$Term\ symbol$
0	0	0	$^1S_0$
0	1	1	$^3S_1$
1	0	1	$^1P_1$
1	1	0, 1, 2	$^3P_{0,1,2}$‡
2	0	2	$^1D_2$
2	1	1, 2, 3	$^3D_{1,2,3}$

‡ This symbol stands for three states of different J values: $^3P_0$, $^3P_1$, $^3P_2$.

To determine the spectroscopic states allowed for an electronic configuration use the following three-step procedure. First, set up a table of the possible orbital arrangements, as shown in Table 11.2 for the $2p^2$ electronic configuration.

Table 11.2 The orbital arrangements for the $2p^2$ configuration

m‡			$M = \Sigma m$	$S = \Sigma s$
1	0	−1		
↑↓			2	0
	↑↓		0	0
		↑↓	−2	0
↑	↑		1	−1, 0, 0, +1
↑		↑	0	−1, 0, 0, +1
	↑	↑	−1	−1, 0, 0, +1

‡ A pair of arrows ↑↓ indicates two electrons of opposite spin, whereas a single arrow ↑ indicates a single electron of *either* spin, $\pm\frac{1}{2}h/2\pi$.

The second step consists of the construction of a single table showing the number of orbital arrangements for each pair of M and S values, as shown in Table 11.3 for the $2p^2$ case. This is called a *number table*. In the third step the number table (Table 11.3) is decomposed into a sum of smaller tables, each smaller table having only 1s as entries and called an *array table*. One usually starts with the entries of highest L value. In the present case, $L = 2$.

Table 11.3 The number of arrangements for each pair of M and S values for $2p^2$

S \ M	-2	-1	0	1	2
-1		1	1	1	
0	1	2	3	2	1
1		1	1	1	

The first spectroscopic state, then, is related to the following array table:

S \ M	-2	-1	0	1	2
0	1	1	1	1	1

The term symbol is identified from the highest values of M and S which occur in the array table: $L = 2$ and $S = 0$ in this present case. This corresponds to a singlet D state with J value of 2: $^1D_2$. The array-table entries are subtracted from the original number table, and the process is continued as shown in Table 11.4.

Table 11.4   Successive subtraction of array tables to yield spectroscopic term symbols

S \ M	-2	-1	0	1	2
-1		1	1	1	
0	1	2	3	2	1
1		1	1	1	

S \ M	-1	0	1
-1	1	1	1
0	1	2	1
1	1	1	1

S \ M	0
0	1

S \ M	-2	-1	0	1	2
0	1	1	1	1	1

S \ M	-1	0	1
-1	1	1	1
0	1	1	1
1	1	1	1

S \ M	0
0	1

$L = 2, S = 0$
$^1D_2$

$L = 1, S = 1$
$^3P_{0,1,2}$

$L = 0, S = 0$
$^1S_0$

The term symbols for many of the common electronic configurations are given in Tables 11.5 and 11.6.

The lowest-energy term, corresponding to the electronic ground state, may be picked from the list of term symbols with the assistance of Hund's rules. The lowest-energy term will be the one with the maximum S and,

Table 11.5 Spectroscopic term symbols for nonequivalent electrons

Electronic configuration	Term symbols‡
ss	^1S, ^3S
sp	^1P, ^3P
sd	^1D, ^3D
pp	^1S, ^1P, ^1D, ^3S, ^3P, ^3D
pd	^1P, ^1D, ^1F, ^3P, ^3D, ^3F
dd	^1S, ^1P, ^1D, ^1F, ^1G, ^3S, ^3P, ^3D, ^3F, ^3G
sss	^2S, ^2S, ^4S
ssp	^2P, ^2P, ^4P
ssd	^2D, ^2D, ^4D
spp	^2S, ^2P, ^2D, ^2S, ^2P, ^2D, ^4S, ^4P, ^4D
spd	^2P, ^2D, ^2F, ^2P, ^2D, ^2F, ^4P, ^4D, ^4F
ppp	$^2S(2)$, $^2P(6)$, $^2D(4)$, $^2F(2)$, $^4S(1)$, $^4P(3)$, $^4D(2)$, $^4F(1)$
ppd	$^2S(2)$, $^2P(4)$, $^2D(6)$, $^2F(4)$, $^2G(2)$, $^4S(1)$, $^4P(2)$, $^4D(3)$, $^4F(2)$, $^4G(1)$
pdf	$^2S(2)$, $^2P(4)$, $^2D(6)$, $^2F(6)$, $^2G(6)$, $^2H(4)$, $^2I(2)$, $^4S(1)$, $^4P(2)$, $^4D(3)$, $^4F(3)$, $^4G(3)$, $^4H(2)$, $^4I(1)$

Source: Taken by permission from G. Herzberg, "Atomic Spectra and Atomic Structure," p. 132, Dover Publications, Inc., New York, 1944.
‡ Numbers in parenthesis indicate the number of such states.

Table 11.6 Spectroscopic term symbols for equivalent electrons

Electronic configuration	Term symbols
s^2	^1S
p^2	^1S, ^1D, ^3P
p^3	^2P, ^2D, ^4S
p^4	^1S, ^1D, ^3P
p^5	^2P
p^6	^1S
d^2	^1S, ^1D, ^1G, ^3P, ^3F
d^3	^2P, $^2D(2)$, ^2F, ^2G, ^2H, ^4P, ^4F
d^4	$^1S(2)$, $^1D(2)$, ^1F, $^1G(2)$, ^1I, $^3P(2)$, ^3D, $^3F(2)$, ^3G, ^3H, ^5D
d^5	^2S, ^2P, $^2D(3)$, $^2F(2)$, $^2G(2)$, ^2H, ^2I, ^4P, ^4D, ^4F, ^4G, ^6S

Source: Taken by permission from G. Herzberg, "Atomic Spectra and Atomic Structure," p. 132, Dover Publications, Inc., New York, 1944.

of terms with the same S, the lowest L. For shells less than half filled the J value will be the lowest J, and for shells more than half filled, the highest J value. Thus, for the d^2 case the $^3P_0$ term is the ground-state term, and for the p^3 case it is the $^4S_{\frac{3}{2}}$ state.

11.2 ATOMIC ENERGY-LEVEL SPLITTING IN CRYSTAL-FIELD THEORY

In both crystal-field theory and ligand-field theory attention is focused on the electron orbitals of the metal atom. Whether the interaction is considered purely electrostatic, as in crystal-field theory, or somewhat covalent, as in ligand-field theory, the ligands are considered to be perturbers of the electronic environment of the atom. The interaction is considered to be electrostatic in nature. The sum result of the electrostatic interaction of the ligands with the metal orbitals is a splitting of the degeneracy of the metal orbitals because of the lowering of the symmetry in the presence of the ligands. Although we cannot compute the magnitude of the splitting, symmetry considerations alone will allow us to determine how the degenerate energy levels are split.

We have already encountered this problem in a somewhat different form. In Chap. 8 we discussed the representations of atomic orbitals in various point groups. We saw that each atomic orbital can be designated by a function which indicates its symmetry, usually as a subscript, for example, $2p_x$ or $3d_{x^2-y^2}$. Further, we noted that these functions are tabulated on the right side of most character tables. Hence, one can easily determine an atomic orbital irreducible representation in a particular point group simply by referring to the appropriate functional form in a character table.

One problem becomes apparent at this point. The symmetry functions for AOs in which $l > 2$ (f orbitals and higher) are not usually tabulated and, further, such symmetry functions are usually excluded from character tables. Hence, this simple approach must be abandoned.[1]

We must now develop a general technique for determining the irreducible representations to which the various AOs belong in the several point groups. We shall consider the wave functions as basis functions for a representation, and we shall find a general formula for the character of the matrices of this representation and then be able to use the general reduction formula, Eq. (6.70), to find the irreducible representations.

Let us take a specific case at this point. Consider a complex with a

---

[1] The reader who wishes to inquire into the transformation problem for f and higher orbitals may consult a table of AOs in L. Pauling and E. B. Wilson, "Introduction to Quantum Mechanics," pp. 132–136, McGraw-Hill Book Company, New York, 1935, and C. J. Ballhausen, "Introduction to Ligand Field Theory," pp. 93–97, McGraw-Hill Book Company, 1962.

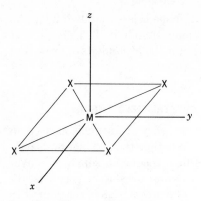

Fig. 11.4   The coordinate system and
molecular arrangement in a square
complex, MX_4, of point group D_4.

square arrangement of ligands in point group D_4, as shown in Fig. 11.4.
The functions which will be used as basis functions here are the hydrogen-
like wave functions $\psi_{n,l,m}(r,\ \theta,\ \phi)$.[1]

$$\psi_{nlm}(r,\ \theta,\ \phi)\ =\ R_{nl}(r)Y_{lm}(\theta,\ \phi)\ =\ R_{nl}(r)P_{lm}(\cos\theta)\Phi_m(\phi)$$

For a single electron in a $3d$ orbital we may write

$$\psi_{3,2,m}(r,\ \theta,\ \phi)\ =\ R_{3,2}(r)P_{2,m}(\cos\theta)\ \frac{e^{im\phi}}{\sqrt{2\pi}}$$

There are, of course, five basis functions here corresponding to the five
values of m: $+2$, $+1$, 0, -1, -2.   Let us now find the matrices which
represent these basis functions in point group D_4, whose character table is
given in Table 11.7.

[1] The $Y_{lm}(\theta,\ \phi)$ are spherical harmonics, solutions of the angular part of the Schrödinger equation for one-electron atoms. $P_{lm}(\cos\theta)$ are the associated Legendre
polynomials.

Table 11.7   The character table for point group D_4

D_4	E	$2C_4$	$C_2\ (=C_4{}^2)$	$2C_2$	$2C_2''$
A_1	1	1	1	1	1
A_2	1	1	1	-1	-1
B_1	1	-1	1	1	-1
B_2	1	-1	1	-1	1
E	2	0	-2	0	0
Γ_d	5	-1	1	1	1

We shall consider only rotations, for reasons which will become apparent as we proceed. The most general manner in which to deal with this problem is to consider a rotation through an angle ω about an arbitrary axis which passes through the center of the molecule. In this manner we must always quantize each orbital about the same arbitrary axis. Thus, a rotation through angle ω will transform $\psi_{nlm}(r, \theta, \phi)$ into $\psi_{rlm}(r, \theta, \phi + \omega)$. Reference to the form of the wave function shows that only the function $\Phi_m(\phi)$ is affected by this transformation and since functions of different m are not mixed, the matrices are diagonal:

$$\Phi_m(\phi + \omega) = \Gamma(\omega)\Phi_m(\phi)$$

$$\frac{1}{\sqrt{2\pi}}\begin{bmatrix} e^{i2(\phi+\omega)} \\ e^{i(\phi+\omega)} \\ e^{0} \\ e^{-i(\phi+\omega)} \\ e^{-i2(\phi+\omega)} \end{bmatrix} = \begin{bmatrix} e^{i2\omega} & 0 & 0 & 0 & 0 \\ 0 & e^{i\omega} & 0 & 0 & 0 \\ 0 & 0 & e^{0} & 0 & 0 \\ 0 & 0 & 0 & e^{-i\omega} & 0 \\ 0 & 0 & 0 & 0 & e^{-i2\omega} \end{bmatrix} \frac{1}{\sqrt{2\pi}} \begin{bmatrix} e^{i2\phi} \\ e^{i\phi} \\ e^{0} \\ e^{-i\phi} \\ e^{-i2\phi} \end{bmatrix}$$

Thus, the character may be written

$$\chi(\omega) = e^{i2\omega} + e^{i\omega} + e^{0} + e^{-i\omega} + e^{-i2\omega}$$

or in the general case for any l value

$$\chi(\omega) = e^{il\omega} + e^{i(l-1)\omega} + \cdots + e^{-i(1-l)\omega} + e^{-il\omega}$$

$$= e^{-il\omega} \sum_{j=0}^{2l} (e^{i\omega})^j \tag{11.1}$$

or

$$\chi(\omega) = \frac{\sin\left[(l + \tfrac{1}{2})\omega\right]}{\sin(\omega/2)} \tag{11.2}$$

For point group D_4 we obtain the character system Γ_d given in Table 11.7 as follows:

$$\Gamma_d(C_2) = \frac{\sin\left[(2 + \tfrac{1}{2})\pi\right]}{\sin(\pi/2)} = \frac{1}{1} = 1 \qquad \omega = \pi$$

$$\Gamma_d(C_4) = \frac{\sin\left[(2 + \tfrac{1}{2})(\pi/2)\right]}{\sin(\pi/4)} = \frac{1}{-1} = -1 \qquad \omega = \frac{\pi}{2}$$

Using the standard reduction formula, Eq. (6.70), we obtain the direct sum

$$\Gamma_d(D_4) = A_1 + B_1 + B_2 + E$$

This result may be easily extended to the centrosymmetric point group D_{4h}. Point group D_{4h} possesses a center of inversion, and the symmetry elements of D_{4h} include those of D_4 plus products of each with the center of inversion. This separation is clearly illustrated in Table 11.8.

Table 11.8   The character table of point group D_{4h} shown as $D_{4h} = D_4 \times i$

D_{4h}	E	$2C_4$	C_2	$2C_2$	$2C_2''$	i	$2S_4$	σ_h	$2\sigma_v$	$2\sigma_d$
A_{1g}	1	1	1	1	1	1	1	1	1	1
A_{2g}	1	1	1	-1	-1	1	1	1	-1	-1
B_{1g}	1	-1	1	1	-1	1	-1	1	1	-1
B_{2g}	1	-1	1	-1	1	1	-1	1	-1	1
E_g	2	0	-2	0	0	2	0	-2	0	0
A_{1u}	1	1	1	1	1	-1	-1	-1	-1	-1
A_{2u}	1	1	1	-1	-1	-1	-1	-1	1	1
B_{1u}	1	-1	1	1	-1	-1	1	-1	-1	1
B_{2u}	1	-1	1	-1	1	-1	1	-1	1	-1
E_u	2	0	-2	0	0	-2	0	2	0	0

One need not usually consider the whole character table in the determination of irreducible representations.   For example, d orbitals are symmetric with respect to inversion.   Therefore, in D_{4h} the d orbitals must belong to even, or *gerade*, irreducible representations.   Thus,

$$\Gamma_d(D_{4h}) = A_{1g} + B_{1g} + B_{2g} + E_g$$

One can proceed in a general manner to determine the irreducible representations to which AOs belong in various point groups.   Use Eq. (11.1) or (11.2) to determine the character system for the rotations, and then if the point group is centrosymmetric, the character table may be split, as in the D_{4h} case.   The irreducible representations are tabulated in Table 11.9 for orbitals s, p, d, f, g, h, and i in several point groups commonly encountered in metal complexes.

Finally, there is the problem of determining the splitting of the Russell-Saunders electronic states in the chemical environment of the ligands.   Because the overall magnetic quantum number M appears in the total wave function just as the individual magnetic quantum number m appears in the one-electron wave functions

$$\Phi_M(\phi) = \frac{1}{\sqrt{2\pi}} e^{iM\phi}$$

Table 11.9 applies equally well to the splitting of the free-ion electronic states.   Further, the splitting of electronic states does not affect the spin multiplicity of the state.

With these considerations in mind, Table 11.10 has been prepared for the splitting of states S, P, D, F, G, H, and I in several commonly encountered point groups.   Since spin multiplicity is unaffected by symmetry splitting, the spin multiplicity is indicated by n for generality.

Table 11.9 Irreducible representations of atomic orbitals in several point groups

Orbital	Point group				
	O_h	T_d	D_{4h}‡	D_3§	D_{2d}
s	A_{1g}	A_1	A_{1g}	A_1	A_1
p	T_{1u}	T_2	$A_{2u} + E_u$	$A_2 + E$	$B_2 + E$
d	$E_g + T_{2g}$	$E + T_2$	$A_{1g} + B_{1g} + B_{2g} + E_g$	$A_1 + 2E$	$A_1 + B_1 + B_2 + E$
f	$A_{2u} + T_{1u} + T_{2u}$	$A_2 + T_1 + T_2$	$A_{2u} + B_{1u} + B_{2u} + 2E_u$	$A_1 + 2A_2 + 2E$	$A_1 + A_2 + B_2 + 2E$
g	$A_{1g} + E_g + T_{1g} + T_{2g}$	$A_1 + E + T_1 + T_2$	$2A_{1g} + A_{2g} + B_{1g} + B_{2g} + 2E_g$	$2A_1 + A_2 + 3E$	$2A_1 + A_2 + B_1 + B_2 + 2E$
h	$E_u + 2T_{1u} + T_{2u}$	$E + T_1 + 2T_2$	$A_{1u} + 2A_{2u} + B_{1u} + B_{2u} + 3E_u$	$A_1 + 2A_2 + 4E$	$A_1 + A_2 + B_1 + 2B_2 + 3E$
i	$A_{1g} + A_{2g} + E_g + T_{1g} + 2T_{2g}$	$A_1 + A_2 + E + T_1 + 2T_2$	$2A_{1g} + A_{2g} + 2B_{1g} + 2B_{2g} + 3E_g$	$3A_1 + 2A_2 + 4E$	$2A_1 + A_2 + 2B_1 + 2B_2 + 3E$

‡ Point-group D_4 representations can be obtained by dropping the u and g subscripts.

§ Point-group D_{2d} representations can be obtained by adding the subscripts u and g in the appropriate manner.

Source: Adapted from F. A. Cotton, "Chemical Applications of Group Theory," pp. 194–195, John Wiley & Sons, Inc., New York, 1964.

Table 11.10 Splitting of Russell-Saunders states by the ligand environment for several point groups

Free-ion terms	Split states in point groups				
	O_h	T_d	D_{4h}	D_{3h}	D_{2d}
^nS	$^nA_{1g}$	$^nA_1$	$^nA_{1g}$	$^nA_1$	$^nA_1$
^nP	$^nT_{1u}$	$^nT_2$	$^nA_{2u}$	$^nA_2$	$^nB_2$
			^nE_u	^nE	^nE
^nD	^nE_g	^nE	$^nA_{1g}\ ^nB_{2g}$	$^nA_1$	$^nA_1\ ^nB_2$
	$^nT_{2g}$	$^nT_2$	$^nB_{1g}\ ^nE_g$	$2\ ^nE$	$^nB_1\ ^nE$
^nF	$^nA_{2u}\ ^nT_{2u}$	$^nA_2\ ^nT_2$	$^nA_u\ ^nB_u$	$^nA_1\ 2\ ^nE$	$^nA_1\ ^nB_2$
	^nT_u	$^nT_1$	$^nB_u\ 2\ ^nE_u$	$2\ ^nA_2$	$^nA_2\ 2\ ^nE$
^nG	$^nA_{1g}\ ^nT_{1g}$	$^nA_1\ ^nT_1$	$2\ ^nA_{1g}\ ^nB_{1g}$	$2\ ^nA_1\ 3\ ^nE$	$2\ ^nA_1\ ^nB_1$
	$^nE_g\ ^nT_{2g}$	$^nE\ ^nT_2$	$^nA_{2g}\ ^nB_{2g}$	$^nA_2$	$^nA_2\ ^nB_2$
			$2\ ^nE_g$		$2\ ^nE$
^nH	$^nE_u\ ^nT_{2u}$	$^nE\ ^nT_2$	$^nA_{1u}\ 2\ ^nA_{2u}$	$^nA_1\ 2\ ^nA_2$	$^nA_1\ ^nA_2$
	$2T_{1u}$	$2\ ^nT_1$	$^nB_{1u}\ ^nB_{2u}$	$4\ ^nE$	$^nB_1\ 2\ ^nB_2$
			$3\ ^nE_u$		$3\ ^nE$
^nI	$^nA_{1g}\ ^nA_{2g}$	$^nA_1\ ^nA_2$	$2\ ^nA_{1g}\ ^nA_{2g}$	$3\ ^nA_1\ 2\ ^nA_2$	$2\ ^nA_1\ ^nA_2$
	$^nE_g\ ^nT_{1g}$	$^nE\ ^nT_1$	$2\ ^nB_{1g}\ 2\ ^nB_{2g}$	$4\ ^nE$	$2\ ^nB_1\ 2\ ^nB_2$
	$2\ ^nT_{2g}$	$2\ ^nT_2$	$3\ ^nE_g$		$3\ ^nE$

Thus, the interaction of the metal atom or ion with the chemical environment of symmetrically arranged ligands generally has the effect of splitting the atomic energy levels which are degenerate in the free ion. To each irreducible representation an energy may be assigned. If the order of the energies is known, an energy-level diagram can be made. Such a diagram is called a *crystal-field-splitting diagram*. Symmetry and group-theory considerations can tell us only the manner in which the orbital degeneracy is lifted; they cannot give us directly the energy splittings or even the order of the various split levels.

11.3 ESTIMATION OF ENERGY-LEVEL ORDERING BY CRYSTAL-FIELD THEORY

Before we can construct energy-level diagrams for the energy levels in metal complexes of various point-group symmetries, we must obtain some notion of the relative ordering of energy levels. The calculation of the energies of the various levels is a quantum-mechanical problem. The details of the quantum-mechanical calculation are somewhat beyond the scope of this book.[1] However, a simple model can be used to establish

[1] See the references listed at the end of this chapter.

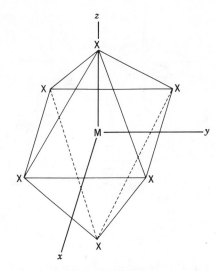

Fig. 11.5 The coordinate system and ligand arrangement in an octahedral point group of O_h symmetry.

the relative ordering of the energy-level scheme. The model is based on the purely electrostatic interaction of the ligands in the complex.

Consider the orientation of the ligands in an octahedral complex, as shown in Fig. 11.5, and the directional properties of the five $3d$ orbitals, as shown in Fig. 11.6. Under the approximation of crystal-field theory each ligand is considered to be a point charge (or point dipole) and the metal-ligand interaction is considered as purely electrostatic. In the free metal ion the five $3d$ orbitals possess the same energy: they are degenerate. However, in the chemical environment set up by the octahedrally arranged ligands, there arises a difference in the energy of the orbitals, and the degeneracy is lifted. Consideration of Fig. 11.5 shows that the regions of maximum probability in both the d_{z^2} and $d_{x^2-y^2}$ orbitals point directly toward the negatively charged ligands. On the other hand, the regions of highest probability for the d_{xy}, d_{xz}, and d_{yz} orbitals lie in between the negatively charged ligands. Thus, as a result of the coulombic repulsion between the negatively charged ligands and (negatively charged) electrons which may occupy the d_{z^2} and $d_{x^2-y^2}$ orbitals, the energy of these two orbitals is raised relative to that of the unsplit fivefold-degenerate case. By contrast the energy of the d_{xy}, d_{xz}, and d_{yz} orbitals is lowered. The sum total of this effect is schematically illustrated in Fig. 11.7.

A similar pictorial approach can be applied to other complex symmetries. The tetrahedral case is illustrated in Figs. 11.8 and 11.9. Since both point groups O_h and T_d belong to what are known as cubic groups

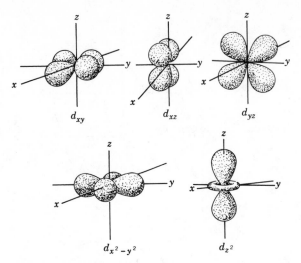

Fig. 11.6 Schematic representation of the $3d$ orbitals. (*Taken by permission from M. C. Day and J. Selbin, "Theoretical Inorganic Chemistry," Reinhold Publishing Corporation, New York*, 1962.)

(containing a combination of two-, three-, and fourfold axes), it may not be surprising to find that the orbital splittings are similar. In T_d, however, the energy-level ordering is reversed relative to the ordering in O_h.

The crystal-field-splitting diagrams for some other symmetry species may be obtained by considering a distortion of a higher symmetry form.

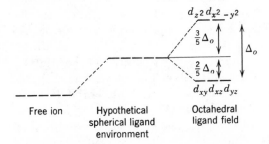

| Free ion | Hypothetical spherical ligand environment | Octahedral ligand field |

Fig. 11.7 A schematic drawing of the relative energies involved in the simple crystal-field model of metal-ligand interaction. (*left*) The five-fold degeneracy of the free ion; (*center*) a hypothetical energy state in which the total negative charge of the ligands is spread into a spherical shell around the metal ion at a distance from the metal equal to the average metal-ligand distance; (*right*) the splitting of the orbital energy levels by the electrostatic field of the six ligands in octahedral symmetry.

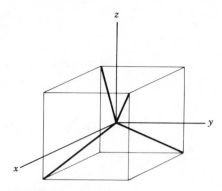

Fig. 11.8 The coordinate system for a tetrahedral complex of point group T_d.

For instance, the crystal-field diagrams for the tetragonally distorted octahedral complex and the square planar complex, both of D_{4h} symmetry, may be determined from the diagram for O_h. Consider a tetragonally distorted octahedral complex in which two "trans" ligands (located on the z axis for simplicity) are moved a short distance further away from the metal atom than the equatorial ligands in the xy plane. As a consequence of lowering the symmetry of the environment, some of the levels which were degenerate in O_h are no longer degenerate in D_{4h}.

Since the ligands are further away along the z axis, d_{z^2} becomes lower in energy relative to $d_{x^2-y^2}$. Likewise, d_{xz} and d_{yz} become lower than d_{xy}. In the extreme case in which the ligands are removed to infinity along the z axis, the square planar arrangement is achieved. The trend in orbital-energy change is also carried to an extreme. The results are illustrated in Fig. 11.10. It must be realized that the precise ordering of orbital energy levels (in these cases) depends upon the exact details of the structure of the complex, i.e., relative metal-to-ligand distances and strength of metal-ligand interaction. Further, another case is possible: the two

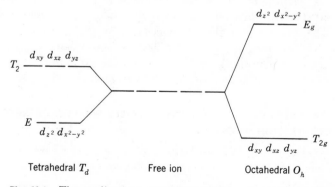

Fig. 11.9 The qualitative crystal-field-splitting diagrams for O_h and T_d symmetry.

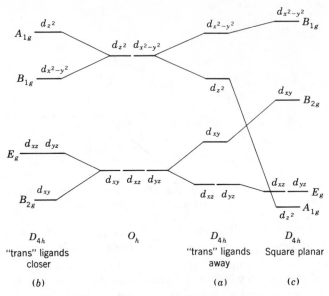

Fig. 11.10 The qualitative crystal-field-splitting diagrams relative to the O_h case for (a) tetragonal distortion of O_h in which two trans ligands are moved a small distance further away from the metal ion; (b) tetragonal distortion of O_h in which two trans ligands are moved closer to the metal ion; (c) the square planar case: two trans ligands are removed from the O_h complex.

trans ligands could be moved closer to the metal ion (or the other four ligands moved away from the metal ion). Inversion of the energy-level scheme takes place, as also shown in Fig. 11.10.

Ballhausen[1] has given the crystal-field diagram for the trigonal distortion of O_h to D_{3d}. This diagram is shown in Fig. 11.11 relative to the octahedral case.

Hence, in this relatively crude but simple pictorial approach the crystal-field diagrams can be obtained for most point groups of interest. The texts listed in the references give more general and accurate methods.

Now that energy-level diagrams have been established, the question arises concerning the nature of the interaction of the ligand field with the various electronic states of the free metal ion.

11.4 ENERGY LEVELS AND CRYSTAL-FIELD-SPLITTING STRENGTH: CORRELATION DIAGRAMS

We have not yet established a definite relation between the ordering of electronic states in a metal complex and the strength of the metal-ligand

[1] C. J. Ballhausen, "Introduction to Ligand Field Theory," p. 132, McGraw-Hill Book Company, New York, 1962.

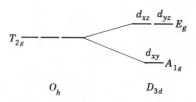

Fig. 11.11 The qualitative crystal-field-splitting diagrams for trigonally distorted O_h to produce D_{3d}. (*Adapted by permission from C. J. Ballhausen, "Introduction to Ligand Field Theory", p. 132, Copyright 1962. McGraw-Hill Book Company.*)

interaction. Since the splitting is caused by the metal-ligand interaction, the ordering and magnitude of splitting may change with the strength of the interaction. We shall now show how to set up a diagram having for its abscissa the strength of the interaction in terms of the crystal-field splitting Δ, for the left ordinate axis the order of energy states in the free ion, and for the right ordinate axis the energy states in a complex characterized by a very large crystal-field splitting. This diagram demonstrates the correlation between states derived from the free ion and states derived from the strong interaction complex, and hence it is called a *correlation diagram.*

The simplest case for d electrons is the single d electron in the octahedral field. The free-ion state for d^1 is ^2D, and reference to Table 11.9 shows that the D state is split into T_{2g} and E_g states by the octahedral ligand field of O_h symmetry. This splitting is shown on the left side of Fig. 11.12a. In the case of large crystal-field splitting, the single electron may either occupy the T_{2g} one-electron level, or it may occupy one of the E_g one-electron levels (see Fig. 11.9). Hence in the case of very large crystal-field splitting there are two possible states, T_{2g}^1 and E_g^1, which are shown on the right side of Fig. 11.12a. We know that both states on the right must be doublets, since only one electron occupies each level.

The diagram can easily be completed now. One simply connects a straight line between the identical states on the two sides of the diagram. The result shows simply that the splitting between T_{2g} and E_g increases as the crystal-field splitting Δ_o increases. With little additional effort one can now set up the correlation diagram for the d^1 case in T_d symmetry.

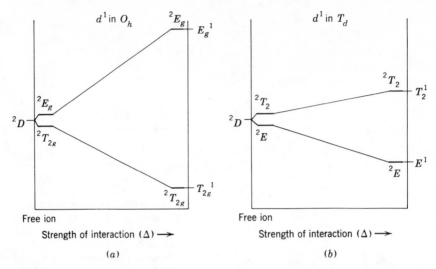

Fig. 11.12 The correlation diagram for the d^1 case. The abscissa is the crystal-field strength. The left side represents the free ion and the way in which the free-ion state is split by the ligand field. (a) An octahedral ligand field; (b) a tetrahedral ligand field.

Table 11.10 shows that the splitting of states is the same in T_d as in O_h except that the states are inverted (see Fig. 11.9). Hence, the correlation diagram for point group T_d can be immediately produced, as in Fig. 11.12b. This inversion of levels between O_h and T_d will be utilized later in a general manner.

For d^n cases in which $n > 1$ the correlation diagram is not produced so simply. An additional concept is required, which for practical purposes we shall develop by means of a specific example. The highest symmetry and least number of electrons provide the simplest example: d^2 in O_h.

Reference to Table 11.6 gives the free-ion states for the d^2 case: ^1S, ^1D, ^1G, ^3P, ^3F. These states are shown in their experimentally determined order on the left side of Fig. 11.13. The designations for the states derived from a very large splitting are determined by consideration of the various ways in which two electrons may be placed into the T_{2g} and E_g^* levels of the O_h crystal-field diagram (see Fig. 11.9). There are three possible arrangements, as shown in Fig. 11.14: T_{2g}^2, $T_{2g}^1 E_g^{*1}$, and E_g^{*2}. These three states have also been added to Fig. 11.13 in approximately the correct order and relative spacings on the right ordinate.

From the considerations of Sec. 11.3 we can determine the manner in which the ligand field splits each electronic state in the weak-field case as well as in the strong-field case. These splittings have also been indi-

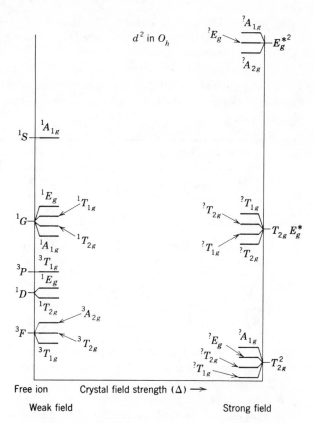

Free ion   Crystal field strength (Δ) $\longrightarrow$

Weak field   Strong field

Fig. 11.13 The preliminary setup for the development of a correlation diagram for the d^2 case. The left ordinate is determined by the electronic states for the free metal ion and the way in which these states are split by the crystal field. The order of energy states in the metal complex is different for a large crystal-field splitting and is indicated on the right ordinate. The spin multiplicities must still be determined.

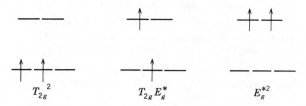

Fig. 11.14 The crystal-field-splitting diagram for the d^2 case in an octahedral field showing the three ways in which two electrons may occupy the T_{2g} and E_g^* levels (without specification of the spin multiplicities).

cated in Fig. 11.13 on an arbitrary scale.   The problem now is that we must yet determine the spin multiplicities of the states on the right-hand side of the correlation diagram.

The manner in which the splittings on the right-hand side of Fig. 11.13 have been obtained depends upon the use of the product representation, as discussed in Sec. 6.4.   The character systems and direct sums are shown here.

O_h	E	$8C_3$	$6C_2$	$6C_4$	$3C_2$	i	$6S_4$	$8S_6$	$3\sigma_h$	$6\sigma_d$
$T_{2g}{}^2$	9	0	1	1	1	9	1	0	1	1
$T_{2g}E_g^*$	6	0	0	0	-2	6	0	0	-2	0
E_g^{*2}	4	1	0	0	4	4	0	1	4	0

Using the standard reduction formula, Eq. (6.70), the following direct sums are obtained:

$$T_{2g}{}^2 = A_{1g} + E_g + T_{1g} + T_{2g}$$
$$T_{2g}E_g^* = T_{1g} + T_{2g}$$
$$E_g^{*2} = A_{1g} + E_g + A_{2g}$$

However, until we know the spin multiplicities of the right-hand states, we cannot correlate those states to the left-hand states.

The most general method which can be used here is called the *method of descent in symmetry*, first used by H. Bethe[1] and further developed by C. K. Jorgensen[2] and C. J. Ballhausen.[3]   This method utilizes two aspects of the effect of lowering the symmetry of an electronic system: (1) degenerate levels are often split into nondegenerate (one-dimensional) representations or sums of nondegenerate representations, and (2) the spin multiplicity of a state is unaffected.   Hence, Bethe showed how to make use of the simpler electronic arrangements in the lower symmetry to determine the spin multiplicities there and in the higher-symmetry case.   We shall now apply the method to the E_g^{*2} in O_h.

First, we must find a lower-symmetry group, a subgroup of O_h, which will lift the degeneracy of the single electron level E_g^* and at the same time provide a unique transformation of each state into a one-dimensional state (or sum of one-dimensional states).   For the present case we shall find that subgroup D_{4h} will suffice.   According to the correlation tables of Appendix II, the state E_g is split into $A_{1g} + B_{1g}$ in D_{4h}.

[1] H. A. Bethe, *Ann. Physik*, (5) **3**:133 (1929), English translation, Consultants Bureau, New York, 1958.
[2] C. K. Jorgensen, *Acta Chem. Scand.*, **9**:116 (1959).
[3] *Op.cit.*

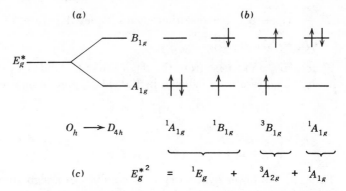

Fig. 11.15 (*a*) Lowering the symmetry of the ligand field from O_h to D_{4h} splits the E_g^* level. (*b*) The two electrons may be placed into the two levels in four different ways, giving rise to four electronic states. (*c*) The three electronic states of the two electrons occupying E_g^* in O_h may be uniquely related to the states arising from E_g^{*2} in D_{4h}.

Figure 11.15 shows the possible ways in which these split states may be occupied by two electrons.

The spin multiplicities of the four states in D_{4h} can now be determined. The leftmost configuration of Fig. 11.15*b* represents two electrons in the A_{1g} state or $A_{1g} \times A_{1g}$. The direct product of any state with itself produces the totally symmetric state, A_{1g} in this case. Since the two electrons occupy the same state, they must have paired spins, and hence this state is a singlet, $^1A_{1g}$. The third configuration from the left in Fig. 11.15*b* represents one electron each in A_{1g} and B_{1g} with spins unpaired. The direct product of the totally symmetric state with any state leaves the state unchanged. Hence, this state is a B_{1g} triplet, $^3B_{1g}$. The other two cases are determined in the same manner.

Now we are in a position to show how the spin multiplicities of the direct product E_g^{*2} can be determined. From the correlation table in Appendix II we obtain the splitting of $E_g^2 = A_{1g} + A_{2g} + E_g$ when the symmetry is lowered from O_h to D_{4h}:

$$E_g^{*2} \begin{cases} A_{1g} \to A_{1g} \\ A_{2g} \to B_{1g} \\ E_g \ \to A_{1g} + B_{1g} \end{cases} \qquad \begin{matrix} O_h & D_{4h} \end{matrix}$$

From Fig. 11.15 we can draw a unique one-to-one equivalence between states obtained from filling split one-electron states (with known spin multiplicities) and states obtained from the split direct product E_g^{*2}. The one triplet $^3B_{1g}$ state cannot be derived from the E_g state in O_h

$(E_g \rightarrow A_{1g} + B_{1g})$ because there is no triplet A_{1g} state:

$$E_g \nrightarrow {}^1A_{1g} + {}^3B_{1g}$$

Hence, ${}^3B_{1g}$ must arise from the A_{2g} state in O_h, and A_{2g} must be a triplet in O_h. The results are shown in Fig. 11.15 and summarized as follows:

$$E_g^{*2} \begin{cases} {}^1A_{1g} \rightarrow {}^1A_{1g} \\ {}^3A_{2g} \rightarrow {}^3B_{1g} \\ {}^1E_g \rightarrow {}^1A_{1g} + {}^1B_{1g} \end{cases} \qquad \begin{matrix} O_h & D_{4h} \end{matrix}$$

Thus, in the lower symmetry it is possible to assign spin multiplicities unambiguously and uniquely. Since the symmetry lowering leaves the spin multiplicity unchanged, the spin multiplicity of the states in the higher symmetry can be assigned—with due attention to detail.

In the case of $T_{2g} \times E_g^* = T_{1g} + T_{2g}$ the states may be both singlet and triplet, since the electrons may be placed independently in either of the two original states. Hence,

$$T_{2g} \times E_g^* = {}^1T_{1g} + {}^1T_{2g} + {}^3T_{1g} + {}^3T_{2g}$$

and the descent-in-symmetry method is not needed.

For the remaining case, $T_{2g}{}^2 = A_{1g} + E_g + T_{1g} + T_{2g}$, the descent-in-symmetry method is needed again. If we attempt to use the subgroup D_{4h} to lower the symmetry, we run into trouble, as we shall see here. D_{4h} splits the T_{2g} triply degenerate level as follows:

$$O_h \rightarrow D_{4h}$$
$$T_{2g} \rightarrow B_{2g} + E_g$$

Also

$$T_{2g}{}^2 = 2A_{1g} + A_{2g} + B_{1g} + B_{2g} + 2E_g$$

as follows for the direct product formed for two electrons in T_{2g}:

$$T_{2g}{}^2 \begin{cases} B_{2g} \times B_{2g} = A_{1g} \\ E_g \times E_g = A_{1g} + A_{2g} + B_{1g} + B_{2g} \\ 2(B_{2g} \times E_g) = 2E_g \end{cases}$$

Now it can be seen that it is not possible to determine the spin multiplicities in the D_{4h} case because of the presence of the two degenerate states, which, of course, arose because of the presence of a degenerate state in the splitting of the triply degenerate level T_{2g}. Hence, we must seek another subgroup in which T_{2g} is split into three *one-dimensional* representations. A survey of the correlation table in Appendix II for O_h shows there are only two such subgroups, C_{2v} and C_{2h}. We shall solve the spin-multiplicity problem for $T_{2g}{}^2$ using subgroup C_{2v}. Again using the correlation table for O_h in Appendix II, we see that in C_{2v} the triply degenerate level T_{2g} is split into A_1, B_1, and B_2:

$$O_h \rightarrow C_{2v}$$
$$T_{2g} \rightarrow A_1 + B_1 + B_2$$

This splitting is shown schematically in the upper half of Fig. 11.16, along with the various ways in which these levels may be occupied by two electrons. The proper symmetry designations for occupancy by two electrons are obtained by taking the direct product of T_{2g}^2 in C_{2v} $(A_1 + B_1 + B_2)^2$. Using the direct-product method the symmetry designation of each state in C_{2v} can be obtained. For example, $A_1^2 = A_1$, $B_1 \times B_2 = A_2$, and $A_1 \times B_2 = B_2$. All these appropriate states are shown in Fig. 11.16c, along with their properly determined spin multiplicities. Notice

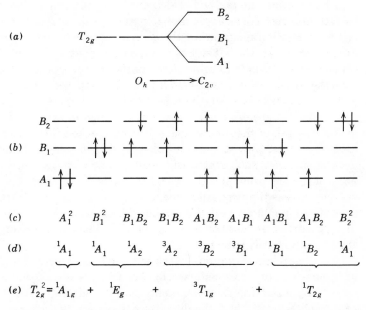

Fig. 11.16 (a) Lowering the symmetry of the ligand field from O_h to C_{2v} splits the T_{2g} level into three nondegenerate levels. (b) The two electrons may be placed into the three levels in nine different ways (c) giving rise to nine electronic states (d) whose direct products can be determined. Spin multiplicities may also be assigned. (e) The states arising from double occupancy of T_{2g} in O_h can be uniquely related to the states arising from T_{2g}^2 in C_{2v}, thus uniquely assigning spin multiplicities to the states in O_h. [The order of the electron configurations in (b) was determined so that the final groupings in (d) would directly correspond to (e). A trial-and-error method is used.]

that there are two possible ways to place two electrons in two different
energy levels, i.e., spins paired or spins unpaired, giving rise to *both* a
singlet and triplet state.

Finally, it is shown on the bottom line of Fig. 11.16 that there is only
one way in which these states can be assigned to states arising from $T_{2g}{}^2$
in O_h: $A_{1g} + E_g + T_{1g} + T_{2g}$.

$$
\begin{array}{cc}
O_h & C_{2v} \\
\end{array}
$$

$$
T_{2g}{}^2 \begin{cases}
{}^1A_{1g} \to {}^1A_1 \\
{}^1E_g \to {}^1A_1 + {}^1A_2 \\
{}^3T_{1g} \to {}^3A_2 + {}^3B_2 + {}^3B_1 \\
{}^1T_{2g} \to {}^1B_1 + {}^1B_2 + {}^1A_1
\end{cases}
$$

The clue to this arrangement is the fact that there are only three spin
triplet states.

Thus, using the method of descent in symmetry, we have been able
to determine the correct spin multiplicities for the states on the right side
of the correlation diagram for the d^2 case. We can now proceed to connect the states on the left side to those on the right. To consider how the
connections are made imagine the hypothetical process in which, starting
with the free ion, the crystal-field interaction is turned on and the strength
of the interaction is slowly increased to a very large value.

Generally speaking, each state will change linearly with the change
in the strength of the interaction. However, when there are two or more
identical states, they will also interact with each other. Hence, the connecting lines for such states will tend to show curvature. Finally, we
need one more principle, the so-called *noncrossing rule:* identical states
cannot cross as the strength of the interaction is varied. With these considerations in mind we can now make all the necessary connections for the
d^2 octahedral case, as shown in Fig. 11.17. The curvature of interacting
states is arbitrarily drawn.

If the preliminary groundwork has been done correctly, there should
be a one-to-one correspondence between states on the left and on the
right. By observing the noncrossing rule the left and right states can be
connected correctly and the diagram completed. Of course, the precise
spacings of levels and the curvature of connection lines must be determined semiempirically: a combination of experimental spectral data and
rather difficult calculations. We are producing here only a qualitative
diagram.

The same procedure as developed above can be used to develop the
correlation diagram for the other d^n ($n = 3, 4, 5, \ldots , 10$) cases in
the point groups of interest. It is probably obvious that as the number
of electrons increases and as the symmetry is lowered, the problem
becomes quite complicated. As a matter of fact, for point groups other

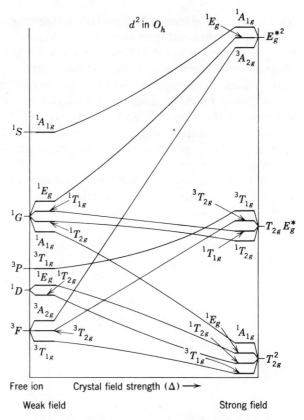

Fig. 11.17 A qualitative correlation diagram for the d^2 case in an octahedral environment.

than O_h, T_d, and D_{4h}, symmetry may be helpful in only a preliminary way. Rather sophisticated calculations may be necessary for the complete solution of the problem. Fortunately, however, there is a set of relationships for d^n cases in octahedral and tetrahedral symmetries which greatly simplifies the problem. Further, a given problem involving a metal complex of lower symmetry may often be related to a higher-symmetry idealized structure in such a way that qualitative information can be obtained for the lower-symmetry structure.

11.5 CORRELATION DIAGRAMS FOR THE d^n CASES IN OCTAHEDRAL AND TETRAHEDRAL LIGAND FIELDS

As was illustrated earlier for the d^1 case, the order of energy levels in T_d point-group symmetry is just the inverse of the order in O_h point-group symmetry. This relationship is known as the octahedral-tetrahedral level inversion. Hence, the correlation diagrams for d^n cases in T_d symmetry can be obtained from those in O_h symmetry simply by inverting the order in each group of split levels on both the left and right sides of the diagram and reconnecting the corresponding states with straight or curved lines, as appropriate. In this manner the diagram of Fig. 11.12b was obtained from the diagram of Fig. 11.12a. We can now produce a diagram for the d^2 case in T_d symmetry from Fig. 11.17. The resulting completed correlation diagram is shown in Fig. 11.18. Notice that the spin multiplicity assignments on the right are the same as in the O_h diagram for d^2.

A second inversion principle is encountered when considering the relation between d^n and d^{10-n} splitting patterns. For example, quanti-

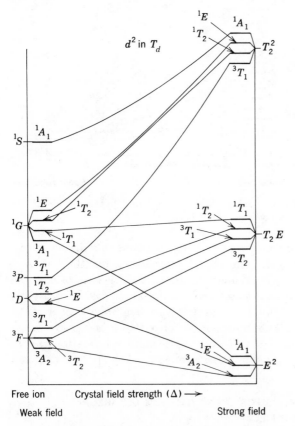

Free ion   Crystal field strength $(\Delta) \longrightarrow$

Weak field   Strong field

Fig. 11.18 A qualitative correlation diagram for the d^2 case in a tetrahedral environment. Notice that the order of levels derived from the splitting of a state is just the inverse of the corresponding octahedral case.

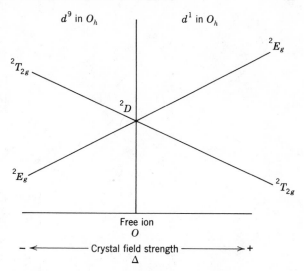

Fig. 11.19 The correlation diagram for both a d^1 and a d^9 case in an O_h ligand field. The free-ion state is at the middle. Notice that the order of the two levels for the d^1 case is just the inverse of the order for the d^9 case.

tatively a d^1 case (one electron) must behave under a purely electrostatic theory just like a d^9 case (one positron) except for a reversal of the sign of the energy of interaction. That is, n electrons behave like n positrons ($10 - n$ electrons). This principle is called the *hole formalism* and results in an inversion of energy levels because of the change in sign of the energy of interaction.

Figure 11.19 on the right side shows the splitting of a d^1 case in the O_h field. The left side, represented by the negative of the energy of interaction, shows the splitting of a d^9 case in the O_h field. The left is just the inverse of the right.

Thus, the order of the splittings of an energy level in a d^n case is just the inverse of the order in a d^{10-n} case in O_h. The same is obviously true for d^n and d^{10-n} levels in T_d. Hence, only five diagrams are necessary for a qualitative description of correlation diagrams in O_h *or* in T_d. The others are obtained by inverting the energies on the right-hand side and reconnecting states.

Further, since $d_{O_h}{}^n$ is the inverse of $d_{O_h}{}^{10-n}$ as well as the inverse of $d_{T_d}{}^n$, more general relations can be established: $d_{O_h}{}^n$ is identical to $d_{T_d}{}^{10-n}$, and $d_{T_d}{}^n$ is identical to $d_{O_h}{}^{10-n}$. Thus, only five diagrams are needed for *both* O_h and T_d. On the basis of these equivalencies and inverse relations rather sophisticated calculations have been used to produce the set of diagrams shown in Fig. 11.20.

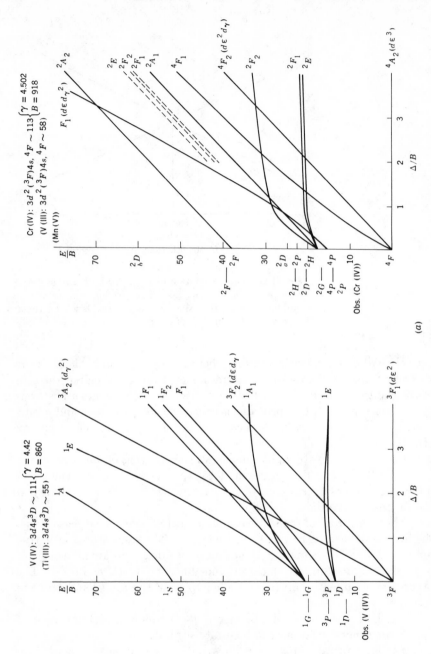

Fig. 11.20 Correlation diagrams for *d* electrons numbering from two to eight electrons. *(Taken by permission from T. M. Dunn, D. S. McClure, and R. G. Pearson, "Some Aspects of Crystal Field Theory," pp. 42–45, Harper & Row, Incorporated, Publishers New York, 1965.)*

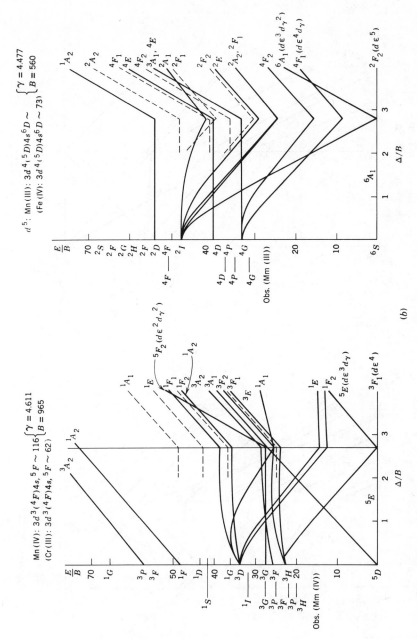

Fig. 11.20 *(Continued.)*

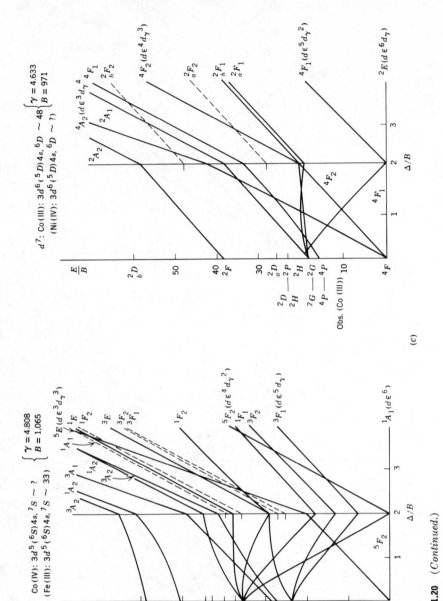

Fig. 11.20 (*Continued.*)

324

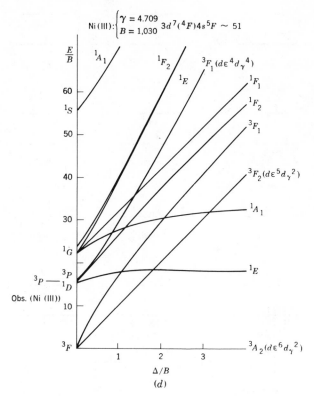

Fig. 11.20 (*Continued.*)

One further phenomenon must be mentioned here. In certain cases the number of unpaired electrons is determined by the size of the crystal-field splitting. Consider the octahedral case. The lower one-electron level is triply degenerate, T_{2g}. In the d^1, d^2, and d^3 cases the electrons will occupy the T_{2g} level as the lowest energy state. However, as shown in Fig. 11.21, in the d^4, d^5, d^6, and d^7 cases a choice is possible. If the energy P required to pair two electrons is greater than the energy difference Δ between T_{2g} and E_g^*, the electrons will be unpaired. Such a state is called a *high-spin state*. When the crystal-field splitting is large compared to the pairing energy, a *low-spin state* is obtained.

Because of this high-spin–low-spin phenomenon there must be a value of the crystal-field strength at which high-spin states are no longer more stable than low-spin states. At such a value of Δ the ground state (as well as excited states) must change. In the correlation diagram, therefore, there must be a point on the abscissa at which an abrupt change

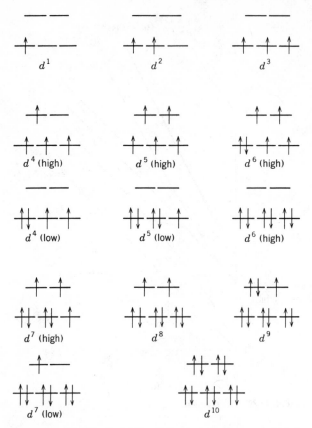

Fig. 11.21 The T_{2g} and E_g^* one-electron levels are occupied by various numbers of electrons in O_h symmetry in ways which depend upon the relative size of the crystal-field splitting Δ_o and the mean pairing energy P. Notice both high- and low-spin configurations for the d^4 to d^7 cases.

in the energy levels takes place. Such abrupt changes can easily be seen in the diagrams of Fig. 11.20, and a demarcation line has been included.

One final consideration will be presented here. There is one important quantitative difference between octahedral and tetrahedral complexes. Tetrahedral complexes possess only four charges, whereas octahedral possess six. Further, the four charges are not arranged as efficiently as in the octahedral case; i.e., the metal orbitals do not point directly at the ligands. Dunn, McClure, and Pearson[1] have shown that this tends to reduce the crystal-field splitting relative to the octahedral case by a

[1] T. M. Dunn, D. S. McClure, and R. G. Pearson, "Some Aspects of Crystal Field Theory," p. 25, Harper & Row, Publishers, Incorporated, New York, 1965.

factor of approximately $\frac{2}{3}$. Hence

$$\Delta_t \approx \frac{4}{6} \cdot \frac{2}{3}\Delta_o$$

or

$$\Delta_t \approx \frac{4}{9}\Delta_o$$

11.6 USE OF CORRELATION DIAGRAMS: SPECTRAL AND MAGNETIC PROPERTIES

In dealing with the interpretation of the ultraviolet and visible spectra of transition-metal compounds it is practical to use a somewhat limited form of correlation diagram developed by L. E. Orgel. The Orgel diagram generally is limited to states originating from the lowest two or three free-ion states. Because of their greater simplicity, these diagrams lend themselves better to the study of spectral transitions. They have been reproduced in Fig. 11.22.

Since most complexes of transition metals absorb light in the visible region, they are colored compounds. The extinction coefficients for the visible transitions are generally quite small for octahedral complexes, 0.01 to 50, and considerably larger for tetrahedral complexes, 10 to 2,000. However, transition-metal compounds also absorb in the ultraviolet, sometimes in a continually rising absorption, with extinction coefficients ranging from 1,000 to 10,000. These spectra are commonly referred to as *charge-transfer spectra* because of the difference in electronic configuration between initial and final state—the transfer of an electron from the ligands to the metal (or vice versa). Such spectra were mentioned in Sec. 10.6 and may be interpreted in terms of the MO diagrams found in Sec. 9.6.

Because they involve only energy levels which arise from the crystal-field splitting of free-ion states, the weak visible transitions are called crystal-field transitions and are of two types: (1) transitions which originate and terminate on states arising from the same free-ion term. These transitions tend to zero value as the crystal-field splitting tends to zero; (2) transitions which terminate on a level arising from a different free-ion state than the state of origin. These transitions tend to the free-ion energy separation as the crystal-field splitting tends to zero. Actually, the energy separations in complexes are usually 70 to 80 per cent of the corresponding separation in the free ion. On the basis of Chap. 10 we can write down two selection rules:

1. *The spin selection rule:* $\Delta S = 0$. Transitions which violate this rule are generally so weak that we can ignore them.

2. *The Laporte rule* (derived from the symmetry selection rule). Transitions between states of the same parity, u or g, are forbidden:

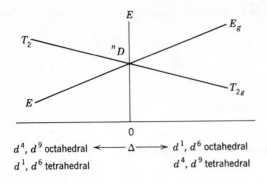

d^4, d^9 octahedral ⟵——Δ——⟶ d^1, d^6 octahedral
d^1, d^6 tetrahedral d^4, d^9 tetrahedral

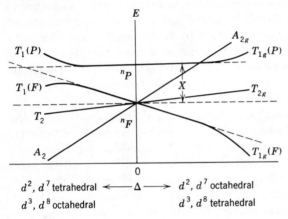

d^2, d^7 tetrahedral ⟵——Δ——⟶ d^2, d^7 octahedral
d^3, d^8 octahedral d^3, d^8 tetrahedral

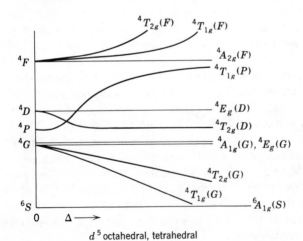

d^5 octahedral, tetrahedral

Fig. 11.22   Orgel diagrams for d electrons in octahedral and tetrahedral symmetry.   (*Taken by permission from T. M. Dunn, D. S. McClure, and R. G. Pearson, "Some Aspects of Crystal Field Theory," pp. 18, 21, and 24, Harper & Row, Publishers, Incorporated, New York, 1965.*)

$u \to g$ and $g \to u$ but $g \not\to g$ and $u \not\to u$. For example, $A_{1g} \to A_{1u}$, but $A_{1u} \not\to A_{1u}$. These transitions become allowed but relatively weak when coupled with a vibrational transition of the proper symmetry (see Sec. 10.4).

Let us now consider a few specific examples. Table 11.11 lists several ions and other useful information, including the number of d electrons.

Table 11.11   Some first-row transition-metal ions and magnetic moments

Ion	No. of d electrons	High-spin complexes‡		Low-spin complexes‡	
		Spin only	Experimental	Spin only	Experimental
Ti^{3+}	1	1.73	1.73		
V^{4+}	1		1.68–1.78		
Ti^{++}	2	2.83	2.75–2.85		
V^{3+}	2		2.75–2.85		
V^{++}	3	3.88	3.80–3.90		
Cr^{3+}	3		3.70–3.90		
Mn^{4+}	3		3.80–4.00		
Cr^{+}	4	4.90	4.75–4.90	2.83	3.20–3.30
Mn^{3+}	4		4.90–5.00		3.18
Mn^{++}	5	5.92	5.65–6.10	1.73	1.80–2.10
Fe^{3+}	5		5.70–6.00		2.00–2.50
Fe^{++}	6	4.90	5.10–5.70		
Co^{3+}	6				
Co^{++}	7	3.88	4.30–5.20	1.73	1.70–2.00
Ni^{3+}	7				1.80–2.00
Ni^{++}	8	2.83	2.80–3.50		
Cu^{++}	9	1.73	1.70–2.20		

Source: Adapted by permission from J. Lewis and R. Wilkins, "Modern Coordination Chemistry," Interscience Publishers, Inc., New York, 1960.

‡ The magnetic moments are given in units of Bohr magnetons.

SPECTRAL PROPERTIES

Both $[Ti(H_2O)_6]^{3+}$ and $[V(H_2O)_6]^{4+}$ are d^1 cases. There is only one spin-allowed transition for these cases, $^2E_g \leftarrow {}^2T_2g$. The spectrum of $[Ti(H_2O)_6]^{3+}$ consists of one broad hump at 20,300 cm^{-1} ($\sim$4900 Å) and a shoulder at $\sim$17,500 cm^{-1}. Both transitions are very weak, with $\epsilon \sim 5$. The double nature of this band is caused by a splitting in the excited state because of the Jahn-Teller effect.[1]

The transition in $[Ti(H_2O)_6]^{3+}$ was first assigned by Ilse and Hart-

[1] A. D. Liehr, *Progr. Inorg. Chem.*, **3**:281 (1962), and T. M. Dunn, The Visible and Ultraviolet Spectra of Complex Compounds, in J. Lewis and R. Wilkins, "Modern Coordination Chemistry," Interscience Publishers, Inc., New York, 1960.

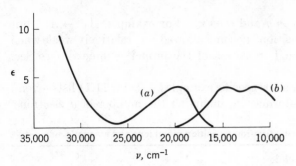

Fig. 11.23 The spectrum of (a) the $[Ti(H_2O)_6]^{++}$ ion in $CsTi(SO_4) \cdot 12H_2O$ and (b) the $[CoF_6]^{3-}$ ion in K_3CoF_6. (*Adapted from T. M. Dunn, D. S. McClure, and R. G. Pearson, "Some Aspects of Crystal Field Theory," p. 40, Harper & Row, Publishers, Incorporated, New York, 1965.*)

mann[1] in 1951.   The Orgel diagram for d^6 shows that a similar transition is possible in the ion $[CoF_6]^{3-}$ as in the compound K_3CoF_6.   The transition occurs at 13,000 cm^{-1}.   The spectra for both $[Ti(H_2O)_6]^{3+}$ and $[CoF_6]^{3-}$ are shown in Fig. 11.23.

The d^4 and d^9 cases may be represented by complexes of Cr^{++}, Mn^{3+}, and Fe^{4+}.   Octahedral complexes of these ions are not common, and theoretical interest in their spectra is low because there is only one predicted transition which can be checked experimentally.   The spectra of $[Cr(H_2O)_6]^{++}$ and $[Cu(H_2O)_6]^{++}$ are shown in Fig. 11.24.

Although the ground state of the d^9 case may be split because of the Jahn-Teller effect, it is possible to assign the transitions in the following

[1] F. E. Ilse and H. Hartmann, *Z. Physik. Chem. Leipzig,* **197**:239 (1951).

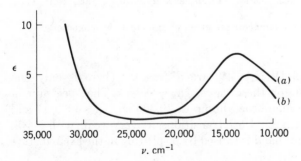

Fig. 11.24 The spectrum of (a) $[Cr(H_2O)_6]^{++}$ and (b) $[Cu(H_2O)_6]^{++}$. (*Adapted from T. M. Dunn, D. S. McClure, and R. G. Pearson, "Some Aspects of Crystal Field Theory," p. 41, Harper & Row, Publishers, Incorporated, New York, 1965.*)

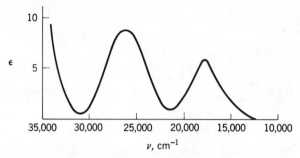

Fig. 11.25 The spectrum of the $[V(H_2O_6)]^{3+}$ ion. (*Adapted from T. M. Dunn, D. S. McClure, and R. G. Pearson, "Some Aspects of Crystal Field Theory," p. 46, Harper & Row, Incorporated, Publishers, New York, 1965.*)

complexes:

Compound	ν, cm^{-1}
$[Cu(H_2O)_6]^{++}$	12,600
$[Cu(NH_3)_6]^{++}$	15,100
$[Cu(en)_3]^{++}$	16,400

These three complex ions illustrate the spectrochemical series in that the crystal-field splitting Δ_o increases as follows: $H_2O < NH_3 <$ ethylenediamine.

For the d^2 and d^7 cases let us cite $[V(H_2O)_6]^{3+}$ and $[Co(H_2O)_6]^{++}$. The spectrum of $[V(H_2O)_6]^{3+}$ is shown in Fig. 11.25 and assignments have been made as follows:

Transition	ν, cm^{-1}
$^3T_{1g}(F) \leftarrow {}^3T_{2g}(F)$	17,700
$^3T_{1g}(F) \leftarrow {}^3T_{1g}(P)$	25,800
$^3T_{1g}(F) \leftarrow {}^3A_{2g}$	37,000

The assignments appear consistent, but the predicted position of ν_3 falls in the region of a very strong charge-transfer band and hence cannot be verified.   The following assignments have been made for the $[Co(H_2O)_6]^{++}$ complex ion:

Transition	ν, cm^{-1}
$^4T_{1g}(F) \leftarrow {}^4T_{2g}(F)$	8,000–9,000
$^4T_{1g}(F) \leftarrow {}^2E_g$	11,000
$^4T_{1g}(F) \leftarrow {}^4A_{2g}$	16,000–18,000
$^4T_{1g}(F) \leftarrow {}^4T_{1g}(P)$	20,000–21,000

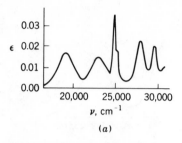
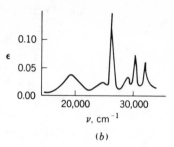

Fig. 11.26   The spectrum of (a) the $[Mn(H_2O)_6]^{++}$ ion as in $Mn(SO_4)_2 \cdot 7H_2O$ and (b) of MnF_2.

These assignments appear consistent, but no independent checks have been made.

Perhaps the most thoroughly studied group of complexes are those of d^3 and d^8 configurations.   The most well known d^3 case is the Cr^{3+} in an Al_2O_3 matrix (commonly called ruby).   The $[Cr(H_2O)_6]^{3+}$ ion has also been studied, and the assignments for both cases are given here.

Ruby	ν, cm^{-1}	Hexahydrate	ν, cm^{-1}
$^2E_g \leftarrow {}^4A_{2g}$	15,000	$^4T_{2g} \leftarrow {}^4A_{2g}$	17,500
$^2T_{1g} \leftarrow {}^4A_{2g}$	15,500	$^4T_{1g}(F) \leftarrow {}^4A_{2g}$	24,700
$^2T_{2g} \leftarrow {}^4A_{2g}$	22,000	$^4T_{1g}(P) \leftarrow {}^4A_{2g}$	37,000

The $[Ni(NH_3)_6]^{++}$ and $[Ni(H_2O)_6]^{++}$ complexes are d^8 cases, and assignments have been made as follows

Transition	ν, cm^{-1}	
	Hexahydrate	Hexammine
$^3T_{2g} \leftarrow {}^3A_{2g}$	8,600	10,700
$^3T_{1g}(F) \leftarrow {}^3A_{2g}$	13,500	17,500
$^3T_{1g}(P) \leftarrow {}^3A_{2g}$	25,300	28,200

In the d^5 case the spectrum of $[Mn(H_2O)_6]^{++}$ is important because it possesses a very sharp transition, as shown in Fig. 11.26 along with that of MnF_2.   The sharp transition must take place between levels which are independent of crystal-field strength because for other transitions there is a range of crystal-field splitting values over which groups of ions may absorb energy, thus creating broad bands.   A glance at the Orgel diagram for d^5 shows that there are several quartet terms which remain constant as a function of Δ.   The following assignments[1] have been made for $[Mn(H_2O)_6]^{++}$:

Transition	ν, cm^{-1}
$^4T_{1g}(G) \leftarrow {}^6A_{1g}$	18,800
$^4T_{2g}(G) \leftarrow {}^6A_{1g}$	23,000
$^4E_g(G) \leftarrow {}^6A_{1g}$	24,900
$^4A_{1g}(G) \leftarrow {}^6A_{1g}$	25,150
$^4T_{2g}(D) \leftarrow {}^6A_{1g}$	28,000
$^4E_g(D) \leftarrow {}^6A_{1g}$	29,700
$^4T_{1g}(P) \leftarrow {}^6A_{1g}$	32,400
$^4A_{2g}(F) \leftarrow {}^6A_{1g}$	35,400
$^4T_{1g}(F) \leftarrow {}^6A_{1g}$	36,900
$^4T_{2g}(F) \leftarrow {}^6A_{1g}$	40,600

We have dealt in more detail with octahedral complexes because spectral assignments for tetrahedral complexes are far less certain.   Dunn, McClure, and Pearson[2] state that only two spectral transitions have been assigned with certainty for tetrahedral complexes: (1) in $[MnCl_4]^{--}$ the $^4A_1(G) \leftarrow A_2$ transition is assigned to the band at 22,450 cm^{-1}; (2) in $[CoCl_4]^{--}$ the $^4T_1 \leftarrow {}^4A_2$ transition is assigned to the band at 6300 cm^{-1}.

In considering the spectra of tetrahedral complexes two features are readily observable.   The intensities are generally larger since the transitions are allowed by the Laporte rule (T_d does not have a center of inversion).   Also the transitions occur at lower energy because $\Delta_t \approx \frac{4}{9}\Delta_o$.

Earlier we alluded to the spectrochemical series of ligands which represents the relative splitting caused by the various ligands.   Following is a list of many common ligands: $I^- < Br^- < -SCN^- \approx Cl^- < NO_3^- < F^- <$ urea $\approx OH^- \approx ONO^- \approx HCOO^- < C_2O_4^{-2} < H_2O < -NCS^- <$ glycine$^- \approx EDTA^{-4} <$ pyridine $\approx NH_3 <$ ethylenediamine $< -NO_2^- \ll CN^-$.

MAGNETIC PROPERTIES

Considerable attention has been given to the magnetic properties of transition-metal complexes.   Valuable information concerning the number of unpaired electrons, oxidation state, and bond type can be obtained from a study of magnetic properties.   We shall, however, only touch upon the first of the three topics.

First, we must relate the experimental quantity, magnetic susceptibility, to theoretical quantities such as quantum numbers and number of

[1] C. K. Jorgensen, *Acta Chem. Scand.*, **11**:53 (1957), and L. E. Orgel, *J. Chem. Phys.*, **23**:1004 (1955).

[2] *Op. cit.*, p. 52.

unpaired electrons.   The total molar magnetic susceptibility χ is defined as

$$\chi = \frac{N^2\mu^2}{3RT}$$

where N^2 = Avogadro's number
μ = permanent magnetic moment
R = molar gas constant
T = temperature, °K

Rearranging and solving for μ, we can write the effective magnetic moment as

$$\mu_{eff} = 2.84 \sqrt{\chi T}$$

The resulting effective magnetic moment is in units of Bohr magnetons (BM); 9.27×10^{-21} erg/gauss ($= eh/4\pi mc$).

Using the symbolism developed earlier, the total spin-angular-momentum quantum number S is given as $S = \sum_i s_i$, and the total orbital-angular-momentum quantum number L is given as $L = \sum_i l_i$.   We should point out that $S = n/2$, where n is the number of unpaired electrons. There are three factors related to the paramagnetism of a complex ion:[1] (1) the number of unpaired electrons, (2) the upper electronic states, which are separated in energy from the ground state by less than $\Delta E = kT$, and (3) both the symmetry and strength of the ligand field.

Let us consider three cases.[2]

1. *Large multiplet separation.*   When the unpaired electrons are well shielded from the ligand field and excited states are not low-lying ($\Delta E \gg kT$), the spin-orbit coupling of the unpaired electrons is significant. There will be $2L + 1$ values of J ranging from $L - S$ to $L + S$ (or $2S + 1$ values if $S < L$).   In this case

$$\mu_{eff} = g \sqrt{J(J + 1)} \qquad \text{BM}$$

where the g factor (Landé g factor) is given as

$$g = 1 + \frac{J(J + 1) + S(S + 1) - L(L + 1)}{2J(J + 1)}$$

For this case each level is split into $2J + 1$ components in a magnetic field, and each component is separated from the next by $\Delta E = g\beta H$, where

[1] M. C. Day and J. Selbin, "Theoretical Inorganic Chemistry," p. 302, Reinhold Publishing Corporation, New York, 1962.
[2] L. E. Orgel, *J. Chem. Phys.*, **23**:1004 (1955); C. K. Jorgensen, *Acta Chem. Scand.*, **11**:53 (1957); L. J. Heidt, G. F. Koster, and A. M. Johnson, *J. Am. Chem. Soc.*, **80**:6471 (1959).

$\beta = eh/4\pi mc$ and H is the magnetic field strength.   The magnetic prop- erties of heavy-metal complexes, particularly rare earths, may be described in this manner since the partially filled shells lie inside the filled shells.

2. *Small multiplet separation.*   When the energy separations between successive J states become small compared to kT, spin-orbit coupling becomes negligible.   The spin and orbital angular momenta act inde- pendently, and μ_{eff} is given as

$$\mu_{eff} = \sqrt{4S(S+1) + L(L+1)} \quad \text{BM}$$

3. *Spin only.*   However, in some complexes, particularly those of the first transition series, the orbital angular momentum appears to be unimportant, and μ_{eff} may be written as

$$\mu_{eff} = \sqrt{4S(S+1)} \quad \text{BM}$$

Since $S = n/2$,

$$\mu_{eff} = \sqrt{n(n+2)} \quad \text{BM}$$

and we have a direct relation between experimental magnetic suscepti- bility and the number of unpaired electrons.

A summary of some experimental and theoretical results is presented in Table 11.11.   In Sec. 11.6 we pointed out that the number of unpaired electrons for d^4 to d^7 cases in O_h symmetry is dependent upon Δ_o and, hence both high- and low-spin cases are possible.   This phenomenon may be observed in the table.

11.7 POLARIZATION OF ELECTRONIC AND VIBRONIC SPECTRA

Although we have already discussed polarization of electronic spectra in Chap. 10, we shall give here a brief review, along with two examples of importance in the study of the spectra of metal complexes.   For com- pounds belonging to point groups in which the electric-dipole operators x, y, and z do not all belong to the same irreducible representation, the absorption of polarized light may be different for different directions of polarization.   That is, light absorbed in a transition characterized by an irreducible representation which transforms as the cartesian component x is polarized parallel to x.   Hence, in O_h, where x, y, and z all belong to T_{1u}, there is no special direction of polarization, but in D_{4h}, where z belongs to A_{2u} and (x, y) to E_u, there may be a difference in absorption between light polarized parallel to the fourfold axis and light polarized perpen- dicular to the fourfold axis.

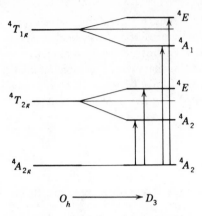

Fig. 11.27 Lowering the symmetry of an O_h complex to D_3 symmetry produces a splitting of energy levels. The D_3 energy-level diagram can be used to understand the electronic spectrum of the $[Cr(C_2O_4)_3]^{3-}$ ion.

For an example let us consider the trisoxalato complex[1] of Cr^{3+}, $[Cr(C_2O_4)_3]^{3-}$, whose structure belongs to point group D_3. The Cr^{3+} ion is a d^3 case, and from the Orgel diagram we see that the states of interest (in O_h) are A_{2g}, T_{2g}, and T_{1g}. Viewing the D_3 symmetry as a distortion of O_h symmetry, we can determine the diagram for D_3 shown in Fig. 11.27. The possible transitions are indicated by arrows. Using the methods of Sec. 10.3, the spectral activity of these transitions has been determined and listed in Table 11.12. Experimentally, Piper and Carlin showed that the ratio of extinction coefficients for polarized light was very small: $\epsilon_{\parallel}/\epsilon_{\perp} = 0.06$, a confirmation of the spectral assignments.

[1] Ballhausen, *op. cit.*; T. S. Piper and R. L. Carlin, *J. Chem. Phys.*, **35**: 1809 (1961).

Table 11.12   Spectral transition in $[Cr(C_2O_4)_3]^{3-}$

Transition	Activity	Polarization‡
$^4A_1 \leftarrow {}^4A_2$	Allowed	z or $\parallel$
$^4A_2 \leftarrow {}^4A_2$	Forbidden	
$^4E \leftarrow {}^4A_2$	Allowed	(x, y) or $\perp$

‡ z or $\parallel$ means transition is allowed for light polarized parallel to the threefold axis; (x, y) or $\perp$ means transition is allowed for light polarized perpendicular to the threefold axis.

Let us now consider the possibilities for violation of the electronic symmetry selection rules through vibronic coupling. According to Sec. 10.4, the direct product of the representations of the upper electronic state and the representations of the cartesian components x, y, z must contain the representations of normal modes of vibration if vibronic coupling may occur. The required direct products for $[Cr(C_2O_4)_3]^{3-}$ are as follows:

Γ_μ	Upper electronic state	Product $(\Gamma_\mu \Gamma_{V_i})$
$A_2 + E$	A_2	$A_1 + E$
$A_2 + E$	E	$A_1 + A_2 + E$

Vibrational analysis of the complex ion shows that normal modes belong to A_1, A_2, and E representations. Hence, all electronic transitions would be allowed under vibronic coupling *with* absorption unaffected by polarization, i.e., allowed for light polarized both parallel and perpendicular to the threefold axis. Since it is observed experimentally that the polarization ratio $\epsilon_\parallel / \epsilon_\perp$ is 0.06, vibronic coupling is unimportant in the ion $[Cr(C_2O_4)_3]^{3-}$. Further, the combined polarization and vibronic coupling analysis tend to confirm the D_3 point-group structure for $[Cr(C_2O_4)_3]^{3-}$.

A much different result is obtained in the vibronic polarization analysis of *trans*-$[Co(en)_2Cl_2]Cl$.[1] The molecular structure of the cobalt complex is shown in Fig. 11.28. It is obvious that the symmetry of the overall structure (including hydrogen atoms) is D_{2h} but, as Ballhausen[2] points

[1] S. Yamada, A. Nakahara, Y. Shimura, and T. Tsuchida, *Bull. Chem. Soc. Japan,* **28**:222 (1955); C. J. Ballhausen, *ibid.*, p. 193; F. A. Cotton, "Chemical Applications of Group Theory," pp. 234–236, John Wiley & Sons, Inc., New York, 1963.
[2] C. J. Ballhausen and W. Moffitt, *J. Inorg. Nucl. Chem.*, **3**:178 (1956).

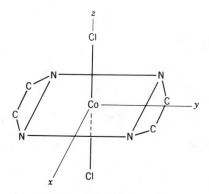

Fig. 11.28 The molecular structure of the complex ion $[Co(en)_2Cl_2]^+$, not showing the hydrogen atoms.

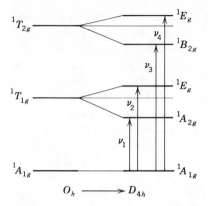

Fig. 11.29 The energy-level diagram for $[Co(en)_2Cl_2]^+$ can be obtained as a tetragonal distortion of O_h to D_{4h}. The splitting pattern and possible spectral transitions are shown here.

out, the effective symmetry is D_{4h}. This means that only the nitrogen atoms of the ethylenediamine ligands are involved in the vibronic coupling. The aliphatic CH_2 linking groups play only a minor role and may be excluded from symmetry considerations.

The possible electronic transitions are shown in Fig. 11.29, and the direct products of the dipole-moment components and the various excited states are as follows:

Transition	$\Gamma_\mu V_i$	
	$\Gamma_z V_i$	$\Gamma_{x,y} V_i$
$A_{2g} \leftarrow A_{1g}$	A_{1u}	E_u
$B_{2g} \leftarrow A_{1g}$	B_{1u}	E_u
$E_g \leftarrow A_{1g}$	E_u	$A_{1u} + A_{2u} + B_{1u} + B_{2u}$

Vibrational analysis of the D_{4h} system of the $[Co(en)_2Cl_2]^{++}$ ion shows that the normal modes belong to the following representations: A_{1g}, B_{1g}, B_{2g}, E_g, A_{2u}, B_{1u}, and E_u. In D_{4h}, $\Gamma_\mu = A_{2u} + E_u$. Thus, we can prepare the following table of spectral activity.

Transition	Activity and polarization	
	Parallel	Perpendicular
$A_{2g} \leftarrow A_{1g}$	Forbidden	Allowed
$B_{2g} \leftarrow A_{1g}$	Allowed	Allowed
$E_g \leftarrow A_{1g}$	Allowed	Allowed

The spectrum of $[Co(en)_2Cl_2]^+$ has been assigned as follows:

Transition	ν, cm^{-1}	Polarization
$A_{2g} \leftarrow A_{1g}$	16,000	Parallel
$E_g \leftarrow A_{1g}$	22,000	Both
$\left.\begin{array}{l} E_g \leftarrow A_{1g} \\ B_{2g} \leftarrow A_{1g} \end{array}\right\}$	27,000–32,000	Both

This agreement of predicted spectral properties and experimental results is confirmation of the proposed importance of vibronic coupling in this compound.

PROBLEMS

11.1. Using the method developed in Sec. 11.2, derive the term symbols for (*a*) a $3d^2$ electronic configuration and (*b*) a $3d^5$ electronic configuration.

11.2. Using the mathematical form of d orbitals given in Chap. 8, show that the $d_{x^2-y^2}$ orbital has an equivalent spatial orientation to the d_{z^2} orbital.

11.3. (*a*) Determine the possible spectroscopic states for the electronic configuration $3d^2 4p^1$.

(*b*) Determine the possible spectroscopic states for the electronic configuration $3d^3$.

11.4. Show that the following table is correct for the ground state for each d^n configuration.

d^1	d^2	d^3	d^4	d^5	d^6	d^7	d^8	d^9
^2D	^3F	^4F	^5D	^6S	^5D	^4F	^3F	^2D

11.5. Derive Eq. (11.2) from Eq. (11.1).

11.6. (*a*) Use Fig. 11.30 to refer the five d orbitals to the threefold axis of the octahedron. Write the d orbitals in the new coordinate system as linear combinations of the usual form of d orbitals. There will still be a triply degenerate T_{2g} and a doubly degenerate E_g orbital.

(*b*) Now consider a distortion of the octahedron along the threefold axis to point group D_{3d}. Determine the splitting of the d orbitals (see Fig. 11.11).

11.7. Using the crystal-field-splitting diagram for the square planar complex in Fig. 11.10, determine the number of unpaired electrons in square planar $Ni(CO)_4$ and in $[PtCl_4]^{--}$.

11.8. Evidence from x-ray crystallography shows that complexes of copper such as $[Cu(H_2O)_6]^{++}$ are distorted from O_h symmetry in that two trans

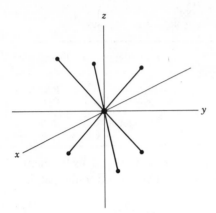

Fig. 11.30 A cartesian coordinate system used to refer the $3d$ orbitals to the threefold axes of an octahedron which lie along the x, y, and z axes.

ligands are not as close as the other four to the metal ion. Use crystal-field theory to develop a crystal-field-splitting diagram which accounts for the spectrum of $[Cu(H_2O)_6]^{++}$.

11.9. Determine the qualitative correlation diagram for the d^3 case in the O_h point group. How is this diagram related to the d^3 case in T_d symmetry?

11.10. Consider the problem of determining the spin multiplicities of the states derived from T_{2g}^2 in O_h symmetry by using the descent-in-symmetry method in subgroup C_{2h}.

11.11. Repeat the method in Prob. 11.10 for T_{2g}^2 in point group T_d.

11.12. Use crystal-field theory to show why $[Cu(H_2O)_6]^{++}$ is pale blue-green, $[Cu(NH_3)_6]^{++}$ is deep blue, and anhydrous $CuSO_4$ is colorless.

11.13. Speculate as to the difference between nickel hydrates and nickel in silicate glasses, a difference which changes the color from pale green in the hydrate to deep purple in the glasses.

11.14. Figure 11.31 shows the spectrum[1] of a tetrahedral complex of Mn^{++}. Compare this spectrum to that in Fig. 11.26 and discuss why the spectra are so similar. Account for any observed differences.

11.15. Using quantitative crystal-field theory it is possible to determine energy expressions for spectral transitions in terms of the crystal-field splitting Δ and the separation in energy between the free-ion states X. For $[V(H_2O)_6]^{3+}$ these equations are

$$E[^3T_{1g}(F) \leftarrow {}^3T_{1g}(P)] = (X^2 + \tfrac{6}{5}\Delta X + \Delta^2)^{\frac{1}{2}}$$

$$E[^3T_{1g}(F) \leftarrow {}^3T_{2g}(F)] = -\tfrac{1}{2}X + \tfrac{1}{2}\Delta + (\tfrac{1}{2}X^2 + \tfrac{6}{5}\Delta X + \Delta^2)^{\frac{1}{2}}$$

[1] S. Buffagni and T. M. Dunn, *Nature*, **188**:937 (1960).

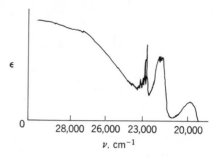

Fig. 11.31 The partial spectrum of a tetrahedral complex of Mn^{++}.

The energies of the first and second transitions are 25,200 and 17,000 cm^{-1}, respectively. Solve for Δ and X. Compare X to the known value of the separation of the ^3P and ^3F in the free V^{3+} ion.

11.16. Using the methods of Sec. 11.2, determine the spectroscopic states for (a) a $4f^1$ electronic configuration and (b) a $4f^2$ electronic configuration.

11.17. (a) Determine which d^n cases may exhibit both a high-spin and low-spin configuration in T_d symmetry.

(b) Discuss the high-spin–low-spin problem in square planar complexes.

11.18. (a) Confirm the normal mode analysis for $[Cr(C_2O_4)_3]^{3-}$ as discussed in Sec. 11.8.

(b) Confirm the crystal-field splitting diagram shown in Fig. 11.27.

(c) Determine the possible spectral transitions for $[Cr(C_2O_4)_3]^{3-}$.

11.19. (a) Perform the normal mode analysis for the D_{4h} form of the trans $[Co(en)_2Cl_2]^{++}$ ion as discussed in Sec. 11.7.

(b) Confirm the table of spectral activity given in the text.

REFERENCES

Ballhausen, C. J.: "Introduction to Ligand Field Theory," McGraw-Hill Book Company, New York, 1962.

Dunn, T. M., D. S. McClure, and R. G. Pearson: "Some Aspects of Crystal Field Theory," Harper & Row Publishers, Incorporated, New York, 1965.

Figgis, B. N.: "Introduction to Ligand Fields," John Wiley & Sons, Inc., New York, 1966.

Griffith, J. S.: "The Theory of Transition Metal Ions," Cambridge University Press, New York, 1961.

Orgel, Leslie E.: "An Introduction to Transition-metal Chemistry: Ligand Field Theory," Methuen & Co. Ltd., London. 1960.

appendix 1
character
tables

See Secs. 6.3 and 6.4 for an explanation of symbols used in these tables.[1]

TYPE I

C_1	E	
A	1	all

C_s	E	σ_h		
A'	1	1	x, y, R_z	x^2, y^2, z^2, xy
A''	1	-1	z, R_x, R_y	yz, xz

C_i	E	i		
A_g	1	1	R_x, R_y, R_z	$x^2, y^2, z^2, xy, xz, yz$
A_u	1	-1	x, y, z	

[1] Tables in Appendix I taken by permission from E. Bright Wilson, Jr., John C. Decius, and Paul C. Cross, "Molecular Vibrations", pp. 323–330, McGraw-Hill Book Company, New York, 1955.

TYPE II

THE C_n GROUPS

C_2	E	C_2		
A	1	1	z, R_z	x^2, y^2, z^2, xy
B	1	-1	x, y, R_x, R_y	yz, xz

C_3	E	C_3	$C_3{}^2$	$\epsilon = \exp(2\pi i/3)$	
A	1	1	1	z, R_z	$x^2 + y^2, z^2$
E	$\begin{Bmatrix} 1 \\ 1 \end{Bmatrix}$	$\begin{matrix} \epsilon \\ \epsilon^* \end{matrix}$	$\begin{Bmatrix} \epsilon^* \\ \epsilon \end{Bmatrix}$	$(x, y); (R_x, R_y)$	$(x^2 - y^2, xy); (yz, xz)$

C_4	E	C_4	C_2	$C_4{}^3$	$i = \sqrt{-1}$	
A	1	1	1	1	z, R_z	$x^2 + y^2, z^2$
B	1	-1	1	-1		$x^2 - y^2, xy$
E	$\begin{Bmatrix} 1 \\ 1 \end{Bmatrix}$	$\begin{matrix} i \\ -i \end{matrix}$	$\begin{matrix} -1 \\ -1 \end{matrix}$	$\begin{Bmatrix} -i \\ i \end{Bmatrix}$	$(x, y); (R_x, R_y)$	(yz, xz)

C_5	E	C_5	$C_5{}^2$	$C_5{}^3$	$C_5{}^4$	$\epsilon = \exp(2\pi i/5)$	
A	1	1	1	1	1	z, R_z	$x^2 + y^2, z^2$
E_1	$\begin{Bmatrix} 1 \\ 1 \end{Bmatrix}$	$\begin{matrix} \epsilon \\ \epsilon^* \end{matrix}$	$\begin{matrix} \epsilon^2 \\ \epsilon^{2*} \end{matrix}$	$\begin{matrix} \epsilon^{2*} \\ \epsilon^2 \end{matrix}$	$\begin{Bmatrix} \epsilon^* \\ \epsilon \end{Bmatrix}$	$(x, y); (R_x, R_y)$	(yz, xz)
E_2	$\begin{Bmatrix} 1 \\ 1 \end{Bmatrix}$	$\begin{matrix} \epsilon^2 \\ \epsilon^{2*} \end{matrix}$	$\begin{matrix} \epsilon^* \\ \epsilon \end{matrix}$	$\begin{matrix} \epsilon \\ \epsilon^* \end{matrix}$	$\begin{Bmatrix} \epsilon^{2*} \\ \epsilon^2 \end{Bmatrix}$		$(x^2 - y^2, xy)$

C_6	E	C_6	C_3	C_2	$C_3{}^2$	$C_6{}^5$	$\epsilon = \exp(2\pi i/6)$	
A	1	1	1	1	1	1	z, R_z	$x^2 + y^2, z^2$
B	1	-1	1	-1	1	-1		
E_1	$\begin{Bmatrix} 1 \\ 1 \end{Bmatrix}$	$\begin{matrix} \epsilon \\ \epsilon^* \end{matrix}$	$\begin{matrix} -\epsilon^* \\ -\epsilon \end{matrix}$	$\begin{matrix} -1 \\ -1 \end{matrix}$	$\begin{matrix} -\epsilon \\ -\epsilon^* \end{matrix}$	$\begin{Bmatrix} \epsilon^* \\ \epsilon \end{Bmatrix}$	(x, y) (R_x, R_y)	(xz, yz)
E_2	$\begin{Bmatrix} 1 \\ 1 \end{Bmatrix}$	$\begin{matrix} -\epsilon^* \\ -\epsilon \end{matrix}$	$\begin{matrix} -\epsilon \\ -\epsilon^* \end{matrix}$	$\begin{matrix} 1 \\ 1 \end{matrix}$	$\begin{matrix} -\epsilon^* \\ -\epsilon \end{matrix}$	$\begin{Bmatrix} -\epsilon \\ -\epsilon^* \end{Bmatrix}$		$(x^2 - y^2, xy)$

C_7	E	C_7	$C_7{}^2$	$C_7{}^3$	$C_7{}^4$	$C_7{}^5$	$C_7{}^6$		$\epsilon = \exp(2\pi i/7)$
A	1	1	1	1	1	1	1	z, R_z	$x^2 + y^2, z^2$
E_1	$\begin{cases}1\\1\end{cases}$	$\begin{matrix}\epsilon\\\epsilon^*\end{matrix}$	$\begin{matrix}\epsilon^2\\\epsilon^{2*}\end{matrix}$	$\begin{matrix}\epsilon^3\\\epsilon^{3*}\end{matrix}$	$\begin{matrix}\epsilon^{3*}\\\epsilon^3\end{matrix}$	$\begin{matrix}\epsilon^{2*}\\\epsilon^2\end{matrix}$	$\begin{matrix}\epsilon^*\\\epsilon\end{matrix}\Big\}$	$\begin{matrix}(x, y)\\(R_x, R_y)\end{matrix}$	(xz, yz)
E_2	$\begin{cases}1\\1\end{cases}$	$\begin{matrix}\epsilon^2\\\epsilon^{2*}\end{matrix}$	$\begin{matrix}\epsilon^{3*}\\\epsilon^3\end{matrix}$	$\begin{matrix}\epsilon^*\\\epsilon\end{matrix}$	$\begin{matrix}\epsilon\\\epsilon^*\end{matrix}$	$\begin{matrix}\epsilon^3\\\epsilon^{3*}\end{matrix}$	$\begin{matrix}\epsilon^{2*}\\\epsilon^2\end{matrix}\Big\}$		
E_3	$\begin{cases}1\\1\end{cases}$	$\begin{matrix}\epsilon^3\\\epsilon^{3*}\end{matrix}$	$\begin{matrix}\epsilon^*\\\epsilon\end{matrix}$	$\begin{matrix}\epsilon^2\\\epsilon^{2*}\end{matrix}$	$\begin{matrix}\epsilon^{2*}\\\epsilon^2\end{matrix}$	$\begin{matrix}\epsilon\\\epsilon^*\end{matrix}$	$\begin{matrix}\epsilon^{3*}\\\epsilon^3\end{matrix}\Big\}$		$(x^2 - y^2, xy)$

C_8	E	C_8	C_4	C_2	$C_4{}^3$	$C_8{}^3$	$C_8{}^5$	$C_8{}^7$		$\epsilon = \exp(2\pi i/8)$
A	1	1	1	1	1	1	1	1	z, R_z	$x^2 + y^2, z^2$
B	1	-1	1	1	1	-1	-1	-1		
E_1	$\begin{cases}1\\1\end{cases}$	$\begin{matrix}\epsilon\\\epsilon^*\end{matrix}$	$\begin{matrix}i\\-i\end{matrix}$	$\begin{matrix}-1\\-1\end{matrix}$	$\begin{matrix}-i\\i\end{matrix}$	$\begin{matrix}-\epsilon^*\\-\epsilon\end{matrix}$	$\begin{matrix}-\epsilon\\-\epsilon^*\end{matrix}$	$\begin{matrix}\epsilon^*\\\epsilon\end{matrix}\Big\}$	$\begin{matrix}(x, y)\\(R_x, R_y)\end{matrix}$	(xz, yz)
E_2	$\begin{cases}1\\1\end{cases}$	$\begin{matrix}i\\-i\end{matrix}$	$\begin{matrix}-1\\-1\end{matrix}$	$\begin{matrix}1\\1\end{matrix}$	$\begin{matrix}-1\\-1\end{matrix}$	$\begin{matrix}-i\\i\end{matrix}$	$\begin{matrix}i\\-i\end{matrix}$	$\begin{matrix}-i\\i\end{matrix}\Big\}$		
E_3	$\begin{cases}1\\1\end{cases}$	$\begin{matrix}-\epsilon\\-\epsilon^*\end{matrix}$	$\begin{matrix}i\\-i\end{matrix}$	$\begin{matrix}-1\\-1\end{matrix}$	$\begin{matrix}-i\\i\end{matrix}$	$\begin{matrix}\epsilon^*\\\epsilon\end{matrix}$	$\begin{matrix}\epsilon\\\epsilon^*\end{matrix}$	$\begin{matrix}-\epsilon^*\\-\epsilon\end{matrix}\Big\}$		$(x^2 - y^2, xy)$

THE D_n GROUPS

D_2	E	$C_2(z)$	$C_2(y)$	$C_2(x)$		
A	1	1	1	1		x^2, y^2, z^2
B_1	1	1	-1	-1	z, R_z	xy
B_2	1	-1	1	-1	y, R_y	xz
B_3	1	-1	-1	1	x, R_x	yz

D_3	E	$2C_3$	$3C_2$		
A_1	1	1	1		$x^2 + y^2, z^2$
A_2	1	1	-1	z, R_z	
E	2	-1	0	$(x, y); (R_x, R_y)$	$(x^2 - y^2, xy); (xz, yz)$

D_4	E	$2C_4$	$C_2 (= C_4{}^2)$	$2C_2$	$2C_2''$		
A_1	1	1	1	1	1		$x^2 + y^2, z^2$
A_2	1	1	1	-1	-1	z, R_z	
B_1	1	-1	1	1	-1		$x^2 - y^2$
B_2	1	-1	1	-1	1		xy
E	2	0	-2	0	0	$(x, y); (R_x, R_y)$	(xz, yz)

D_5	E	$2C_5$	$2C_5{}^2$	$5C_2$		
A_1	1	1	1	1		$x^2 + y^2,\ z^2$
A_2	1	1	1	-1	$z,\ R_z$	
E_1	2	$2\cos 72°$	$2\cos 144°$	0	$(x,\ y);\ (R_x,\ R_y)$	$(xz,\ yz)$
E_2	2	$2\cos 144°$	$2\cos 72°$	0		$(x^2 - y^2,\ xy)$

D_6	E	$2C_6$	$2C_3$	C_2	$3C_2'$	$3C_2''$		
A_1	1	1	1	1	1	1		$x^2 + y^2,\ z^2$
A_2	1	1	1	1	-1	-1	$z,\ R_z$	
B_1	1	-1	1	-1	1	-1		
B_2	1	-1	1	-1	-1	1		
E_1	2	1	-1	-2	0	0	$(x,\ y);\ (R_x,\ R_y)$	$(xz,\ yz)$
E_2	2	-1	-1	2	0	0		$(x^2 - y^2,\ xy)$

THE C_{nv} GROUPS

C_{2v}	E	C_2	$\sigma_v(xz)$	$\sigma_v'(yz)$		
A_1	1	1	1	1	z	$x^2,\ y^2,\ z^2$
A_2	1	1	-1	-1	R_z	xy
B_1	1	-1	1	-1	$x,\ R_y$	xz
B_2	1	-1	-1	1	$y,\ R_x$	yz

C_{3v}	E	$2C_3$	$3\sigma_v$		
A_1	1	1	1	z	$x^2 + y^2,\ z^2$
A_2	1	1	-1	R_z	
E	2	-1	0	$(x,\ y);\ (R_x,\ R_y)$	$(x^2 - y^2,\ xy);\ (xz,\ yz)$

C_{4v}	E	$2C_4$	C_2	$2\sigma_v$	$2\sigma_d$		
A_1	1	1	1	1	1	z	$x^2 + y^2,\ z^2$
A_2	1	1	1	-1	-1	R_z	
B_1	1	-1	1	1	-1		$x^2 - y^2$
B_2	1	-1	1	-1	1		xy
E	2	0	-2	0	0	$(x,\ y);\ (R_x,\ R_y)$	$(xz,\ yz)$

C_{5v}	E	$2C_5$	$2C_5^2$	$5\sigma_v$		
A_1	1	1	1	1	z	$x^2 + y^2, z^2$
A_2	1	1	1	-1	R_z	
E_1	2	$2\cos 72°$	$2\cos 144°$	0	(x, y); (R_x, R_y)	(xz, yz)
E_2	2	$2\cos 144°$	$2\cos 72°$	0		$(x^2 - y^2, xy)$

C_{6v}	E	$2C_6$	$2C_3$	C_2	$3\sigma_v$	$3\sigma_d$		
A_1	1	1	1	1	1	1	z	$x^2 + y^2, z^2$
A_2	1	1	1	1	-1	-1	R_z	
B_1	1	-1	1	-1	1	-1		
B_2	1	-1	1	-1	-1	1		
E_1	2	1	-1	-2	0	0	(x, y); (R_x, R_y)	(xz, yz)
E_2	2	-1	-1	2	0	0		$(x^2 - y^2, xy)$

THE C_{nh} GROUPS

C_{2h}	E	C_2	i	σ_h		
A_g	1	1	1	1	R_z	x^2, y^2, z^2, xy
B_g	1	-1	1	-1	R_x, R_y	xz, yz
A_u	1	1	-1	-1	z	
B_u	1	-1	-1	1	x, y	

C_{3h}	E	C_3	C_3^2	σ_h	S_3	S_3^5		$\epsilon = \exp(2\pi i/3)$
A'	1	1	1	1	1	1	R_z	$x^2 + y^2, z^2$
E'	$\begin{cases}1 \\ 1\end{cases}$	$\begin{matrix}\epsilon \\ \epsilon^*\end{matrix}$	$\begin{matrix}\epsilon^* \\ \epsilon\end{matrix}$	$\begin{matrix}1 \\ 1\end{matrix}$	$\begin{matrix}\epsilon \\ \epsilon^*\end{matrix}$	$\begin{matrix}\epsilon^* \\ \epsilon\end{matrix}$	(x, y)	$(x^2 - y^2, xy)$
A''	1	1	1	-1	-1	-1	z	
E''	$\begin{cases}1 \\ 1\end{cases}$	$\begin{matrix}\epsilon \\ \epsilon^*\end{matrix}$	$\begin{matrix}\epsilon^* \\ \epsilon\end{matrix}$	$\begin{matrix}-1 \\ -1\end{matrix}$	$\begin{matrix}-\epsilon \\ -\epsilon^*\end{matrix}$	$\begin{matrix}-\epsilon^* \\ -\epsilon\end{matrix}$	(R_x, R_y)	(xz, yz)

C_{4h}	E	C_4	C_2	C_4^3	i	S_4^3	σ_h	S_4		$i = \sqrt{-1}$
A_g	1	1	1	1	1	1	1	1	R_z	$x^2 + y^2, z^2$
B_g	1	-1	1	-1	1	-1	1	-1		$x^2 - y^2, xy$
E_g	$\begin{cases}1 \\ 1\end{cases}$	$\begin{matrix}i \\ -i\end{matrix}$	$\begin{matrix}-1 \\ -1\end{matrix}$	$\begin{matrix}-i \\ i\end{matrix}$	$\begin{matrix}1 \\ 1\end{matrix}$	$\begin{matrix}i \\ -i\end{matrix}$	$\begin{matrix}-1 \\ -1\end{matrix}$	$\begin{matrix}-i \\ i\end{matrix}$	(R_x, R_y)	(xz, yz)
A_u	1	1	1	1	-1	-1	-1	-1	z	
B_u	1	-1	1	-1	-1	1	-1	1		
E_u	$\begin{cases}1 \\ 1\end{cases}$	$\begin{matrix}i \\ -i\end{matrix}$	$\begin{matrix}-1 \\ -1\end{matrix}$	$\begin{matrix}-i \\ i\end{matrix}$	$\begin{matrix}-1 \\ -1\end{matrix}$	$\begin{matrix}-i \\ i\end{matrix}$	$\begin{matrix}1 \\ 1\end{matrix}$	$\begin{matrix}i \\ -i\end{matrix}$	(x, y)	

C_{5h}	E	C_5	$C_5{}^2$	$C_5{}^3$	$C_5{}^4$	σ_h	S_5	$S_5{}^7$	$S_5{}^3$	$S_5{}^9$		$\epsilon = \exp(2\pi i/5)$
A'	1	1	1	1	1	1	1	1	1	1	R_z	$x^2 + y^2,\ z^2$
E_1'	$\begin{cases}1\\1\end{cases}$	$\begin{matrix}\epsilon\\\epsilon^*\end{matrix}$	$\begin{matrix}\epsilon^2\\\epsilon^{2*}\end{matrix}$	$\begin{matrix}\epsilon^{2*}\\\epsilon^2\end{matrix}$	$\begin{matrix}\epsilon^*\\\epsilon\end{matrix}$	$\begin{matrix}1\\1\end{matrix}$	$\begin{matrix}\epsilon\\\epsilon^*\end{matrix}$	$\begin{matrix}\epsilon^2\\\epsilon^{2*}\end{matrix}$	$\begin{matrix}\epsilon^{2*}\\\epsilon^2\end{matrix}$	$\begin{matrix}\epsilon^*\\\epsilon\end{matrix}\Big\}$	(x, y)	
E_2'	$\begin{cases}1\\1\end{cases}$	$\begin{matrix}\epsilon^2\\\epsilon^{2*}\end{matrix}$	$\begin{matrix}\epsilon^*\\\epsilon\end{matrix}$	$\begin{matrix}\epsilon\\\epsilon^*\end{matrix}$	$\begin{matrix}\epsilon^{2*}\\\epsilon^2\end{matrix}$	$\begin{matrix}1\\1\end{matrix}$	$\begin{matrix}\epsilon^2\\\epsilon^{2*}\end{matrix}$	$\begin{matrix}\epsilon^*\\\epsilon\end{matrix}$	$\begin{matrix}\epsilon\\\epsilon^*\end{matrix}$	$\begin{matrix}\epsilon^{2*}\\\epsilon^2\end{matrix}\Big\}$		$(x^2 - y^2,\ xy)$
A''	1	1	1	1	1	-1	-1	-1	-1	-1	z	
E_1''	$\begin{cases}1\\1\end{cases}$	$\begin{matrix}\epsilon\\\epsilon^*\end{matrix}$	$\begin{matrix}\epsilon^2\\\epsilon^{2*}\end{matrix}$	$\begin{matrix}\epsilon^{2*}\\\epsilon^2\end{matrix}$	$\begin{matrix}\epsilon^*\\\epsilon\end{matrix}$	$\begin{matrix}-1\\-1\end{matrix}$	$\begin{matrix}-\epsilon\\-\epsilon^*\end{matrix}$	$\begin{matrix}-\epsilon^2\\-\epsilon^{2*}\end{matrix}$	$\begin{matrix}-\epsilon^{2*}\\-\epsilon^2\end{matrix}$	$\begin{matrix}-\epsilon^*\\-\epsilon\end{matrix}\Big\}$	(R_x, R_y)	(xz, yz)
E_2''	$\begin{cases}1\\1\end{cases}$	$\begin{matrix}\epsilon^2\\\epsilon^{2*}\end{matrix}$	$\begin{matrix}\epsilon^*\\\epsilon\end{matrix}$	$\begin{matrix}\epsilon\\\epsilon^*\end{matrix}$	$\begin{matrix}\epsilon^{2*}\\\epsilon^2\end{matrix}$	$\begin{matrix}-1\\-1\end{matrix}$	$\begin{matrix}-\epsilon^2\\-\epsilon^{2*}\end{matrix}$	$\begin{matrix}-\epsilon^*\\-\epsilon\end{matrix}$	$\begin{matrix}-\epsilon\\-\epsilon^*\end{matrix}$	$\begin{matrix}-\epsilon^{2*}\\-\epsilon^2\end{matrix}\Big\}$		

C_{6h}	E	C_6	C_3	C_2	$C_3{}^2$	$C_6{}^5$	i	$S_3{}^5$	$S_6{}^5$	σ_h	S_6	S_3		$\epsilon = \exp(2\pi i/6)$
A_g	1	1	1	1	1	1	1	1	1	1	1	1	R_z	$x^2 + y^2,\ z^2$
B_g	1	-1	1	-1	1	-1	1	-1	1	-1	1	-1		
E_{1g}	$\begin{cases}1\\1\end{cases}$	$\begin{matrix}\epsilon\\\epsilon^*\end{matrix}$	$\begin{matrix}-\epsilon^*\\-\epsilon\end{matrix}$	$\begin{matrix}-1\\-1\end{matrix}$	$\begin{matrix}-\epsilon\\-\epsilon^*\end{matrix}$	$\begin{matrix}\epsilon^*\\\epsilon\end{matrix}$	$\begin{matrix}1\\1\end{matrix}$	$\begin{matrix}\epsilon\\\epsilon^*\end{matrix}$	$\begin{matrix}-\epsilon^*\\-\epsilon\end{matrix}$	$\begin{matrix}-1\\-1\end{matrix}$	$\begin{matrix}-\epsilon\\-\epsilon^*\end{matrix}$	$\begin{matrix}\epsilon^*\\\epsilon\end{matrix}\Big\}$	(R_x, R_y)	(xz, yz)
E_{2g}	$\begin{cases}1\\1\end{cases}$	$\begin{matrix}-\epsilon^*\\-\epsilon\end{matrix}$	$\begin{matrix}-\epsilon\\-\epsilon^*\end{matrix}$	$\begin{matrix}1\\1\end{matrix}$	$\begin{matrix}-\epsilon^*\\-\epsilon\end{matrix}$	$\begin{matrix}-\epsilon\\-\epsilon^*\end{matrix}$	$\begin{matrix}1\\1\end{matrix}$	$\begin{matrix}-\epsilon^*\\-\epsilon\end{matrix}$	$\begin{matrix}-\epsilon\\-\epsilon^*\end{matrix}$	$\begin{matrix}1\\1\end{matrix}$	$\begin{matrix}-\epsilon^*\\-\epsilon\end{matrix}$	$\begin{matrix}-\epsilon\\-\epsilon^*\end{matrix}\Big\}$		$(x^2 - y^2,\ xy)$
A_u	1	1	1	1	1	1	-1	-1	-1	-1	-1	-1	z	
B_u	1	-1	1	-1	1	-1	-1	1	-1	1	-1	1		
E_{1u}	$\begin{cases}1\\1\end{cases}$	$\begin{matrix}\epsilon\\\epsilon^*\end{matrix}$	$\begin{matrix}-\epsilon^*\\-\epsilon\end{matrix}$	$\begin{matrix}-1\\-1\end{matrix}$	$\begin{matrix}-\epsilon\\-\epsilon^*\end{matrix}$	$\begin{matrix}\epsilon^*\\\epsilon\end{matrix}$	$\begin{matrix}-1\\-1\end{matrix}$	$\begin{matrix}-\epsilon\\-\epsilon^*\end{matrix}$	$\begin{matrix}\epsilon^*\\\epsilon\end{matrix}$	$\begin{matrix}1\\1\end{matrix}$	$\begin{matrix}\epsilon\\\epsilon^*\end{matrix}$	$\begin{matrix}-\epsilon^*\\-\epsilon\end{matrix}\Big\}$	(x, y)	
E_{2u}	$\begin{cases}1\\1\end{cases}$	$\begin{matrix}-\epsilon^*\\-\epsilon\end{matrix}$	$\begin{matrix}-\epsilon\\-\epsilon^*\end{matrix}$	$\begin{matrix}1\\1\end{matrix}$	$\begin{matrix}-\epsilon^*\\-\epsilon\end{matrix}$	$\begin{matrix}-\epsilon\\-\epsilon^*\end{matrix}$	$\begin{matrix}-1\\-1\end{matrix}$	$\begin{matrix}\epsilon^*\\\epsilon\end{matrix}$	$\begin{matrix}\epsilon\\\epsilon^*\end{matrix}$	$\begin{matrix}-1\\-1\end{matrix}$	$\begin{matrix}\epsilon^*\\\epsilon\end{matrix}$	$\begin{matrix}\epsilon\\\epsilon^*\end{matrix}\Big\}$		

THE D_{nh} GROUPS

D_{2h}	E	$C_2(z)$	$C_2(y)$	$C_2(x)$	i	$\sigma(xy)$	$\sigma(xz)$	$\sigma(yz)$		
A_g	1	1	1	1	1	1	1	1		$x^2,\ y^2,\ z^2$
B_{1g}	1	1	-1	-1	1	1	-1	-1	R_z	xy
B_{2g}	1	-1	1	-1	1	-1	1	-1	R_y	xz
B_{3g}	1	-1	-1	1	1	-1	-1	1	R_x	yz
A_u	1	1	1	1	-1	-1	-1	-1		
B_{1u}	1	1	-1	-1	-1	-1	1	1	z	
B_{2u}	1	-1	1	-1	-1	1	-1	1	y	
B_{3u}	1	-1	-1	1	-1	1	1	-1	x	

D_{3h}	E	$2C_3$	$3C_2$	σ_h	$2S_3$	$3\sigma_v$		
A_1'	1	1	1	1	1	1		$x^2 + y^2,\ z^2$
A_2'	1	1	-1	1	1	-1	R_z	
E'	2	-1	0	2	-1	0	(x, y)	$(x^2 - y^2,\ xy)$
A_1''	1	1	1	-1	-1	-1		
A_2''	1	1	-1	-1	-1	1	z	
E''	2	-1	0	-2	1	0	(R_x, R_y)	(xz, yz)

D_{4h}	E	$2C_4$	C_2	$2C_2'$	$2C_2''$	i	$2S_4$	σ_h	$2\sigma_v$	$2\sigma_d$		
A_{1g}	1	1	1	1	1	1	1	1	1	1		$x^2+y^2,\ z^2$
A_{2g}	1	1	1	-1	-1	1	1	1	-1	-1	R_z	
B_{1g}	1	-1	1	1	-1	1	-1	1	1	-1		x^2-y^2
B_{2g}	1	-1	1	-1	1	1	-1	1	-1	1		xy
E_g	2	0	-2	0	0	2	0	-2	0	0	(R_x, R_y)	(xz, yz)
A_{1u}	1	1	1	1	1	-1	-1	-1	-1	-1		
A_{2u}	1	1	1	-1	-1	-1	-1	-1	1	1	z	
B_{1u}	1	-1	1	1	-1	-1	1	-1	-1	1		
B_{2u}	1	-1	1	-1	1	-1	1	-1	1	-1		
E_u	2	0	-2	0	0	-2	0	2	0	0	(x, y)	

D_{5h}	E	$2C_5$	$2C_5^2$	$5C_2$	σ_h	$2S_5$	$2S_5^3$	$5\sigma_v$		
A_1'	1	1	1	1	1	1	1	1		$x^2+y^2,\ z^2$
A_2'	1	1	1	-1	1	1	1	-1	R_z	
E_1'	2	$2\cos 72°$	$2\cos 144°$	0	2	$2\cos 72°$	$2\cos 144°$	0	(x, y)	
E_2'	2	$2\cos 144°$	$2\cos 72°$	0	2	$2\cos 144°$	$2\cos 72°$	0		(x^2-y^2, xy)
A_1''	1	1	1	1	-1	-1	-1	-1		
A_2''	1	1	1	-1	-1	-1	-1	1	z	
E_1''	2	$2\cos 72°$	$2\cos 144°$	0	-2	$-2\cos 72°$	$-2\cos 144°$	0	(R_x, R_y)	(xz, yz)
E_2''	2	$2\cos 144°$	$2\cos 72°$	0	-2	$-2\cos 144°$	$-2\cos 72°$	0		

D_{6h}	E	$2C_6$	$2C_3$	C_2	$3C_2'$	$3C_2''$	i	$2S_3$	$2S_6$	σ_h	$3\sigma_d$	$3\sigma_v$		
A_{1g}	1	1	1	1	1	1	1	1	1	1	1	1		$x^2+y^2,\ z^2$
A_{2g}	1	1	1	1	-1	-1	1	1	1	1	-1	-1	R_z	
B_{1g}	1	-1	1	-1	1	-1	1	-1	1	-1	1	-1		
B_{2g}	1	-1	1	-1	-1	1	1	-1	1	-1	-1	1		
E_{1g}	2	1	-1	-2	0	0	2	1	-1	-2	0	0	(R_x, R_y)	(xz, yz)
E_{2g}	2	-1	-1	2	0	0	2	-1	-1	2	0	0		(x^2-y^2, xy)
A_{1u}	1	1	1	1	1	1	-1	-1	-1	-1	-1	-1		
A_{2u}	1	1	1	1	-1	-1	-1	-1	-1	-1	1	1	z	
B_{1u}	1	-1	1	-1	1	-1	-1	1	-1	1	-1	1		
B_{2u}	1	-1	1	-1	-1	1	-1	1	-1	1	1	-1		
E_{1u}	2	1	-1	-2	0	0	-2	-1	1	2	0	0	(x, y)	
E_{2u}	2	-1	-1	2	0	0	-2	1	1	-2	0	0		

THE D_{nd} GROUPS

D_{2d}	E	$2S_4$	C_2	$2C_2'$	$2\sigma_d$		
A_1	1	1	1	1	1		$x^2+y^2,\ z^2$
A_2	1	1	1	-1	-1	R_z	
B_1	1	-1	1	1	-1		x^2-y^2
B_2	1	-1	1	-1	1	z	xy
E	2	0	-2	0	0	$(x, y);\ (R_x, R_y)$	(xz, yz)

D_{3d}	E	$2C_3$	$3C_2$	i	$2S_6$	$3\sigma_d$		
A_{1g}	1	1	1	1	1	1		$x^2+y^2,\ z^2$
A_{2g}	1	1	-1	1	1	-1	R_z	
E_g	2	-1	0	2	-1	0	(R_x, R_y)	$(x^2-y^2,\ xy);\ (xz,\ yz)$
A_{1u}	1	1	1	-1	-1	-1		
A_{2u}	1	1	-1	-1	-1	1	z	
E_u	2	-1	0	-2	1	0	(x, y)	

D_{4d}	E	$2S_8$	$2C_4$	$2S_8{}^3$	C_2	$4C_2'$	$4\sigma_d$		
A_1	1	1	1	1	1	1	1		$x^2+y^2,\ z^2$
A_2	1	1	1	1	1	-1	-1	R_z	
B_1	1	-1	1	-1	1	1	-1		
B_2	1	-1	1	-1	1	-1	1	z	
E_1	2	$\sqrt{2}$	0	$-\sqrt{2}$	-2	0	0	(x, y)	
E_2	2	0	-2	0	2	0	0		$(x^2-y^2,\ xy)$
E_3	2	$-\sqrt{2}$	0	$\sqrt{2}$	-2	0	0	(R_x, R_y)	$(xz,\ yz)$

D_{5d}	E	$2C_5$	$2C_5{}^2$	$5C_2$	i	$2S_{10}{}^3$	$2S_{10}$	$5\sigma_d$		
A_{1g}	1	1	1	1	1	1	1	1		$x^2+y^2,\ z^2$
A_{2g}	1	1	1	-1	1	1	1	-1	R_z	
E_{1g}	2	$2\cos 72°$	$2\cos 144°$	0	2	$2\cos 72°$	$2\cos 144°$	0	(R_x, R_y)	$(xz,\ yz)$
E_{2g}	2	$2\cos 144°$	$2\cos 72°$	0	2	$2\cos 144°$	$2\cos 72°$	0		$(x^2-y^2,\ xy)$
A_{1u}	1	1	1	1	-1	-1	-1	-1		
A_{2u}	1	1	1	-1	-1	-1	-1	1	z	
E_{1u}	2	$2\cos 72°$	$2\cos 144°$	0	-2	$-2\cos 72°$	$-2\cos 144°$	0	(x, y)	
E_{2u}	2	$2\cos 144°$	$2\cos 72°$	0	-2	$-2\cos 144°$	$-2\cos 72°$	0		

D_{6d}	E	$2S_{12}$	$2C_6$	$2S_4$	$2C_3$	$2S_{12}{}^5$	C_2	$6C_2'$	$6\sigma_d$		
A_1	1	1	1	1	1	1	1	1	1		$x^2+y^2,\ z^2$
A_2	1	1	1	1	1	1	1	-1	-1	R_z	
B_1	1	-1	1	-1	1	-1	1	1	-1		
B_2	1	-1	1	-1	1	-1	1	-1	1	z	
E_1	2	$\sqrt{3}$	1	0	-1	$-\sqrt{3}$	-2	0	0	(x, y)	
E_2	2	1	-1	-2	-1	1	2	0	0		$(x^2-y^2,\ xy)$
E_3	2	0	-2	0	2	0	-2	0	0		
E_4	2	-1	-1	2	-1	-1	2	0	0		
E_5	2	$-\sqrt{3}$	1	0	-1	$\sqrt{3}$	-2	0	0	(R_x, R_y)	$(xz,\ yz)$

THE S_n GROUPS

S_4	E	S_4	C_2	$S_4{}^3$		$i = \sqrt{-1}$
A	1	1	1	1	R_z	$x^2 + y^2,\ z^2$
B	1	-1	1	-1	z	$x^2 - y^2,\ xy$
E	$\begin{cases}1 \\ 1\end{cases}$	$\begin{matrix}i \\ -i\end{matrix}$	$\begin{matrix}-1 \\ -1\end{matrix}$	$\begin{matrix}-i \\ i\end{matrix}$	$(x, y);\ (R_x, R_y)$	$(xz,\ yz)$

S_6	E	C_3	$C_3{}^2$	i	$S_6{}^5$	S_6		$\epsilon = \exp(2\pi i/3)$
A_g	1	1	1	1	1	1	R_z	$x^2 + y^2,\ z^2$
E_g	$\begin{cases}1 \\ 1\end{cases}$	$\begin{matrix}\epsilon \\ \epsilon^*\end{matrix}$	$\begin{matrix}\epsilon^* \\ \epsilon\end{matrix}$	$\begin{matrix}1 \\ 1\end{matrix}$	$\begin{matrix}\epsilon \\ \epsilon^*\end{matrix}$	$\begin{matrix}\epsilon^* \\ \epsilon\end{matrix}$	(R_x, R_y)	$(x^2 - y^2,\ xy);\ (xz,\ yz)$
A_u	1	1	1	-1	-1	-1	z	
E_u	$\begin{cases}1 \\ 1\end{cases}$	$\begin{matrix}\epsilon \\ \epsilon^*\end{matrix}$	$\begin{matrix}\epsilon^* \\ \epsilon\end{matrix}$	$\begin{matrix}-1 \\ -1\end{matrix}$	$\begin{matrix}-\epsilon \\ -\epsilon^*\end{matrix}$	$\begin{matrix}-\epsilon^* \\ -\epsilon\end{matrix}$	(x, y)	

S_8	E	S_8	C_4	$S_8{}^3$	C_2	$S_8{}^5$	$C_4{}^3$	$S_8{}^7$		$\epsilon = \exp(2\pi i/8)$
A	1	1	1	1	1	1	1	1	R_z	$x^2 + y^2,\ z^2$
B	1	-1	1	-1	1	-1	1	-1	z	
E_1	$\begin{cases}1 \\ 1\end{cases}$	$\begin{matrix}\epsilon \\ \epsilon^*\end{matrix}$	$\begin{matrix}i \\ -i\end{matrix}$	$\begin{matrix}-\epsilon^* \\ -\epsilon\end{matrix}$	$\begin{matrix}-1 \\ -1\end{matrix}$	$\begin{matrix}-\epsilon \\ -\epsilon^*\end{matrix}$	$\begin{matrix}-i \\ i\end{matrix}$	$\begin{matrix}\epsilon^* \\ \epsilon\end{matrix}$	$(x, y);\ (R_x, R_y)$	
E_2	$\begin{cases}1 \\ 1\end{cases}$	$\begin{matrix}i \\ -i\end{matrix}$	$\begin{matrix}-1 \\ -1\end{matrix}$	$\begin{matrix}-i \\ i\end{matrix}$	$\begin{matrix}1 \\ 1\end{matrix}$	$\begin{matrix}i \\ -i\end{matrix}$	$\begin{matrix}-1 \\ -1\end{matrix}$	$\begin{matrix}-i \\ i\end{matrix}$		$(x^2 - y^2,\ xy)$
E_3	$\begin{cases}1 \\ 1\end{cases}$	$\begin{matrix}-\epsilon^* \\ -\epsilon\end{matrix}$	$\begin{matrix}-i \\ i\end{matrix}$	$\begin{matrix}\epsilon \\ \epsilon^*\end{matrix}$	$\begin{matrix}-1 \\ -1\end{matrix}$	$\begin{matrix}\epsilon^* \\ \epsilon\end{matrix}$	$\begin{matrix}i \\ -i\end{matrix}$	$\begin{matrix}-\epsilon \\ -\epsilon^*\end{matrix}$		$(xz,\ yz)$

S_{10}	E	C_5	$C_5{}^2$	$C_5{}^3$	$C_5{}^4$	i	$S_{10}{}^7$	$S_{10}{}^9$	S_{10}	$S_{10}{}^3$		$\epsilon = \exp(2\pi i/5)$
A_g	1	1	1	1	1	1	1	1	1	1	R_z	z^2
A_u	1	1	1	1	1	-1	-1	-1	-1	-1	z	
E_{1g}	$\begin{cases}1 \\ 1\end{cases}$	$\begin{matrix}\epsilon \\ \epsilon^*\end{matrix}$	$\begin{matrix}\epsilon^2 \\ \epsilon^{2*}\end{matrix}$	$\begin{matrix}\epsilon^{2*} \\ \epsilon^2\end{matrix}$	$\begin{matrix}\epsilon^* \\ \epsilon\end{matrix}$	$\begin{matrix}1 \\ 1\end{matrix}$	$\begin{matrix}\epsilon \\ \epsilon^*\end{matrix}$	$\begin{matrix}\epsilon^2 \\ \epsilon^{2*}\end{matrix}$	$\begin{matrix}\epsilon^{2*} \\ \epsilon^2\end{matrix}$	$\begin{matrix}\epsilon^* \\ \epsilon\end{matrix}$	(R_x, R_y)	
E_{1u}	$\begin{cases}1 \\ 1\end{cases}$	$\begin{matrix}\epsilon \\ \epsilon^*\end{matrix}$	$\begin{matrix}\epsilon^2 \\ \epsilon^{2*}\end{matrix}$	$\begin{matrix}\epsilon^{2*} \\ \epsilon^2\end{matrix}$	$\begin{matrix}\epsilon^* \\ \epsilon\end{matrix}$	$\begin{matrix}-1 \\ -1\end{matrix}$	$\begin{matrix}-\epsilon \\ -\epsilon^*\end{matrix}$	$\begin{matrix}-\epsilon^2 \\ -\epsilon^{2*}\end{matrix}$	$\begin{matrix}-\epsilon^{2*} \\ -\epsilon^2\end{matrix}$	$\begin{matrix}-\epsilon^* \\ -\epsilon\end{matrix}$	(x, y)	
E_{2g}	$\begin{cases}1 \\ 1\end{cases}$	$\begin{matrix}\epsilon^2 \\ \epsilon^{2*}\end{matrix}$	$\begin{matrix}\epsilon^* \\ \epsilon\end{matrix}$	$\begin{matrix}\epsilon \\ \epsilon^*\end{matrix}$	$\begin{matrix}\epsilon^{2*} \\ \epsilon^2\end{matrix}$	$\begin{matrix}1 \\ 1\end{matrix}$	$\begin{matrix}\epsilon^2 \\ \epsilon^{2*}\end{matrix}$	$\begin{matrix}\epsilon^* \\ \epsilon\end{matrix}$	$\begin{matrix}\epsilon \\ \epsilon^*\end{matrix}$	$\begin{matrix}\epsilon^{2*} \\ \epsilon^2\end{matrix}$		
E_{2u}	$\begin{cases}1 \\ 1\end{cases}$	$\begin{matrix}\epsilon^2 \\ \epsilon^{2*}\end{matrix}$	$\begin{matrix}\epsilon^* \\ \epsilon\end{matrix}$	$\begin{matrix}\epsilon \\ \epsilon^*\end{matrix}$	$\begin{matrix}\epsilon^{2*} \\ \epsilon^2\end{matrix}$	$\begin{matrix}-1 \\ -1\end{matrix}$	$\begin{matrix}-\epsilon^2 \\ -\epsilon^{2*}\end{matrix}$	$\begin{matrix}-\epsilon^* \\ -\epsilon\end{matrix}$	$\begin{matrix}-\epsilon \\ -\epsilon^*\end{matrix}$	$\begin{matrix}-\epsilon^2 \\ -\epsilon^2\end{matrix}$		

S_{12}	E	S_{12}	C_6	S_4	C_3	$S_{12}{}^5$	C_2	$S_{12}{}^7$	$C_3{}^2$	$S_4{}^3$	$C_6{}^5$	$S_{12}{}^{11}$		$\epsilon = \exp{(i\pi/6)}$
A	1	1	1	1	1	1	1	1	1	1	1	1	R_z	$x^2 + y^2$
B	1	-1	1	-1	1	-1	1	-1	1	-1	1	-1	z	
E_1	$\begin{cases}1 \\ 1\end{cases}$	$\begin{matrix}\epsilon \\ \epsilon^*\end{matrix}$	$\begin{matrix}\epsilon^2 \\ \epsilon^{2*}\end{matrix}$	$\begin{matrix}-i \\ i\end{matrix}$	$\begin{matrix}-\epsilon^{2*} \\ -\epsilon^2\end{matrix}$	$\begin{matrix}-\epsilon^* \\ -\epsilon\end{matrix}$	$\begin{matrix}-1 \\ -1\end{matrix}$	$\begin{matrix}-\epsilon \\ -\epsilon^*\end{matrix}$	$\begin{matrix}-\epsilon^2 \\ -\epsilon^{2*}\end{matrix}$	$\begin{matrix}i \\ -i\end{matrix}$	$\begin{matrix}\epsilon^{2*} \\ \epsilon^2\end{matrix}$	$\begin{matrix}\epsilon^* \\ \epsilon\end{matrix}$	$\begin{matrix}(x, y); \\ (R_x, R_y)\end{matrix}$	
E_2	$\begin{cases}1 \\ 1\end{cases}$	$\begin{matrix}\epsilon^2 \\ \epsilon^{2*}\end{matrix}$	$\begin{matrix}-\epsilon^{2*} \\ -\epsilon^2\end{matrix}$	$\begin{matrix}-1 \\ -1\end{matrix}$	$\begin{matrix}\epsilon^2 \\ \epsilon^{2*}\end{matrix}$	$\begin{matrix}-\epsilon^{2*} \\ -\epsilon^2\end{matrix}$	$\begin{matrix}1 \\ 1\end{matrix}$	$\begin{matrix}-\epsilon^{2*} \\ -\epsilon^2\end{matrix}$	$\begin{matrix}\epsilon^{2*} \\ \epsilon^2\end{matrix}$	$\begin{matrix}-1 \\ -1\end{matrix}$	$\begin{matrix}\epsilon^2 \\ \epsilon^{2*}\end{matrix}$	$\begin{matrix}\epsilon^{2*} \\ \epsilon^2\end{matrix}$		
E_3	$\begin{cases}1 \\ 1\end{cases}$	$\begin{matrix}-i \\ i\end{matrix}$	$\begin{matrix}-1 \\ -1\end{matrix}$	$\begin{matrix}i \\ -i\end{matrix}$	$\begin{matrix}1 \\ 1\end{matrix}$	$\begin{matrix}-i \\ i\end{matrix}$	$\begin{matrix}-1 \\ -1\end{matrix}$	$\begin{matrix}i \\ -i\end{matrix}$	$\begin{matrix}1 \\ 1\end{matrix}$	$\begin{matrix}-i \\ -i\end{matrix}$	$\begin{matrix}-1 \\ -1\end{matrix}$	$\begin{matrix}i \\ -i\end{matrix}$		
E_4	$\begin{cases}1 \\ 1\end{cases}$	$\begin{matrix}-\epsilon^{2*} \\ -\epsilon^2\end{matrix}$	$\begin{matrix}-\epsilon^2 \\ -\epsilon^{2*}\end{matrix}$	$\begin{matrix}1 \\ 1\end{matrix}$	$\begin{matrix}-\epsilon^{2*} \\ -\epsilon^2\end{matrix}$	$\begin{matrix}-\epsilon^2 \\ -\epsilon^{2*}\end{matrix}$	$\begin{matrix}1 \\ 1\end{matrix}$	$\begin{matrix}-\epsilon^{2*} \\ -\epsilon^2\end{matrix}$	$\begin{matrix}-\epsilon^2 \\ -\epsilon^{2*}\end{matrix}$	$\begin{matrix}1 \\ 1\end{matrix}$	$\begin{matrix}-\epsilon^{2*} \\ -\epsilon^2\end{matrix}$	$\begin{matrix}-\epsilon^2 \\ -\epsilon^{2*}\end{matrix}$		
E_5	$\begin{cases}1 \\ 1\end{cases}$	$\begin{matrix}-\epsilon^* \\ -\epsilon\end{matrix}$	$\begin{matrix}\epsilon^{2*} \\ \epsilon^2\end{matrix}$	$\begin{matrix}-i \\ i\end{matrix}$	$\begin{matrix}-\epsilon^2 \\ -\epsilon^{2*}\end{matrix}$	$\begin{matrix}\epsilon \\ \epsilon^*\end{matrix}$	$\begin{matrix}-1 \\ -1\end{matrix}$	$\begin{matrix}\epsilon^* \\ \epsilon\end{matrix}$	$\begin{matrix}-\epsilon^{2*} \\ -\epsilon^{2*}\end{matrix}$	$\begin{matrix}i \\ -i\end{matrix}$	$\begin{matrix}\epsilon^2 \\ \epsilon^{2*}\end{matrix}$	$\begin{matrix}-\epsilon \\ -\epsilon^*\end{matrix}$		

TYPE III

THE CUBIC GROUPS

T	E	$4C_3$	$4C_3{}^2$	$3C_2$		
A	1	1	1	1		$x^2 + y^2 + z^2$
E	$\begin{cases}1 \\ 1\end{cases}$	$\begin{matrix}\epsilon \\ \epsilon^*\end{matrix}$	$\begin{matrix}\epsilon^* \\ \epsilon\end{matrix}$	$\begin{matrix}1 \\ 1\end{matrix}$		$(3z^2 - r^2, x^2 - y^2)$
T	3	0	0	-1	$\begin{matrix}(x, y, z); (xy, xz, yz) \\ (R_x, R_y, R_z)\end{matrix}$	

T_d	E	$8C_3$	$3C_2$	$6S_4$	$6\sigma_d$		
A_1	1	1	1	1	1		$x^2 + y^2 + z^2$
A_2	1	1	1	-1	-1		
E	2	-1	2	0	0		$(2z^2 - x^2 - y^2, x^2 - y^2)$
T_1	3	0	-1	1	-1	(R_x, R_y, R_z)	
T_2	3	0	-1	-1	1	(x, y, z)	(xy, xz, yz)

O	E	$8C_3$	$3C_2$	$6C_2$	$6C_4$		
A_1	1	1	1	1	1		$x^2 + y^2 + z^2$
A_2	1	1	1	-1	-1		
E	2	-1	2	0	0		$(3z^2 - r^2, x^2 - y^2)$
T_1	3	0	-1	-1	1	$(x, y, z); (R_x, R_y, R_z)$	
T_2	3	0	-1	1	-1	(xy, xz, yz)	

O_h	E	$8C_3$	$6C_2$	$6C_4$	$3C_2 \ (= C_4{}^2)$	i	$6S_4$	$8S_6$	$3\sigma_h$	$6\sigma_d$		
A_{1g}	1	1	1	1	1	1	1	1	1	1		$x^2 + y^2 + z^2$
A_{2g}	1	1	-1	-1	1	1	-1	1	1	-1		
E_g	2	-1	0	0	2	2	0	-1	2	0		$(2z^2 - x^2 - y^2, x^2 - y^2)$
T_{1g}	3	0	-1	1	-1	3	1	0	-1	-1	(R_x, R_y, R_z)	
T_{2g}	3	0	1	-1	-1	3	-1	0	-1	1		(xz, yz, xy)
A_{1u}	1	1	1	1	1	-1	-1	-1	-1	-1		
A_{2u}	1	1	-1	-1	1	-1	1	-1	-1	1		
E_u	2	-1	0	0	2	-2	0	1	-2	0		
T_{1u}	3	0	-1	1	-1	-3	-1	0	1	1	(x, y, z)	
T_{2u}	3	0	1	-1	-1	-3	1	0	1	-1		

THE GROUPS $C_{\infty v}$ AND $D_{\infty h}$ FOR LINEAR MOLECULES

$C_{\infty v}$	E	$2C_\infty{}^\Phi$	$\cdots$	$\infty \sigma_v$		
$A_1 \equiv \Sigma^+$	1	1	$\cdots$	1	z	$x^2 + y^2, z^2$
$A_2 \equiv \Sigma^-$	1	1	$\cdots$	-1	R_z	
$E_1 \equiv \Pi$	2	$2 \cos \Phi$	$\cdots$	0	$(x, y); (R_x, R_y)$	(xz, yz)
$E_2 \equiv \Delta$	2	$2 \cos 2\Phi$	$\cdots$	0		$(x^2 - y^2, xy)$
$E_3 \equiv \Phi$	2	$2 \cos 3\Phi$	$\cdots$	0		
$\cdots \cdots$	$\cdots \cdots \cdots \cdots \cdots \cdots$					

$D_{\infty h}$	E	$2C_\infty{}^\Phi$	$\cdots$	$\infty \sigma_v$	i	$2S_\infty{}^\Phi$	$\cdots$	∞C_2		
$\Sigma_g{}^+$	1	1	$\cdots$	1	1	1	$\cdots$	1		$x^2 + y^2, z^2$
$\Sigma_g{}^-$	1	1	$\cdots$	-1	1	1	$\cdots$	-1	R_z	
Π_g	2	$2 \cos \Phi$	$\cdots$	0	2	$-2 \cos \Phi$	$\cdots$	0	(R_x, R_y)	(xz, yz)
Δ_g	2	$2 \cos 2\Phi$	$\cdots$	0	2	$2 \cos 2\Phi$	$\cdots$	0		$(x^2 - y^2, xy)$
$\cdots$										
$\Sigma_u{}^+$	1	1	$\cdots$	1	-1	-1	$\cdots$	-1	z	
$\Sigma_u{}^-$	1	1	$\cdots$	-1	-1	-1	$\cdots$	1		
Π_u	2	$2 \cos \Phi$	$\cdots$	0	-2	$2 \cos \Phi$	$\cdots$	0	(x, y)	
Δ_u	2	$2 \cos 2\Phi$	$\cdots$	0	-2	$-2 \cos 2\Phi$	$\cdots$	0		
$\cdots$										

THE ICOSAHEDRAL GROUP

I_h	E	$12C_5$	$12C_5^2$	$20C_3$	$15C_2$	i	$12S_{10}$	$12S_{10}^3$	$20S_6$	15σ		
A_g	1	1	1	1	1	1	1	1	1	1		$x^2+y^2+z^2$
T_{1g}	3	$\frac{1}{2}(1+\sqrt{5})$	$\frac{1}{2}(1-\sqrt{5})$	0	-1	3	$\frac{1}{2}(1-\sqrt{5})$	$\frac{1}{2}(1+\sqrt{5})$	0	-1	(R_x, R_y, R_z)	
T_{2g}	3	$\frac{1}{2}(1-\sqrt{5})$	$\frac{1}{2}(1+\sqrt{5})$	0	-1	3	$\frac{1}{2}(1+\sqrt{5})$	$\frac{1}{2}(1-\sqrt{5})$	0	-1		
G_g	4	-1	-1	1	0	4	-1	-1	1	0		$(2z^2-x^2-y^2,$ $x^2-y^2,$ $xy, yz, zx)$
H_g	5	0	0	-1	1	5	0	0	-1	1		
A_u	1	1	1	1	1	-1	-1	-1	-1	-1		
T_{1u}	3	$\frac{1}{2}(1+\sqrt{5})$	$\frac{1}{2}(1-\sqrt{5})$	0	-1	-3	$-\frac{1}{2}(1-\sqrt{5})$	$-\frac{1}{2}(1+\sqrt{5})$	0	1	(x, y, z)	
T_{2u}	3	$\frac{1}{2}(1-\sqrt{5})$	$\frac{1}{2}(1+\sqrt{5})$	0	-1	-3	$-\frac{1}{2}(1+\sqrt{5})$	$-\frac{1}{2}(1-\sqrt{5})$	0	1		
G_u	4	-1	-1	1	0	-4	1	1	-1	0		
H_u	5	0	0	-1	1	-5	0	0	1	-1		

Correlation tables[1] relate the symmetry species of a point group (as found in the character tables) to the species of the subgroups. Such correlations are important and useful in any situation where one wishes to relate a high-symmetry point group to a low-symmetry point group. Examples are given in Sec. 11.5 and in Chap. 8 of "Molecular Vibrations."[2]

[1] Adapted by permission from E. Bright Wilson, Jr., John C. Decius, and Paul C. Cross, "Molecular Vibrations," pp. 333–340, McGraw-Hill Book Company, copyright 1955.

[2] *Ibid.*

D_{4h}	D_4	$C_2' \to C_2'$ D_{2d}	$C_2'' \to C_2'$ D_{2d}	C_{4v}	C_{4h}	C_2' D_{2h}	C_2'' D_{2h}	C_4	S_4
A_{1g}	A_1	A_1	A_1	A_1	A_g	A_g	A_g	A	A
A_{2g}	A_2	A_2	A_2	A_2	A_g	B_{1g}	B_{1g}	A	A
B_{1g}	B_1	B_1	B_2	B_1	B_g	A_g	B_{1g}	B	B
B_{2g}	B_2	B_2	B_1	B_2	B_g	B_{1g}	A_g	B	B
E_g	E	E	E	E	E_g	$B_{2g} + B_{3g}$	$B_{2g} + B_{3g}$	E	E
A_{1u}	A_1	B_1	B_1	A_2	A_u	A_u	A_u	A	B
A_{2u}	A_2	B_2	B_2	A_1	A_u	B_{1u}	B_{1u}	A	B
B_{1u}	B_1	A_1	A_2	B_2	B_u	A_u	B_{1u}	B	A
B_{2u}	B_2	A_2	A_1	B_1	B_u	B_{1u}	A_u	B	A
E_u	E	E	E	E	E_u	$B_{2u} + B_{3u}$	$B_{2u} + B_{3u}$	E	E

D_{4h} (cont.)	C_2' D_2	C_2'' D_2	C_2, σ_v C_{2v}	C_2, σ_d C_{2v}	C_2' C_{2v}	C_2'' C_{2v}
A_{1g}	A	A	A_1	A_1	A_1	A_1
A_{2g}	B_1	B_1	A_2	A_2	B_1	B_1
B_{1g}	A	B_1	A_1	A_2	A_1	B_1
B_{2g}	B_1	A	A_2	A_1	B_1	A_1
E_g	B_2+B_3	B_2+B_3	B_1+B_2	B_1+B_2	A_2+B_2	A_2+B_2
A_{1u}	A	A	A_2	A_2	A_2	A_2
A_{2u}	B_1	B_1	A_1	A_1	B_2	B_2
B_{1u}	A	B_1	A_2	A_1	A_2	B_2
B_{2u}	B_1	A	A_1	A_2	B_2	A_2
E_u	B_2+B_3	B_2+B_3	B_1+B_2	B_1+B_2	A_1+B_1	A_1+B_1

D_{4h} (cont.)	C_2 C_{2h}	C_2' C_{2h}	C_2'' C_{2h}	C_2 C_2	C_2' C_2	C_2'' C_2	σ_h C_s	σ_v C_s	σ_d C_s	C_i
A_{1g}	A_g	A_g	A_g	A	A	A	A'	A'	A'	A_g
A_{2g}	A_g	B_g	B_g	A	B	B	A'	A''	A''	A_g
B_{1g}	A_g	A_g	B_g	A	A	B	A'	A'	A''	A_g
B_{2g}	A_g	B_g	A_g	A	B	A	A'	A''	A'	A_g
E_g	$2B_g$	A_g+B_g	A_g+B_g	$2B$	$A+B$	$A+B$	$2A''$	$A'+A''$	$A'+A''$	$2A_g$
A_{1u}	A_u	A_u	A_u	A	A	A	A''	A''	A''	A_u
A_{2u}	A_u	B_u	B_u	A	B	B	A''	A'	A'	A_u
B_{1u}	A_u	A_u	B_u	A	A	B	A''	A''	A'	A_u
B_{2u}	A_u	B_u	A_u	A	B	A	A''	A'	A''	A_u
E_u	$2B_u$	A_u+B_u	A_u+B_u	$2B$	$A+B$	$A+B$	$2A'$	$A'+A''$	$A'+A''$	$2A_u$

D_{3d}	D_3	C_{3v}	S_6	C_3	C_{2h}	C_2	C_3	C_i
A_{1g}	A_1	A_1	A_g	A	A_g	A	A'	A_g
A_{2g}	A_2	A_2	A_g	A	B_g	B	A''	A_g
E_g	E	E	E_g	E	A_g+B_g	$A+B$	$A'+A''$	$2A_g$
A_{1u}	A_1	A_2	A_u	A	A_u	A	A''	A_u
A_{2u}	A_2	A_1	A_u	A	B_u	B	A'	A_u
E_u	E	E	E_u	E	A_u+B_u	$A+B$	$A'+A''$	$2A_u$

T	D_2	C_3	C_2
A	A	A	A
E	$2A$	E	$2A$
T	$B_1+B_2+B_3$	$A+E$	$A+2B$

T_d	T	D_{2d}	C_{3v}	S_4	D_2	C_{2v}	C_3	C_2	C_s
A_1	A	A_1	A_1	A	A	A_1	A	A	A'
A_2	A	B_1	A_2	B	A	A_2	A	A	A''
E	E	A_1+B_1	E	$A+B$	$2A$	A_1+A_2	E	$2A$	$A'+A''$
T_1	T	A_2+E	A_2+E	$A+E$	$B_1+B_2+B_3$	$A_2+B_1+B_2$	$A+E$	$A+2B$	$A'+2A''$
T_2	T	B_2+E	A_1+E	$B+E$	$B_1+B_2+B_3$	$A_1+B_1+B_2$	$A+E$	$A+2B$	$2A'+A''$

O	T	D_4	D_3	C_4	$3C_2$ D_2	$C_2, 2C_2'$ D_2	C_3	C_2	C_2
A_1	A	A_1	A_1	A	A	A	A	A	A
A_2	A	B_1	A_2	B	A	B_1	A	A	B
E	E	A_1+B_1	E	$A+B$	$2A$	$A+B_1$	E	$2A$	$A+B$
T_1	T	A_2+E	A_2+E	$A+E$	$B_1+B_2+B_3$	$B_1+B_2+B_3$	$A+E$	$A+2B$	$A+2B$
T_2	T	B_2+E	A_1+E	$B+E$	$B_1+B_2+B_3$	$A+B_2+B_3$	$A+E$	$A+2B$	$2A+B$

O_h‡	O	T_d	T_h	D_{4h}	D_{3d}
A_{1g}	A_1	A_1	A_g	A_{1g}	A_{1g}
A_{2g}	A_2	A_2	A_g	B_{1g}	A_{2g}
E_g	E	E	E_g	$A_{1g}+B_{1g}$	E_g
T_{1g}	T_1	T_1	T_g	$A_{2g}+E_g$	$A_{2g}+E_g$
T_{2g}	T_2	T_2	T_g	$B_{2g}+E_g$	$A_{1g}+E_g$
A_{1u}	A_1	A_2	A_u	A_{1u}	A_{1u}
A_{2u}	A_2	A_1	A_u	B_{1u}	A_{2u}
E_u	E	E	E_u	$A_{1u}+B_{1u}$	E_u
T_{1u}	T_1	T_2	T_u	$A_{2u}+E_u$	$A_{2u}+E_u$
T_{2u}	T_2	T_1	T_u	$B_{2u}+E_u$	$A_{1u}+E_u$

‡ To find correlations with smaller subgroups, carry out the correlation in two steps; for example, if the correlation of O_h with C_{2v} is desired, use the above table to pass from O_h to T_d and then employ the table for T_d to go on to C_{2v}.

appendix 3

computer
program
for
Eigenvalue
problems

Many of the areas in chemistry to which group theory may be applied involve the solution of an eigenvalue problem, sometimes referred to as matrix diagonalization. Therefore, a short and simple computer program for solving eigenvalue problems has been included in this text.

The computer program has been written in an elementary type of the Fortran IV language and should be directly usable on any computer which possesses Fortran capability.

The program is quite simple to use. The input instructions are described on comment cards in the program. The required information consists of the size of the matrix (number of rows or columns), N, and the value of each of the nonzero matrix elements, one per card. See the sample data for an example of input.

The program writes out each eigenvalue and a column of numbers for each eigenvector as shown in the sample output. The program, as it appears here, is written for a matrix with a maximum dimension of 12. The DIMENSION statement may be changed, however, to accommodate larger matrices.

PROGRAM TO COMPUTE EIGENVALUES AND EIGENVECTORS BY JACOBI METHOD
*********** INPUT CARD FORMATS *********************************

```
    CARD ONE    TITLE        (1X,18A4)
    CARD TWO    SIZE OF THE MATRIX N  (I5)
    ONE CARD EACH FOR EACH NON-ZERO MATRIX ELEMENT
                I,J,A(I,J),IND        (I5,I5,F10.4,50X,I2)
    LAST CARD   ISTOP    (I5)
                BLANK TO TERMINATE PROGRAM
                ANY POSITIVE INTERGER IF ANOTHER MATRIX IS TO FOLLOW

    DIMENSION A(12,12), S(12,12)

    CALL ROUTINE TO SET THE VARIABLES FOR THE TAPE DESIGNATIONS

    CALL TAPES (IN,IOUT,IPU,ISC)
    INPUT NAME OF COMPOUND
135    READ (IN,7)
    INPUT ARRAY SIZE
    READ (IN,2) N
    SET EIGENVALUE MATRIX TO ZERO
    GENERATE IDENTITY MATRIX AS FIRST APPROXIMATION TO S
    DO 150 I = 1,N
    DO 150 J = 1,N
    A(I,J) = 0.0
    IF (I-J) 100, 101, 100
100 S(I,J) = 0.0
    GO TO 150
101 S(I,J) = 1.0
150 CONTINUE
    SET INDICATOR WHICH CHECKS OFF-DIAGONAL ELEMENTS
    INDIC = 0
    INPUT ARRAY TO BE SOLVED
152 READ (IN,2) I,J,FA,IND
    A (I,J) = -FA
    A (J,I) = -FA
    IF (IND) 151, 152, 151
    COMPUTE INITIAL NORM
151 VI = 0.0
    DO 106 I = 1,N
    DO 106 J = 1,N
    IF (I-J) 107, 106, 107
107 VI = VI + A(I,J) ** 2
106 CONTINUE
    VI = SQRT  (VI)
    COMPUTE FINAL NORM
    VF = VI * 0.1E - 07
    COMPUTE THRESHOLD NORM
    AN = N
128 VI = VI/AN
    SET UP SYSTEMATIC SEARCH
137 IQ = 1
124 IQ = IQ + 1
    IP = 0
121 IP = IP + 1
    IF (A(IP,IQ)) 108, 120, 109
108 IF (-A(IP, IQ) - VI) 120, 112, 112
109 IF (A(IP,IQ) - VI) 120, 112, 112
112 INDIC = 1
    COMPUTE SINE AND COSINE OF MATRIX ROTATION ANGLE
    ALAM = -A(IP,IQ)
```

```
          AMU = 0.5*A(IP,IP) - A(IQ,IQ)
          IF (AMU) 113, 114, 114
   113 SGN = -1.0
          GO TO 115
   114 SGN = +1.0
   115 OMEGA = SGN* ALAM/SQRT   (ALAM** 2 + AMU** 2)
          STHT = OMEGA/SQRT  (2.0 + 2.0*SQRT  (1.0 - OMEGA*OMEGA))
          CTHT = SQRT  (1.0 - STHT** 2)
C      TRANSFORM ELEMENTS OF THE PTH AND QTH COLUMN
          DO 116 I = 1,N
          IF (I-IP) 117, 118, 117
   117 IF (I-IQ) 119, 118, 119
C      ROTATE THE SECULAR MATRIX
   119 AIPI  = A(IP,I)* CTHT - A(IQ,I)* STHT
          AIQI  = A(IP,I)* STHT + A(IQ,I)* CTHT
          A (IP,I) = AIPI
          A (IQ,I) = AIQI
C      ROTATE THE MATRIX OF COEFFICIENTS
   118 AIPI  = S (I,IP)* CTHT - S(I,IQ)* STHT
          AIQI  = S (I,IP)* STHT + S(I,IQ)* CTHT
          S (I,IP) = AIPI
   116 S (I,IQ) = AIQI
          AIPI =A(IP,IP)*CTHT**2+A(IQ,IQ)*STHT**2-2.0*A(IP,IQ)*STHT*CTHT
          AIQI =A(IP,IP)*STHT**2+A(IQ,IQ)*CTHT**2+2.0*A(IP,IQ)*STHT*CTHT
          AIPIQ = (A(IP,IP)-A(IQ,IQ))*CTHT*STHT+A(IP,IQ)*(CTHT**2-STHT**2)
          A (IP,IP) = AIPI
          A (IQ,IQ) = AIQI
          A (IP,IQ) = AIPIQ
          A (IQ,IP) = A (IP,IQ)
C      TRANSFORM MATRIX
          DO 123 I = 1,N
          A (I,IP) = A(IP,I)
   123 A (I,IQ) = A (IQ,I)
   120 IF (IP-IQ+1)  121, 122, 122
   122 IF (IQ-N) 124, 125, 125
   125 IF (INDIC) 126, 127, 126
   126 INDIC = 0
          GO TO 137
   127 IF (VI - VF) 129, 129, 128
C      OUTPUT COMPOUND NAME
   129 WRITE (IOUT,8)
          WRITE (IOUT,7)
          WRITE (IOUT,9)
C      OUTPUT ROOTS TO POLYNOMIAL
          DO 130 I = 1,N
          DO 130 J = 1,N
          IF (I-J)  130, 131, 130
   131 WRITE (IOUT,5) I, A(I,J)
C      OUTPUT CORRESPONDING COEFFICIENTS
          WRITE (IOUT,6)  J
          DO 208 IP = 1,N
   208 WRITE (IOUT,3) IP, J, S (IP,J)
   130 CONTINUE
C      BRANCH TO THE BEGINNING OF THE PROGRAM
          READ (IN,10000) ISTOP
10000 FORMAT ( I5)
          IF(ISTOP) 400,400,135
   400 CONTINUE
          STOP
C      FORMAT STATEMENTS
```

```
2 FORMAT (I5, I5, F10.4, 25X, 25X, I2)
3 FORMAT (4X, I5, I5, E20.8)
5 FORMAT (//2X, 16H EIGENVALUE NO. ,I3,3H = , E15.8)
6 FORMAT (//2X31HCOEFFICIENTS OF EIGENVECTOR   (I3,1H) //)
7 FORMAT (1X,18A4)
8 FORMAT (1H1)
9 FORMAT (//)
  END
  SUBROUTINE TAPES (IN,IOUT,IPU,ISC)
  IN = 5
  IOUT = 6
  IPU = 7
  RETURN
  END
```

************** SAMPLE DATA   ***

```
PYRIDINE  4X4   SIMPLE HUCKEL MO
  4
  1    1  1.5
  1    2 1.414
  2    3  1.0
  3    4 1.414
```
                                                                            1

************** SAMPLE OUTPUT   ***

```
PYRIDINE  4X4   SIMPLE HUCKEL MO
```

EIGENVALUE NO.   1 = -0.14305763E 01

COEFFICIENTS OF EIGENVECTOR   (1)

```
    1    1      0.43204618E 00
    2    1     -0.21197002E-01
    3    1     -0.64123893E 00
    4    1     -0.63378781E 00
```

EIGENVALUE NO.   2 = 0.59402204E 00

COEFFICIENTS OF EIGENVECTOR   (2)

```
    1    2     -0.44297653E 00
    2    2      0.65601575E 00
    3    2      0.23667532E 00
    4    2     -0.56337243E 00
```

EIGENVALUE NO.   3 = -0.25257225E 01

COEFFICIENTS OF EIGENVECTOR   (3)

```
    1    3      0.75460839E 00
    2    3      0.54742819E 00
    3    3      0.31566751E 00
```

         4   3   0.17671818F 00

  EIGENVALUE NO.   4 =   0.18623352E 01

COEFFICIENTS OF EIGENVECTOR   (4)

         1   4   -0.21831495E 00
         2   4   0.51913881E 00
         3   4   -0.65813297F 00
         4   4   0.49968326F 00

formula index

subject index

This book was set in Modern by The Maple Press Company, and printed on permanent paper and bound by The Maple Press Company. The designer was Marsha Cohen; the drawings were done by J. & R. Technical Services, Inc. The editors were James L. Smith and Janet Wagner. William P. Weiss supervised the production.